David Smart;
5, Roseway,
June 90

D1639685

A Doctor's
Story

A DOCTOR'S STORY

Ann Dally

MACMILLAN
LONDON

First published 1990 by
MACMILLAN LONDON LIMITED
4 Little Essex Street London WC2R 3LF
and Basingstoke

Associated companies in Auckland, Delhi, Dublin, Gaborone,
Hamburg, Harare, Hong Kong, Johannesburg, Kuala Lumpur,
Lagos, Manzini, Melbourne, Mexico City, Nairobi, New York,
Singapore and Tokyo

A CIP catalogue record for this book is available from the
British Library.

ISBN 0-333-49718-X

Typeset by Matrix, 21 Russell Street, London WC2

Printed and bound by WBC Print Ltd, Bristol & Maesteg

To PHILIP
with love

Contents

Preface and Acknowledgements

This is the story of my professional life as a doctor. It begins with my childhood desire to be a doctor and describes my training at St Thomas's Hospital in London and my life as a junior doctor in the early years of the National Health Service. It recounts my efforts to practise while raising a family in the fifties, sixties and seventies, when it was almost impossible for a woman to choose both a family and a career. It is also about my work in psychiatry, which led ultimately to my 'rebellion'.

I became a rebel doctor by mistake and towards the end of my professional life. I had never intended to be more than mildly critical of some members of the medical establishment, pointing out certain imperfections that I thought were not in the interests of patients, and putting the remedies into practice in so far as I was able. I had done this before and had found that, if well presented, such criticism did not cause offence, usually made doctors more aware and sometimes led to improvements in practice. Until my profound disagreement with the medical establishment over drug addiction I would have regarded myself almost as a member of that establishment. I certainly never intended to fight the doctors in power, nor did I have any idea how entrenched were their positions, how illogical their arguments, or even how dishonest some of them were. When the trouble started, my daughter Emma predicted, 'They'll find to their surprise that they've been attacking one of their own.' She was wrong. Their attitudes and actions made me realise that I am not, and never could be, 'one of them'.

I also realised that if an area of medical practice lacks contact with other specialties, vested interests may develop to the detriment of patients and, as described in this book, such interests may harm the rest of society even if the doctors act in good faith. Not only is *glasnost* essential in medicine, but doctors need to know what is going on even in specialties that they dislike, despise and may wish to ignore. They also need to be aware of how far their practice, and that of their colleagues, reflects popular prejudices and damages individual patients. Medicine tends to confine itself to problems regarded as respectable, and doctors have often been to the fore in imposing prejudice in the name of science, wisdom or 'a lifetime of experience'. As an example of this, one has only to look at some of the past medical crazes and the authoritative manner in which doctors assured their patients that these were necessary. The most obvious of these was bleeding, the antithesis of treatment today, which for many centuries was regarded as essential in the treatment of most sickness.

Inevitably, much of this book is about my discovery of deficiencies and irregularities in the treatment of drug addiction, my disagreements with that part of the medical establishment responsible for dealing with this, and the three cases brought against me by the General Medical Council. I believe these will continue to have repercussions beyond those evident at the time.

I have been uncertain as to how much I should write on the subject of drug dependency. Some readers will wish for information in order to understand the story fully, but too much detail would be tedious. I have therefore written only what I felt would clarify the rest of the book. Whenever possible I have given explanations of technical terms in the text, but readers unfamiliar with drug problems may find it helpful to look at the glossary before embarking on the book.

Apart from a few necessary changes of name, everything in the book is true as I saw it. Inevitably, I have had to omit much that happened. This was largely for reasons of length, but sometimes it was in order not to hurt or defame. Many remarks made in private have been reproduced in the book; where I thought their inclusion might upset the speaker I have made them anonymous. If any comments that remain give offence to any of my friends, I ask their forgiveness.

I thank everyone who has helped me, particularly the friends and colleagues, too numerous to name, who stood by me. Some of them, such as the obstetrician Wendy Savage, already understood what was going on. Others had their eyes opened and were astonished at what they saw.

I should also like to thank the magnificent team of lawyers assembled by my old friend, the solicitor John Calderan. They included Neil Taylor QC, William Gage QC, Christopher Sumner and John Kelleher. Each of them expressed a belief in what I was trying to achieve and supported me through a difficult time.

I thank those friends and colleagues who appeared as witnesses for me. They gave evidence on my behalf with a generosity and courage that concealed the danger some of them ran by doing so. To those who suffered as a result, I can only affirm my friendship and repeat my appreciation.

I thank my husband and family, without whose encouragement and support I would have found it difficult to survive intact. I am particularly grateful to my daughter Emma for her tireless work on the case, including giving evidence for me, and to her husband, Richard Ehrlich, for his spicy American comments as he watched the British medical establishment in action, and also for his practical help with this book. I thank my secretaries, Anne Lingham and Diana Tomlins, who have stood by and given much of themselves in support. I also thank my agent, Shân Morley-Jones, for suggesting that I write the book in the first place, and both her and my editors at Macmillan, Adam Sisman, Katie Owen and others, for their encouragement and helpful suggestions.

Lastly I give thanks for my grandchildren, Rebecca, Alice and Anna for being born so appropriately when I most needed encouragement and for reminding me that what I have achieved in my professional life goes towards making a better world for their generation.

ANN DALLY
London and Graffham 1989

Foreword

I hope that Ann Dally's account of her life as a doctor and the ordeal which led to her being forced to abandon some of her work and prevented her from looking after her patients as she would wish, will have a wide readership. In particular I hope that the leaders of the medical profession and those in positions of power and influence within the establishment will consider her arguments and the injustice resulting from the case that was brought against her by the General Medical Council (GMC).

The primary duty of a doctor is to his or her patient, and because so much of his or her work is based on custom and accepted methods, not hard scientific data, there is a wide spectrum of acceptable practice. Normally this leads doctors to accept differences in opinion and to tolerate diversity of approach within medicine. In addition, because all doctors have made mistakes – some minor, others not – and have had to learn to deal with their distress or self-doubt when having wished to help they have harmed a patient, they are usually unwilling to criticise another doctor in public. Like other professions they have jealously guarded their right to discipline their colleagues and the GMC is legally bound to discharge this task. The public has a right to expect that doctors will uphold the highest professional standards and ensure that those who are unfit to practise are removed from the register maintained by the GMC. Over the last few years the GMC's inability or unwillingness to tackle clinical complaints about professional negligence or incompetence, and the concentration of power to decide when to proceed within the hands of one man, has drawn increasing criticism.

Ann Dally's case also provides evidence of another problem: the possibility that the GMC can be manipulated by powerful doctors to ensure that their theories of correct management are imposed on independent professionals. I do not believe that this tendency if unchecked will be in the interests of patients, and therefore welcome this book, which shows clearly the details of what happened to Ann.

In my own case (which did not involve the GMC), the argument that criticisms of clinical care should be based on scientific evidence and the totality of one's work as a doctor was upheld by the panel, who dismissed the charge of incompetence made against me. Despite evidence from a few brave practising clinicians that the change in policy towards the treatment of long-term drug addicts was detrimental to the interests of those patients, and the lack of any scientific evidence to support the new policies, Ann Dally was found guilty. The public debate that ensued from the medical and media coverage of her case probably prevented her from being struck off the register but her ability to prescribe freely was restricted for fourteen months.

I found this a painful book to read. Ann describes well the stressful situation of the doctor caught up in the slow and tortuous medico-legal process and the disappointments when known and trusted colleagues withdraw their support. It reawakened my own barely contained feelings, which have been reinforced by the experiences of at least twenty doctors who have contacted me in the last four years and who have been attacked or unjustly suspended as a result of actions by their medical colleagues. It is the experience of listening to doctors whose careers have been destroyed that led me to give such cautious and pessimistic advice to Ann Dally.

Jean Robinson's recent critique of the GMC, the current series of articles by Richard Smith in the *British Medical Journal* and this book will, I hope, start a debate both within the medical profession and more widely about the way that doctors maintain standards. As Jean Robinson says, 'I find it increasingly hard to reconcile the collective behaviour of the profession with the individual care, kindness and decency of the many doctors I know.' There appears to be something about the process by which doctors (and others) rise through the hierarchy that is potentially damaging to integrity and honesty. In medicine, which is so close to the mysteries of life and death and where doctors are privileged to work with people during critical periods of their lives, it seems worse to me when power or money becomes a dominant motive for any doctor.

Many people have expressed surprise that I should have supported Ann Dally, a private practitioner working with drug addicts in Harley

Street – several miles from the underprivileged borough of Tower Hamlets where, as an academic, I work only with NHS patients. What we have in common is that we both believe that patients come first and have questioned aspects of current practice in our respective fields. Also, we both believed that as long as one did one's work honestly and competently and could defend one's position intellectually that in a democratic society one was entitled to free speech and to practise one's profession as one thought best. I was fortunate to win my battle and be able to care for pregnant women and patients again. Ann Dally has fought bravely for a group of people who do not inspire such sympathy and support as pregnant women but I predict that history will support her position and censure the actions of the profession as represented by the GMC.

I hope that we as a profession will learn from this book and take a renewed look at the care and treatment of drug addicts who are suffering from present policies, as are their families. Effective research is needed in this country to find the best way of helping these patients so that they are treated humanely. We must not create the same problems as occur in the USA where most research has been conducted on different populations living in diverse environments.

Lastly, I hope that doctors will look at the way our profession governs itself so that those who question the system do not find themselves in the same position as Ann Dally and the other doctors I know who have been professionally assassinated.

WENDY SAVAGE, FRCOG.
Senior Lecturer in Obstetrics and Gynaecology

Chapter 1

Deciding to be a Doctor

My desire to be a doctor began, like so many of my interests, with books.

I was born on 29 March 1926, at 27 Welbeck Street, a fashionable maternity home in Marylebone, in the heart of 'medical London' and only 500 yards from where I have lived for more than half my adult life.

My father, Claud Mullins, a lawyer who devoted much of his time to law reform, was famous during my childhood as an outspoken and reforming Metropolitan magistrate and writer. His brother was an architect and their father, Edwin Roscoe Mullins, had been a prominent Victorian sculptor. My mother Gwen Brandt, became a weaver and craftswoman. Her father was a businessman and banker who headed the firm of William Brandt's Sons in the City. The only doctor in the family was my American great-uncle Jasper Garmany, from Georgia, but I didn't even know then that he was a doctor.

My medical aspirations came from the books that filled the rooms of our house in Epsom. I still remember the excitement of learning to read in kindergarten. The knowledge that I could read anything made me feel a kind of omnipotence.

My conscious desire to become a doctor probably started with Dr Dolittle, who spoke the language of his animals and who had wonderful adventures with them. Dr Dolittle studied the world about him and tried to understand it, as I was trying to do. When I was older, perhaps eight or nine, my decision was confirmed by other books. Two were unusual autobiographies, Axel Munthe's *Story of San Michele* and George Sava's *The Healing Knife*. But the book that probably influenced me most was A.J. Cronin's *The Citadel*, which was published when I was eleven. In it an idealistic doctor becomes entangled with a rigid medical establishment, does what he believes is best for a patient and is charged before the General Medical Council. Rereading this book recently, I realised how prophetic it was of my own life – except that the fictional doctor persuaded the GMC that his ideas were right.

I nurtured my determination to be a doctor through an education strongly biased against science, nor were my parents interested in medicine. Indeed some people considered doctors 'NQOC', Not Quite Our Class – for doctors, like tradesmen, came when summoned. The human body was usually concealed, mysterious and unmentionable.

One of my parents' few doctor friends was Letitia Fairfield, medical officer to the London County Council. She sometimes worked with my father on matters of social and legal reform. Through her my parents also became friendly with her sister and brother-in-law, Cicely and Henry Andrews. Cicely was better known as the writer Rebecca West.

Among my father's many pioneering interests were the movements for marriage guidance and for birth control. He was a founder of both the Marriage Guidance Council and the Family Planning Association. Through his work for the birth control movement he became friendly with Dr Marie Stopes. I remember her chiefly for the Guy Fawkes firework parties she gave in the garden of her mansion near Dorking. My father told me that she genuinely believed that her first child had been killed by the prayers of Catholics. On one occasion, just as the bonfire was being lit, he stood with her away from the crowd. As the flames began to lick round the feet of the guy, she shook her fist and hissed triumphantly: 'Ah! You were a *Catholic*!'

Some members of my family rejected conventional medicine in favour of 'natural' remedies: yoga, unconventional methods such as Abraham's 'black box', or the diagnosis of disease by examination of the hand. My medical ambitions probably also satisfied the childish desire for rebellion.

My maternal grandparents were different. Neither had grown up in Britain and both distrusted British doctors; they travelled regularly to Paris, Zurich and Berlin when they needed medical advice. I grew up believing that good doctors, at least of the conventional kind, were found only on the Continent. My grandmother took medicine prescribed by her doctor in Paris which her butler brought to the dining room in a little glass jug with a silver hinged lid. The medicine was light brown and she sipped it daintily after, and sometimes during, meals. I was grown up before I realised that it was brandy.

Soon I read other books from which I learned what it was like to be a doctor. The life of Marie Curie was particularly inspiring. I had no wish to work in a laboratory, but I greatly admired her belief in what she did, her hard work in the face of difficulty, and, perhaps more than anything, the fact that she was a woman.

I also read the books of 'James Harpole', the pseudonym of a practising surgeon, which had titles such as *Leaves from a Surgeon's Casebook* and *The White-Coated Army*. In these he gave case histories and described how he had cured people of their disease. It all seemed amazing and exciting, and I longed to follow James Harpole in this career. I wanted to reorganise the world so that disease could be cured and prevented. I read about medical missionaries, particularly in India, and yearned to join them.

However fantastic and absurd my feelings about becoming a doctor, two things remained constant and clear in my mind. One was a need to try to make more sense of the world, preferably by discovering or inventing something new. The other was a feeling of satisfaction whenever, even as a child, I 'made someone better'. I believed, and still believe, that these are what being a doctor is about.

In 1937, aged eleven, I was sent to board at Wychwood, a small girls' school in Oxford. Once quite a good school, it had fallen on hard times and was declining slowly under its ageing joint headmistresses, two elderly spinsters of uncertain purpose and mental state. I now think that they were unfit to care for the young. One of them, Miss Lee, seemed to be obsessed with hierarchies of excellence, and she made it clear that I was low in the hierarchy. One thing I remember about her with pleasure was her recipe for, I think, writing, though perhaps it was for living:

'Observe, Brood, Express, Polish.'

Wychwood was 'advanced'. In theory it was run entirely by the pupils except for matters of 'health, chaperonage and curriculum'. But I soon realised that these three headings could cover almost anything. Bedtime was strictly fixed and early for reasons of health. It was forbidden to post a letter in the red pillar-box ten yards from the school gate because that came under 'chaperonage'. Pupils had to study whatever they were told because that was 'curriculum'. This was the first time I became conscious of adult hypocrisy and saw how it could be used to control the helpless and vulnerable.

I quickly acquired a reputation for being naughty, not unjustified but much of it due, I now realise, to my being the youngest in my class. Some of the girls were as much as three years older than I and the average age was nearly two years older. I don't think the teachers took any account of this when they criticised and punished me, which they did frequently. They also wrote to my mother about every peccadillo. Occasionally I managed to intercept letters to and from my mother, since they were 'posted' in the box on the hall table with the incoming mail piled beside it. Thus I learned that grown-ups tell lies and twist facts if it suits them.

Feeling that I had to make my mark with the older classmates, I became known for my daring. On an expedition to a church, someone challenged me to climb the tower on a ladder left by workmen. I did it and was punished. Back at school, in a bathroom at the very top of the building I unwound an entire roll of lavatory paper and let it float from the window. It broke in the wind and draped itself round the top of an elm tree. During the row that followed, an aggrieved teacher told me: 'You have disgraced the school. That tree can be seen all over North Oxford.' I also became skilled at making water bombs. One day I was leaning out of the classroom window with my latest bomb in my hand when Miss Lee appeared, accompanying a prospective parent. Dared by my classmates, I took aim and dropped the bomb. It landed on top of Miss Lee's head.

A frequent punishment was being made to walk round the netball court before breakfast for half an hour, learning poetry or prose by heart. This was an unexpected blessing: I learned, among much else, the whole of Macaulay's 'Horatius', all Keats's Odes, hundreds of lines of *Paradise Lost* and many of the speeches of Edmund Burke.

Miss Lee favoured girls she could regard as geniuses. Some of her favourites, however, were not geniuses but peculiarities. One was an eccentric called Joy, who had no capacity for learning school subjects but devoted all her time to birthdays. Whenever a new girl arrived Joy would interrogate her about the dates of her birthday and those of her family. She knew the birthday of every pupil, every member of staff, including domestic staff, and even of everybody's parents and grandparents, brothers and sisters, cousins and friends and whomever they mentioned or invented. I have since wondered whether she was an example of that rare and interesting condition, *idiot savant*. She certainly stimulated my interest in strange personalities.

Joan Aiken was more like a real genius. Daughter of the American poet Conrad Aiken, she had more or less been brought up to be a genius. Miss Lee boasted about her to prospective parents. Joan, now a distinguished writer, has remained a close friend, despite the disapproval of Miss Lee, who thought me a bad influence on her favourite.

Denigrating certain children was one of the school's specialities. I don't think this was done sadistically, but it could be very hurtful. One system of denigration was the 'Pig Table', where those with unacceptable table manners were obliged to sit for a week at a time. I still find this type of discrimination distasteful, and fighting it later in my life led me into trouble.

Besides books, my other childish passion was horses. Through them I made my first woman doctor friend, someone much older than me who valued me in a way I never felt valued at school.

We were allowed to ride by arrangement with an older day girl, Rosemary Nasmyth. She and her brother Jan ran a riding school in their spare time. I looked forward all week to Saturday afternoons, when a few girls from the school took the bus to Boar's Hill, above Oxford. There we rode and played with ponies and had tea with the Nasmyth family. But to me, just as exciting as the riding and the tea was talking to Rosemary's and Jan's mother.

Dorothea Nasmyth, née Maude, was the sister of 'Golden Gorse', who was at that time well known to small girls as the author of the first pony books. I had read both her books repeatedly.

As the sister of 'Golden Gorse' Mrs Nasmyth seemed to open up vistas for me; I too hoped to write pony books.

I didn't know at that time that Mrs Nasmyth was a doctor – I thought she was a riding instructor. I liked her because she took children seriously and was genuinely interested in what we said and thought. But I learned that there was much more to her. She was one of the most remarkable women of her time, though so modest that she was never well known. She too had wanted to become a doctor from an early age. She excelled academically and had a father who believed in educating women. In 1898 she went up to Somerville and became the first woman ever to read physiology at Oxford. She took a first in a subject in which it was always said to be more difficult to gain a first than in any other. She was offered a fellowship and the chance to do distinguished work in the university but declined. She wanted to be a practising doctor.

She studied clinical medicine at the Royal Free Hospital, which housed the London School of Medicine for Women. It was still run by Elizabeth Garrett Anderson, the first English woman doctor. Dorothea often talked about this pioneering woman and the men who supported the early women doctors. After qualifying, she worked at the Royal Free and at several other hospitals. When the First World War broke out, she joined the Women's Auxiliary Medical Services and served in Belgium, France, Corfu, Serbia and Macedonia. Eventually she became the first female general practitioner in Oxford, combining the practice with raising her family.

In 1937 Dorothea was nearly sixty years old. She now practised from the house that she and her husband had built on Boar's Hill. As she grew older and more frail, her practice shrank and she seemed to care mainly for a retired academic clientele, many of them distinguished and most of them personal friends. Dorothea talked much about medicine, and this strengthened my interest while also giving me a more realistic view of it.

Through her I also became friends with another outstanding woman doctor, Sylvia Payne, Dorothea's closest friend since they were students together at the Royal Free Hospital. Sylvia was a trained surgeon and married another surgeon from the hospital. Later she became a psychoanalyst and eventually president of the Psycho-Analytical Society. She lived to the age of ninety-five, and I saw her frequently until she became too ill to enjoy company.

I watched the Battle of Britain through the summer of 1940 and experienced air-raids during school holidays, but the war which dominated everyone's lives seemed remote from our cloistered world in Oxford.

As I moved up the school, my determination to be a doctor was somewhat flattened by the prospect of having to do science. In the sixth form it would mean studying virtually nothing else. The only interesting science lessons we had at Wychwood were from a young, newly married biologist called Jean Medawar. She taught us for one term only, soon after I arrived. One day she was ill and her husband Peter came to teach us instead. This caused much excitement, not least among the spinster teachers. I don't remember what Peter Medawar taught us but I do remember that he was tall, dark, handsome and charming. Not many doctors can boast that they were taught by a future Nobel Prize winner before they were twelve.

In 1940 Wychwood, having declined for years, was unable to continue as an independent school and became a boarding house for the Oxford High School. I was about to begin my School Certificate year and was already well on with the syllabus. Wychwood continued to provide lessons for some of its more eccentric or slow-learning children who could not have coped with the academic pressures of the High School, though these suited me well. Attending the High School during the day made me see what good education was like.

Eventually I was expelled from Wychwood for being a 'bad influence'. Miss Lee did her best to make me leave Oxford altogether and told my parents that I would never be any good at anything. She said that the High School was also rejecting me, and since I was apparently ineducable, the best thing would probably be to put me into the Women's Land Army. No one else would want me. My father had the sense to check this information and discovered that it was completely untrue. The teachers at the High School thought I showed promise and that I was an asset to the school. Miss Stack, the headmistress, spent her Easter weekend unravelling what had happened and finding me somewhere to live.

The Oxford High School was highly academic, mostly in classics and arts subjects. Science was taught by an eccentric lady called Miss Davies, known as 'Auntie May'. Her lessons were boring, her thinking was woolly, and she couldn't keep order. As a result, the thought of doing science seriously, as I would have to do in the sixth form, appalled me. I was fourteen years old and becoming interested in literature, history and foreign languages. If I did science, there would be time for little else.

I had two days of adolescent agony, during which time I was acutely aware that the decision was likely to affect my whole future, which seemed awesome. Miss Stack was tolerant of my indecision and eventually I chose history, English and languages, ancient and modern. I was lucky to be younger than most of the others, for it meant that, if all went well and unless the government changed the regulations, I would have my full honours degree by the time I was twenty, the call-up age for university students. Most women at the time had to be content with a condensed two-year course leading only to a 'war' degree. The school taught me so well that at sixteen I won an open exhibition in modern history to Somerville. My friend Sally Plimsoll was awarded the top scholarship at Lady Margaret Hall. Several others in the class won awards and everyone got at least a place at Oxford or Cambridge. We worked hard for a few months but with enjoyment and without straining ourselves.

At the time, we did not appreciate the effort and care of our teachers. Ungrateful children, we took it for granted. Later I learned that Oxford High was one of the top schools in the country for this kind of achievement and I have since felt that it was more their triumph than mine. Responding gladly to the stimulation of those who taught me, I was privileged to receive it.

There were forty undergraduates in my year at Somerville, far fewer than nowadays, and no postgraduate students.

In the same examination, another girl from a school in the East Midlands just missed a place at Somerville and was put high on the waiting list. Her name was Margaret Roberts, later Margaret Thatcher. By the beginning of the autumn term there was still no place for her, so she returned to school. Before the university term started someone dropped out, so Margaret left school and came up to Somerville with the rest of us.

If I had been told that the first woman prime minister would be one of us, I would not have put Margaret among my first six guesses. This was because most of us found her boring and I think it did not occur to us in those heady days that anyone who was boring could possibly reach high places. Margaret also seemed very ordinary, though she differed from the rest of us in that she was a Conservative. In wartime Oxford most students were left wing, especially at Somerville. We had all been influenced by Beveridge, with his vision of freedom and the coming welfare state, the new Jerusalem. Most of us were avowed socialists and many belonged to the Communist Club. I have never been a political person but I certainly thought of myself as a socialist. It seemed the only thing to be and we used to laugh at Margaret Roberts when she knocked on our doors and tried to sell us tickets for the Conservative Club ball or a similar event. She seemed so solemn and assured about it and we were intolerant of other people's certainties.

I did not envy Margaret her scientific studies. She read chemistry and had to spend most of the day in the laboratory. Oxford's social life went on during the day and, as arts students, we felt we got the best from Oxford – even though it was a weakened, wartime Oxford. Medical students, like other scientists, also spent their days in laboratories or in the hospital. I was glad that I wasn't among them.

I don't think anyone at Somerville or Oxford University saw Margaret's immense potential. Most of us regarded her as undistinguished. She didn't seem particularly bright, though she was made a scholar at the end of the first year so she must have impressed someone. Our chief complaint against her was that she wasn't fun to talk to – unforgivable at Somerville. She seemed to have no sense of humour. Dr Janet Vaughan, later Dame Janet, who became Principal in our second year, found her intolerable and did not invite her to her house on Sunday mornings as she did anyone she found remotely interesting. I remember Janet making remarks that showed interest in Margaret's relentless Conservatism but which were also hostile to it. Janet, whom I came to know well, persisted in this view and has talked about it in public, on a BBC programme.

In 1952, six years after we went down from Oxford, everyone in our year was invited to a 'Gaudy', the traditional reunion at Oxford colleges. Several generations were invited to each Gaudy, spanning about six to ten years. Our year was the youngest group to be invited. A representative of each generation was invited to dine on High Table and speak after dinner. The generation above us was represented by Iris Murdoch, just becoming known and admired as a writer. Her speech was appropriate, witty and penetrating. The speaker for our generation was Margaret Thatcher. When we heard that she was going to speak, we feared the worst, and so it was. She had recently become a parliamentary candidate and was about the only member of our year to have achieved anything in the world so far. It was then fashionable for young women graduates to marry and have babies as soon as they graduated.

When Irish Murdoch had finished, Margaret rose. She had lost the Midlands accent that her fellow students had known. Now she sounded more like Princess Elizabeth, who was not yet Queen and had not yet learned the appropriate mode of delivery that she later perfected. Margaret had not yet perfected her accent, and the speech was disconcerting in content. Princess Elizabeth used to talk of 'May hesband and Ay', which was quite a joke among our (her) generation. To our surprise, Margaret, newly married, now said just that and we, her contemporaries, felt ashamed that one of us could be so embarrassing. She then gave us her views on marriage and home life expressed in such sanctimonious platitudes that we were even more embarrassed to be associated with her. She didn't talk about children because at that stage she had none, though most of us were already mothers. The following year she upstaged us all by producing twins and one of her most vociferous Somerville critics exclaimed, 'How typical of Margaret! She *would* have twins!'

This was sad. Had we felt any kinship with her, we would have revelled in her success and been proud to be members of the year that produced the outstanding woman politician of all time. But to us she seemed not unpleasant or bossy, as many of her critics label her today, but alien and uncongenial. Of course, had she been 'one of us', she would not have been so successful.

When the Gaudy dinner was over I found myself talking to Janet Vaughan, the Principal. She looked glum and spoke angrily. 'That was *dreadful*. I'll *never* invite her to speak again.'

But Dr Vaughan did invite her again – to the very next Gaudy, four years later. No one else in our year had distinguished herself so much.

'Nobody thought anything of her,' Janet Vaughan told a Radio Four audience in the series of programmes called *The Thatcher Phenomenon* in 1985. 'She was a perfectly good second class chemist, a beta chemist.' She clearly remembered Margaret's next Gaudy speech better than I, so I will quote her:

> 'She came down to a Gaudy when she was Education Secretary, and she had been asked to make a speech. A Gaudy is a gay time, as you know: good food and good drink and good speeches. Up got Margaret to make her speech. "Hello, Somervillians and taxpayers," and she gave us a lecture on tax law. And this Somerville has never forgiven her for. But that is typical of her, absolutely typical. I suppose now she'd have people who would protect her from doing that sort of thing.'

Somerville women are fond of saying that Margaret is Britain's first woman prime minister but not Somerville's. This was Indira Gandhi, who went up in 1937.

I also came to know girls who were medical students. One of these, with whom I had been at kindergarten, was Zaida Megrah, later Dr Zaida Hall and, later still, Lady Ramsbotham. I was also friendly with beautiful Marie Woolf, niece of Leonard and Virginia. She and her sister Philippa had been at the Oxford High School with me and were both reading medicine at Somerville. Through the Woolfs I got to know another clever family of sisters called Scott Stokes. Forty years later, one of them, Susan, now Dr Sue Openshaw, and I comforted each other when we both became victims of professional and political attacks.

I envied the medical students because they were on the way to becoming doctors, but I was sure that my history course was more interesting than theirs.

During my last year, however, my old desire to be a doctor returned. This may have been partly because of my admiration for Dr Janet Vaughan, who was a distinguished haematologist. She was keen on my studying medicine, as was Dorothea Nasmyth. My parents generously agreed to support me further and finally I decided that I would go ahead. I was offered a place at St Thomas's Hospital in London, although I had to wait a year before they accepted women.

I spent the intervening year lecturing for the War Office, mostly in British-occupied Austria and Germany. My job was to tour the British zones lecturing on historical topics to soldiers as part of their compulsory hours of education. The alternative to attending my lectures was 'fatigues', such as cleaning the latrines, so my lectures were always well attended, but on the whole the British soldiery was not excited by historical subjects. I am sure that I learned more during that year than did my audiences.

It was strange to talk German again. I had spoken it with some fluency as a child, largely because of my friendship with a Russian-German cousin called Tamara, who never learned English. But my language had not kept pace with my age, and in German-speaking countries I found that I could only speak in the manner of a child, talking about animals and dolls as Mara and I had done. Unable to manage the polite address, I could only address everyone as *Du*. Since most Germans were very formal it was embarrassing. I couldn't even ask the way to the ladies' cloakroom but could only say something like 'Ich muss auf's Klo' or 'Ich muss mal', which caused great amusement. The equivalent in English might be to go up to a stranger and say, 'I want to go wee-wee!'

Being out in the world made me hesitate briefly about becoming a student again and embarking on the long medical course. Other offers of agreeable and even dazzling careers were made. But deep down I knew that I wanted to be a doctor, and I was not deflected. Finally I decided to take up my place at St Thomas's.

Chapter 2

Training

I entered the medical school at St Thomas's – London's second oldest hospital and one of the twelve that trained doctors as well as nurses – in October 1947. That was the year the London teaching hospitals were forced to accept women students. Before then the government money these hospitals received had depended on their taking either women or blacks. Now they had to accept both. It was a hundred years almost to the day since Elizabeth Blackwell, the first woman to gain a medical degree in the United States, had entered the medical school at Geneva, New York. The length of her course of studies was fourteen months; mine was seven years.

When I started at St Thomas's the new National Health Service was still nine months away. There had been strong opposition to it from the medical profession. One of the first things I saw when I arrived at Thomas's was a huge slogan, BOOT OUT BEVAN, painted on the river wall of the House of Commons, which faced the hospital across the Thames. It was already too late to do this, and it was left to the doctors to make the best of it.

The hospitals were aiming to build up the numbers of women to 10 per cent. This figure is low by today's standards, but at that time it seemed progressive and even daring. Six hundred suitably qualified women applied to St Thomas's for the first places. In the first year there were about seventy men and three women.

The other two women were both about six years older than I was. One of them, Elizabeth Cross (later Fletcher), became a close friend. Elizabeth had already worked in the Foreign Office in Italy and Egypt. Later, after raising four children, she became Chief Medical Officer to the BBC.

Soon after we arrived, Professor Barnard, Dean of the Medical School, spoke to the women with disarming frankness: 'We didn't want you, but since we have to have you, we'll do our best to make you welcome.'

There was little overt hostility towards us, but sexism was implicit, largely unnoticed because that was how it was. It did not bother us unless it was extreme, as was to happen in our final examination in pathology. We were even given our own 'women's tutor', a physiologist called Maureen, who was foolish enough to tell us that the best spare-time occupation for young women was bell-ringing. We had other ideas.

The women students were given a room in the basement, a glorified cloakroom but with a comfortable sofa. 'We arranged for the sofa so that you can rest when you are indisposed,' one of the male lecturers told us.

The hospital authorities, for all their desire to make things comfortable for us, regarded women students as unimportant. Then, as now, women were unlikely to be accepted in the upper echelons of the hospital or to rise far in the medical hierarchy.

Not having studied science beyond School Certificate biology, I was at a disadvantage compared with the other students who had studied chemistry and physics for years. I had eight months in which to learn these subjects to Higher Certificate (A-level) standard.

When I saw what this entailed, I felt foolish for having spent the previous year in non-academic pursuits. Failure in the First MB exam would mean instant expulsion. We would be allowed 'referral' or marginal failure in one subject if we achieved a reasonable mark, but even that would mean repeating the whole year. I was appalled at what I had taken on.

What I did have, however, was a higher level of general education than most of my peers. The subjects I had studied meant nothing to many of them or were even openly scorned. When a lecturer mentioned a work of literature or a great figure from history, he would be greeted with guffaws of contempt. Sadly, it was already the British tradition for future doctors and scientists to start specialising at an early age, often as young as twelve. Both students and teachers often seemed to feel that anything that could not be measured was unimportant.

This contempt for the arts and the past was accompanied by a disregard for the history of medicine. Anything more than about twenty years old was laughable. The history of medicine was simply an account of the march of progress, preparatory discoveries on the road to the present apex of knowledge. The only historical background we received was a fleeting impression of some 'great doctors' of the past, mostly through the diseases to which they gave their names. We learned that, if one diagnosed Bright's Disease during an oral examination, the examiner was likely to ask who Bright was. We were told that if we didn't know, the best bet was to say, 'Bright was a great surgeon of the nineteenth century' (or 'a great physician', depending on the exam and the disease). Unfortunately, sometimes the famous man who had identified the disease was the examiner himself. Bored by long hours spent questioning students, some examiners would pass the time by trying to catch candidates out in this way.

The enormous emphasis on the function and malfunction of the human body made it difficult to grasp the concept of the 'whole person'. We were exhorted to consider this, but often it meant no more than remembering that there were other systems and parts of the body. Focusing on one system at a time was essential in diagnosis, but it was also restricting. The psyche might not have existed.

In the first year we studied biology, physics and inorganic chemistry. Each had its laboratory in the long corridor of the medical school.

On the other side was an intriguing series of doors leading to a different world. This was the anatomy lab, the mysterious preserve of second- and third-year students where corpses lay naked on marble slabs. The doors to the anatomy lab were marked: NO ADMITTANCE TO UNAUTHORISED PERSONS. This made it seem all the more intriguing to us first-year students, who were forbidden to enter that laboratory. Meanwhile, across the corridor, we dissected humbler forms of life, first dogfish, then rabbits, cockroaches and worms.

I was incompetent at this – the worst of all the students. Though normally quite good with my hands, I always seemed to slip and cut vital vessels. This was probably because of my absurd fastidiousness about touching these dead creatures: I dissected them with a 'no-touch technique', holding scalpel and forceps in a way that kept my hands clean but which was liable to damage the specimen. I had never been bottom of the class before.

In charge of biology was Professor William Rushton, a doughty Lancastrian with a great admiration for my father. He always prefaced his comments with 'Ee!' and his cry rang out frequently over the class. 'Ee, Miss Mullins . . .' (he pronounced it Moollins), ' . . . daughter of a fa-a-a-mous father! 'Ave anoother dogfish!' Then he would present me with yet another fish, spotty, gritty and reeking of formalin. Everyone would laugh, but he assured me that I would eventually get the hang of it.

Most students managed to get through the whole biology course with just one or two dogfish. I used up eight. But Willie Rushton remained tolerant and kind and in the end he was rewarded. In the practical exam in biology during First MB, I suddenly found I could dissect. Before we had even left the laboratory at the end of the exam, old Willie was calling out to everyone in his inimitable voice: 'Ee! 'Oo do y'think's doon the best dissection? That Miss Moollins!'

Physics too opened a new world to me, even though I was bottom of the class again. I had had no idea how things worked before and I was surprised and rather ashamed that my natural curiosity, normally active, had allowed me to ignore such matters.

To my surprise, I managed to pass all three subjects and so qualified for pre-clinical studies, anatomy, physiology and organic chemistry, leading to the Second MB eighteen months later. But I knew I would never be a really scientific doctor.

Most of us probably felt curious but queasy on the day we were due to begin anatomy. Even now, more than forty years later, I can recall the slight feeling of dread in my stomach.

The technician opened the doors and we went in. There was a strong smell of formalin. The laboratory was much larger than our old ones. It was filled with two rows of long tables and on each table perched a long parcel, wrapped in a white sheet.

The Professor of Anatomy, Professor 'Dai' Davies, told us that we were to dissect in pairs, two pairs of students working on each body or limb. He expected us to attend all dissecting sessions, which were four half-days a week, to arrive punctually and stay until the end. Anatomy seemed to be taken more seriously than any other subject: no other department was so strict.

I was allotted a table on the extreme left. Its parcel lay wrapped in its sheet and smelling, as they all did, of formalin. I stood back as the two students on the other side eagerly unwrapped the parcel. Inside was the body of a little old man of spare build, somewhat shrivelled. The white-yellow colour of his skin tinged with grey surprised me. I had never seen that precise colour before. My feeling of dread persisted but I felt I could come to terms with it because the body was so anonymous. But then I saw the label. It was tied round his ankle and it said 'ALFRED SEXTON, aged 74'. Suddenly this impersonal body was a person, with a name and an age.

Even though I became quite fond of Alfred Sexton, I was even more reluctant to touch him than I had been to touch the dogfish in biology. Indeed I scarcely ever did: my earlier experience in no-touch dissecting stood me in good stead. I never got used to touching dead bodies or cutting living flesh, and I still get a funny feeling when I see a surgeon make an incision through intact flesh, though I have made many myself. I would much prefer, for instance, to deliver a baby with my bare hands, as one has to do if things move too quickly for preparation, than make a cut through skin wearing protective gear.

Of course every future doctor needs a grounding in anatomy, but the detail with which we studied it was a relic of the days when there was little else to learn. For most of us the detail was a waste of time. Even those intending to be surgeons would have to study it again in greater detail while working for their fellowship of the Royal College of Surgeons. We would have been better off studying subjects such as psychology and statistics, medical history, social medicine and even logic, but these were barely touched on.

Physiology wasn't much better. We were simply expected to learn the answers to questions we were likely to be asked in the examinations. When I was at school even irregular verbs had been learned in small and manageable doses, interspersed with matters of greater interest. Here the daily grind of learning without questioning was depressing.

Had it not been for exciting developments in my personal life, I would have been discouraged. The man in my life was Peter Dally, a fellow student. He had been a regular sailor, a lieutenant in the Royal Navy. He came from a naval family but was unsuited to naval life and at the end of the war, given the opportunity of being invalided out he welcomed the chance and decided to study medicine.

Peter was the most exciting man I had ever met. He soon moved into lodgings in Barnsbury Street, Islington, near where I lived in Canonbury Square. We did most of our studying together and this greatly relieved the tedium.

Much of the physiology course consisted of estimating gases, usually in blood, by methods used in the nineteenth century. There were already easier methods, and this knowledge did not increase our enthusiasm for the old apparatus.

Other aspects of physiology were more interesting. For example, we were shown neurological patients who had conditions that could clearly be linked with what we were learning. This glimpse of real patients was exciting, and it helped one to learn by providing 'pegs' for learning. One of the most interesting physiology teachers was a young demonstrator, Jim Tanner, who later became famous for his work on child development. He taught us something of genetics and statistics by designing simple experiments that we could do on ourselves and each other. We charted each other's height and the colour of our hair and tested our partners for colour-blindness. We tasted a bitter substance, phenyl-thiourea, to discover how many of us were unable to taste it, a hereditary trait. I was a 'non-taster' but I never knew if this had significance.

One day in a physiology class the subject of education was mentioned. Dr Vass, the senior lecturer, called out to one of the students with his customary directness: 'Education! What's that? Hey, you in the corner! Wake up! Tell me, what is education?'

The student was startled. 'Education, sir? Er – er – education is facts.'

'Wrong!' cried Dr Vass. 'I'll tell you what education is. *Education is getting – facts – out – of – people!*'

I have always thought that this summed up our pre-clinical education, and, to some extent, the whole medical course.

Two days after passing our Second MB, in March 1950, Peter and I were married. After five days' honeymoon in Paris we started hospital work in Casualty at St Thomas's.

Seeing patients every day, we felt we were now taking part in real medical practice. All day and most of the night ambulances drove up the slope, discharged the people they carried, and drove out down the other side. We were called 'dressers' and were expected to do routine work. We also assisted at minor operations and if we showed aptitude were soon allowed to do some ourselves. I didn't care for this: I have always preferred my patients to be conscious.

I came to understand better some of the doubts and certainties of medicine. Sewing people up, diagnosing their problems and comforting them seemed to be completely right. One can seldom be so sure of oneself as when sewing up an injury. I was less certain about the methods we used and some of the things we were taught. Although in theory patients were held to be more important than anything else, this didn't always seem to be so in practice. Some doctors seemed hard and uncaring. In particular, few of them had much understanding of women's problems. For instance, a woman lying on her back naked from the waist down with her feet tied to poles, in the 'lithotomy' position, might be expected to answer questions from students, nurses and doctors. Even the senior nurses, energetic and efficient as they were – and almost all spinsters – weren't in tune with women and their problems.

Many of these problems were so immense and so far outside our experience or the ability of the hospital to deal with that they were simply ignored. For example, a woman with twelve children under the age of fourteen and a drunken husband who had beaten her up might have her head stitched up without even an acknowledgement of her real state.

One procedure we all had to learn was putting a 'Wassermann' needle into a vein. It was easier to take blood with a syringe but took longer and required more sterilising. There was little disposable equipment in those days and I hate to think of the viruses these needles may have spread, but no one talked of viruses in that connection.

Wassermann needles were used in taking blood for tests, sometimes for the Wassermann test for syphilis. This was routine for every patient with symptoms that were not straightforward. Patients were rarely told what we were testing for; permission was certainly not sought, and I don't think they were usually told even if the disease was found. Had we considered the ethics of this, which we did not, I am sure we would have said that simply by presenting himself the patient gave tacit permission for any investigation we thought necessary, and that it would not be possible to explain or get permission for every test.

The first patient from whom I took blood was a hefty workman. As he stood at the end of the long wooden bench crowded with patients and held out his arm, I was thankful to see big veins standing out under his skin. I knew where to plunge the needle and felt confident that I would succeed. And I did, in the sense that I put the needle into the right place. But as it entered his arm, he fainted and fell to the marble floor. Ashamed and embarrassed, I learned two fundamental lessons from this incident. First, always sit the patient down before inserting a needle. Second, think of the possible consequences before you do anything to a patient.

This last was underlined by some splendid advice given by several of our teachers: 'Don't just do something. Stand there!' In other words, if you aren't sure what to do in an emergency, frenzied activity can make things worse. So stand and think. Wait and see. Have the patience and courage to do nothing and to be seen to do nothing. Distinguish between what is possible and what is not, between what might help the patient and what merely makes the doctor feel better. This is sometimes difficult if patients and their relatives expect action, and think you are a bad doctor if you don't take it.

For most of us, Casualty was our first sustained exposure to some of the strange people who attend hospitals. I saw my first 'Saturday night paralysis', damage to the radial nerve in the arm which can be caused by resting the arm over the back of a chair and being too drunk to notice when it 'goes to sleep'. 'Hospital addicts' always came up with some excuse or other in the hope of being admitted. The worst of these – later known, incorrectly, as suffering from 'Munchausen syndrome' – seek surgical operations. When recognised or correctly diagnosed, they rise from their beds and depart to seek another hospital.

More sinister were mothers who damaged their children in the hope of having them admitted. In those days no one gave much thought to this kind of behaviour. There was widespread resistance to the idea that parents might deliberately injure their children. In 1948, when radiologists said that this was the only logical explanation of children's X-rays showing multiple fractures of different ages, other doctors, including paediatricians, could not accept it. Most of our training was geared to diagnosing physical disease, for that was regarded as the only respectable thing to do. It also seemed dangerous not to do it in case there really was something physically wrong. It was considered much better to make a false physical diagnosis and exacerbate a psychiatric disorder than to miss a 'physical diagnosis', even if it had nothing to do with the symptoms and could not be treated.

I learned the folly of this later as a house physician. One patient in the ward, a house-painter, was being investigated for long-standing fatigue and consequent inability to work. My boss, a physician with a great understanding of psychiatry, clearly thought that his troubles were 'functional', meaning psychological. But I made a diagnosis of myxoedema or low levels of thyroid hormone, which I cleverly proceeded to prove with the appropriate tests. When I proudly told my chief, he laughed and said: 'Well, you've made the diagnosis. Now cure the condition! I bet you a fiver he'll never work again.'

He was right. I cured the myxoedema and for a week the patient said he felt better. Later I realised that this was due to the increased attention he had received. When the question arose of his returning to work, his symptoms returned.

Even when psychological disorder was recognised, it was seldom dealt with skilfully, partly because of the distaste most doctors felt for things psychiatric. The attitude was that if the patient was 'unmasked', the best thing to do was to discharge him rather than try to help him.

I slowly realised that medicine as viewed at St Thomas's had little to do with healing. It was concerned chiefly with diagnosis, and particularly the intellectual exercise known as 'differential diagnosis'. This is a game in which the doctor thinks of all the possible causes of the patient's symptoms and eliminates them one by one. Diagnosis was all-important because, once made, the treatment could be looked up in a book. This is not entirely true, although diagnosis certainly has its place. Too many doctors and 'therapists' offer treatment without making a diagnosis.

After three months in Casualty we spent another three months in pathology and then returned to the hospital wards for the main part of the course: six months each of medicine, surgery and anaesthetics, and midwifery and gynaecology. After that came a further six months for minor special subjects, none of which was regarded as very important. These included eyes, then ear, nose and throat, skins, fevers, tuberculosis, venereal disease, psychiatry and so on.

As clinical students, we were allocated patients to look after. We had to 'take a full history' and then examine the patient, make a diagnosis and recommend the appropriate treatment. Everything had to be written up, partly to inform others and partly for our teachers to criticise. 'Taking a history' is a methodical way of getting to know as much as possible about a patient. In practice it may mean little more than finding out something about his past illnesses and the story of his present complaint, but we were taught that it can, and should, cover much more. A good history can illuminate and reveal many important factors in a patient's condition. It may involve early childhood, schooling, brothers and sisters, and much else about the family's past. Sometimes the circumstances of birth and the lives of forebears may be relevant. The history will cover the present circumstances of the patient's life, including his habits, marriage, family, work and interests. Any of these may be relevant in ways that are often subtle and sometimes practical. I remember two patients with lead poisoning: both these mysteries were solved by careful history-taking. The cause in one was traced to his wife poisoning him and in the other to a habit of drinking a glass of water first thing in the morning without first letting the tap run.

In learning about the patient's work we were told to pay special attention to what he or she actually did. I remember a brewery worker with mysterious symptoms whose job in the brewery was to polish the copper pipes, and so copper poisoning, as well as alcoholism, had to be excluded as a possible cause of his illness.

We had to know every detail of these histories and examinations without looking at the notes, so that we knew far more about the patient as a person than did the doctors in charge. We were also expected to refer to the patient by name. This excellent custom may have been peculiar to St Thomas's: I have seldom observed it in doctors trained elsewhere. We took specimens for laboratory tests, carried out minor medical and surgical procedures, and assisted the consultant surgeon or registrar at any operation the patient might have. This was by far the most interesting part of the course.

We learned that the word 'medicine' has several meanings. It can cover the whole subject, as in 'studying medicine', and it also distinguishes certain specialties or branches of practice, in contrast to 'surgery'. The difference is largely one of the type of treatment regarded as appropriate and of the training of the doctor who performs it. Traditionally, doctors were categorised as 'physicians', who at one time did not touch their patients but listened, observed, advised and prescribed, and 'surgeons', originally 'barber-surgeons', who, as well as cutting hair, dealt mostly with external problems – abscesses, accidents and fractures, especially in limbs. The basic division remains today but it is more complicated. If the patient's problem is damage to the body from an accident or a condition which might be relieved by a surgical operation, it is treated by a surgeon, who may never operate on it. Otherwise it is 'medical' and treated by a physician, at least until such time as he hands the problem over to a surgeon. 'Medicine' as practised by a 'physician' is often used in the sense in which those from other countries use the term 'internal medicine', practised by an 'internist'. These refer to specialism in disease which mostly lies inside the body. The distinction is not absolute and has developed partly through chance and convenience of practice.

Medicine became my great interest: under other circumstances I might have stayed with it. I disliked surgery for reasons which by now must be apparent.

Midwifery, on the other hand, brought me unprecedented satisfaction. There is something about a newborn baby that defies all the problems of living. There it is, perfect, the embodiment of hope. The miracle of birth has never ceased to fill me with awe and joy. The best obstetricians are those who never lose that feeling.

We did part of our midwifery training 'on the district', just as Somerset Maugham had done when he was studying medicine at St Thomas's. Most babies were delivered at home, even if conditions there were not good, and a student accompanied the midwife and was expected to stay until the baby was born. Sometimes there was no lavatory or running water, newspapers were used instead of blankets and there was nowhere to cook. But even a woman expecting her first baby had no right to a hospital bed. These were reserved for 'complicated deliveries' and for 'grand multips', women who had had at least four previous babies.

I remember a delivery in a tenement building near Waterloo station. We had to turn the children out of the flat because there was no room for them and the delivery. As the baby was born a sound came from above. I looked up and saw a row of small faces pressed against the skylight.

The first midwife I went out with taught me how to sleep under such conditions. Sometimes one had to wait many hours, even days, and often there was no sofa or even an armchair. The midwife showed me how one can sleep facing backwards astride an upright wooden chair, resting one's head on one's arms. It was surprisingly comfortable.

By the time I qualified I had two babies of my own. Since the hours I would have had to work at St Thomas's would have been unfair to them, I did not apply for a job there. Hours were somewhat better in non-teaching hospitals but jobs were hard to find. Eventually I heard that Dr Alexander Kahan, Consultant Physician at St James' Hospital, Balham, was looking for a house physician. Dr Kahan was said to be sympathetic to working mothers. His wife, a doctor and working mother, had recently died. He gave me the job, but with the warning that 'if the baby gets measles, you can't have any time off'. I promised not to take such liberties and hoped desperately that such a disaster would not arise.

St James' was a general hospital with 650 beds and a new out-patient building which, the administrators boasted, was 'the only hospital building built since the Second World War'.

By the time I qualified as a doctor in 1953, the National Health Service was past its teething troubles. The service then was probably as good as it would ever be, though many of us had visions of perpetual improvement. This was the period when the NHS had the reputation for being 'the envy of the world'. We had a sense of participating in an important step forward in the march of humanity. Despite lingering remnants of old traditions, we were sure that this was the beginning of the new era of advanced social and scientific medicine. Never again would people die because they could not afford medical treatment.

At times the advance of science seemed paradoxical, even absurd.

For instance, we saw a number of cases of a disease known as thyroiditis or 'woody thyroid', for which the traditional treatment was tablets of thyroid extract. Suddenly everyone seemed to be excited about this disease. I believe it was one of the first 'auto-immune' diseases to be identified. Procedures for investigating it were enlarged and changed. The patient was admitted to hospital and submitted to a range of laboratory tests. When the investigations were complete, the patient was discharged with the appropriate treatment. And what was that? The same tablets of thyroid extract as before.

Sometimes the absurdity gave me a peculiar prickly sensation, making me think of the story of the Emperor's new clothes. I have always found it interesting to study this feeling when I get it, particularly if others are reacting differently. After some years I realised that it arises when I confront a certain type of hypocrisy or pretence – especially an unconscious pretence. I am sure that the Emperor and his admirers believed consciously that his clothes were real, but they must have known somewhere that they were not. The ability to recognise these unconscious lies is important in a doctor and essential in a psychiatrist. Sometimes the unconscious lie is external and relatively simple, involving no obvious internal conflict. I suppose that this is why I got my uncomfortable feeling in the 'metabolic ward' at St Thomas's, a research ward run by an endocrinologist called Dr Prunty.

Of all the wards in the hospital, his, we were told, was the most expensive to run. It was the only one with air-conditioning, which was almost unknown in those days. Measurements were made of the oxygen entering the ward and the carbon dioxide leaving it. All food brought in from the hospital kitchens was taken to a special laboratory kitchen, where it was analysed and weighed on 'chemical' rather than 'kitchen' scales. Everything eaten and drunk by each patient was weighed, measured and meticulously analysed.

The ward was divided into small rooms, each containing two or three patients. One of these rooms contained two patients of outstanding interest in relation to calcium metabolism. The first was a woman in early middle age who continued to excrete large amounts of calcium even though she was on a special calcium-free diet. The other was a young girl, also thought to have a disease of calcium metabolism, who failed to gain weight despite being given large quantities of food and extra supplements. All this was demonstrably true: the charts of both women showed the results of the many chemical tests as well as of the 'input–output' of each patient, a record of everything that the patient had taken in or given out. Keeping those charts involved an enormous amount of skilled time. It was impressive, and Dr Prunty was pleased with the research that he and his team were doing. But I became aware of my prickly feeling.

The explanation came some weeks after both women had been discharged, and probably after Dr Prunty and his team had written up the results for a learned journal. The older woman attended the out-patients department and was allotted to a student who, according to the custom, talked to her and examined her before she saw the consultant. She said: 'I had a lovely time in hospital because the girl in the other bed used to give me all her milk!'

Looking back on it now, I can see that the middle-aged woman was probably physically normal but suffering from problems at home while the girl was a classical case of anorexia nervosa. In those days this was such a rare condition that if it was diagnosed, all the students in the hospital were told to go and look. No one liked to make psychiatric diagnoses if they could avoid it, and we were continually warned of the dangers of doing so in patients who then turned out to have 'organic' disease. So our teachers preferred to accept these patients at their face value.

I don't think anyone had the heart to tell Prunty the true explanation of his 'interesting cases'.

In the early years of the National Health Service, we doctors believed that there was a 'backlog' of disease which we were now able to treat and which, when this had been done, would not recur because better medical care would lead to prevention. Although much has since been made of the fallacy of this argument, there was also truth in it. Nowadays people recognise that the 'infinite demand' for medical care can never be satisfied, and this is sometimes used as an argument for not providing it. But I remember many people with painful conditions which any competent surgeon could have prevented years earlier.

Many patients bore unmistakable marks of the Depression, particularly signs of former malnourishment. The inner suburbs of London were still full of undersized men and women who had suffered from tuberculosis and other serious infections, from disasters of childbirth and social catastrophe. In enquiring about a patient's past health, doctors often asked, 'What was your best weight?', meaning, 'What is the most you have ever weighed?' Today, 'best weight' would be more likely to mean 'lowest ever adult weight'.

These conditions are much rarer today. The backlog of disease has largely disappeared. Even so, more could have been done. I think I first realised this when I was newly qualified and working at St James'. Among the junior doctors was Bob Spencer, an energetic young surgeon from New Zealand who was senior surgical registrar at St James'. One of Bob's duties was to attend surgical emergencies that arose in Springfield, the local mental hospital. During his visits there he noticed many chronic mental patients who needed operations. But no one appeared to be concerned unless the patient was in danger of dying. It did not seem to have occurred to the rather sleepy psychiatrists running the hospital that, for instance, a hernia might be better dealt with before it became life-threatening, or that a patient's mental state might improve if he was relieved of chronic pain or disability.

In the true spirit of the NHS, Bob decided to devote his scanty free time to holding a weekly surgical out-patients' clinic at Springfield and to operate on patients needing operations at St James'. We all encouraged him and offered help. If this meant a few more disturbed nights, it was worth it for the increased health we would bring to the mental patients. Even the consultants were willing to work a little harder and allow a little more pressure on their staff.

But Bob had reckoned without the administrators. There were few of them in those days but he was summoned and told that he had no right to do this work and was to stop seeing these patients immediately. The person who summoned Bob was the Medical Superintendent's secretary, a middle-aged woman called Mrs Harrington. Shutting down the Springfield clinic clearly gave her pleasure; we suspected that it had been her idea. This was the first time I saw essential medical treatment being deliberately withheld because it did not suit those in power. Years later I was to remember it forcefully.

Mrs Harrington was a stickler for rules. She would scour the hospital pursuing a doctor who had missed a day's holiday and then, often in front of his patients, would accuse him of theft: because he had worked when he should have had a day off, he had drunk coffee and eaten food to which he was not entitled. This, she said, was an offence. She would force doctors to leave what they were doing, especially at inconvenient moments, and go to her office to sort out a minor administrative detail. 'It's important to have *all* papers in order in *every* detail *all* the time. Otherwise why have papers?'

Later I realised that Mrs Harrington was an example of an extreme authoritarian personality. Seeing all relationships in terms of dominance and submission, she exerted her power with visible satisfaction. She was the first person I met who openly enjoyed persecuting doctors. Later I discovered that the characteristic is not uncommon, especially in those who work with doctors but lack their training or their power to prescribe drugs.

Most of the consultants understood Mrs Harrington and conspired with their juniors to outwit her, but the Medical Superintendent always seemed to support her; he was said to be afraid of her. Several doctors' contracts were not renewed when everyone knew they should have been. Several times to my knowledge Mrs Harrington told patients or their relatives that she thought the doctors had not done their job properly. Luckily this was before the days when patients sued readily.

We junior doctors dealt with our anxieties about Mrs Harrington by regarding her as a joke. Looking back, I am surprised at our compliance. But jobs were scarce, especially in London. Junior doctors had short contracts, some for only six months. Mrs Harrington probably had the power to ensure that rebellious doctors would be replaced.

The hospital consultants had permanent appointments and could not be dismissed unless they did something dreadful: they could have done more to protect the patients. As I found to my cost later, many people will sympathise with someone who is being treated unjustly, but few are willing to give positive help.

Chapter 3

Priorities

In my early years as a doctor I noticed only a little discrepancy between the idealism of my youth and medicine as it was practised. Nearly everyone showed dedication and a spirit of service to patients. This, we were told repeatedly, was the first priority. And by and large it was; the exceptions usually arose from ignorance and insensitivity rather than a deliberate will to harm.

The first exception I came across was administrative nonsense such as Mrs Harrington loved to create. In her world, rules are made to be kept and nothing was more important than papers in order.

The other exception was more serious. While most people tried to do their best for the patients, understanding and warmth were often lacking in students and still more in those who taught us. Some consultants did ward rounds without speaking to a patient at all, or talked about a patient in his presence as though he weren't there, and in technical language which it was assumed he would not understand. In fact the patient was likely to understand partially and to misinterpret what was said. There was no feeling that better decisions might be made if the patient was brought into the discussions: this would have been regarded as undignified and unscientific.

One way of dealing with this problem was not to teach at all in the presence of patients. Mr Bowes, an obstetrician, a warm and jolly man, used to take his group or 'firm' round the ward in comparative silence, then ask us to bring chairs into the ward bathroom. There he would teach us about what we had seen. When I asked him why he did this, he smiled and said: 'Once I was teaching at the bedside of a newly delivered mother, describing to students what it's like to have a baby. Suddenly the mother looked up and said, "Sez you!" Since then I have preferred to talk to students on their own.'

Much of the coldness of his colleagues resulted from the hierarchical structure of the teaching hospital. The consultant was firmly at the top and the patient at the bottom. Another reason was the need for doctors and students to deal with their own anxieties. These are often unconscious in students learning to look after sick people and to explore the mysteries of birth and death. Yet no one talked about or helped us with these problems. I think our teachers were unaware of them even in themselves.

One way that these anxieties were dealt with was to increase and emphasise control over the patients. This aim was, and often still is, common in hospitals; whole systems devoted to it can develop within the hospital structure. The attitude is epitomised in the story of a patient who had overheard the doctors talking about her. She asked the nurse: 'Sister, is it true that I'm expecting twins?'

'Mind your own business,' snapped the nurse.

Deliberate cruelty towards patients was, however, rare. Most of those who acted inhumanely would have been upset to know the effect they had on the patients.

When I first arrived at St James' as a house physician in my first job, I was lucky to work under Morag Arkeson, an exceptional young doctor. I learned more about humane attitudes from watching her than I had ever done in medical school. Morag was a little younger than I but had already been qualified for several years. She had been working as a locum in the job that I was about to do while she waited to become the paediatric registrar. This post would not be vacant for a few days, so she was asked to stay on to initiate me into the duties of a house physician.

As Morag took me round the hospital and introduced me to patients and staff, I was immediately impressed by her quiet way with patients. She made a rapport even with those who were in severe discomfort, raving or cantankerous. I had not seen this skill in action before, perhaps because St Thomas's had been much more formal and perhaps because I had never been taught clinical medicine by a woman. Not that all women have the gift of inspiring confidence and closeness: some are as bad as the worst men.

In hospital it is easy to become unwittingly involved in inhuman processes. One patient has haunted me for more than thirty years.

Her name was Vera Protts. She was brought into Casualty one Saturday afternoon when I was the gynaecological house surgeon on duty. Although she was clearly ill and in pain, we liked each other instantly.

Vera, twenty-eight, was married with a son aged six and was five months pregnant. She had booked for her confinement at the hospital, but then her marriage broke down. Things were so bad that she felt she had to leave her husband. She found a job as a barmaid where she could live in. Her son was welcome, but her employers would not accept a baby. She became desperate. Still early in her pregnancy, she visited the hospital social worker (we called them almoners or 'lady almoners') to say that she wished to have the baby adopted because she couldn't provide a good home.

The almoner was unsympathetic. Since Vera was legally married, she told her, there was no possibility of having the baby adopted. She offered no help and made no further appointment.

Vera was frantic. This was long before the Abortion Act of 1967, so it was impossible for her to get a legal abortion. She tried hard to find another job, but in vain. So she went to a back-street abortionist in Hoxton, East London. 'He hurt me dreadfully,' she said, 'and since then I've had a different kind of pain and feel ill. My mother called the doctor. He called the ambulance.'

The doctor had also informed the police. This was rare: there were so many illegal abortions that the police were interested only in those with fatal outcome. Clearly the doctor realised Vera might die.

He was right to fear that. Vera had had a septic abortion and was infected with the dreaded 'gas gangrene' organisms that had killed so many wounded soldiers on the battlefields. I looked after her for a month, during which she remained seriously ill. At times she felt better and liked to talk. She gave the police a clear description of the abortionist, someone they had long been trying to arrest. They hoped that she would soon be well enough to testify, but we knew Vera would never go to court. If she died, the statement she had made to the police could not be used as evidence.

If Vera was not going to recover, the only way of using her statement was by a 'Dying Declaration'. A magistrate would come to the ward and Vera would have to acknowledge that she was dying and sign her statement in front of him. Then the police could arrest the man and bring him to trial.

My consultant said that since Vera knew me better than anyone else in the hospital, I was the one who should explain the situation to her and persuade her to sign. She told me to wait until I thought Vera was about to fall into a final coma, and I could then set the machinery in motion.

Vera had never mentioned death. She had always talked of getting well, returning to her little boy and starting her new job. But my seniors persuaded me that by now she knew she was dying, and the police inspector who told me the procedure was charming and persuasive. 'You wouldn't want to be responsible for other young women meeting the same fate, now would you, doctor? . . . You are easily the best person to do it, doctor.' There was always that flattering, ingratiating 'doctor'.

This was probably true. 'If it has to be done,' I said, 'I wouldn't want anyone else to do it.' And I persuaded myself that Vera must have realised by then that she was dying.

It was late at night. I did my last ward round and realised that she was beginning to slip away. It was now or never. I rang the magistrate and he came, a big, red-faced man; I could see his pyjamas under his coat. There seemed to be a lot of policemen. Not wanting the other patients to hear, I asked the nurses to push Vera's bed into the corridor. The ward was full of women who had had illegal abortions.

I carried a stool out and sat down beside the bed as I had done so often before. I still remember the conversation.

'Vera, I think you know that you are very ill, don't you?'

'Yes, I know.' She spoke slowly and sleepily.

I took a deep breath and sought courage.

'And I think you know that you may not recover from this.'

Her reaction startled me. A moment before she had been semiconscious. Suddenly she was alert, even lifting herself on her elbow, which she had been unable to do for days. She almost shouted at me: *'I'm not going to die!'*

I didn't get anywhere near the subject of the Dying Declaration. Vera became acutely distressed, almost wild. I had to sedate her and send the police and the magistrate home.

For some days Vera's health improved. The incident seemed to have stimulated her into some sort of recovery; we even had hopes that it might be permanent. But she would have nothing more to do with me. Other doctors looked after her and gave me glowing reports of her progress.

Her improved state lasted for two weeks. Then one evening I was on duty at the Obstetric Hospital three miles away when John

Holmes, the gynaecological registrar, came in and spoke in a solemn voice. 'Vera Protts has joined the great majority!'

I had to give evidence at an inquest at the coroner's court in Sheepcote Lane. The police were there. So were the abortionist and his wife, who declared that they had never seen Vera. No one mentioned the Dying Declaration. The police told me that the file would stay open and that the charge would be murder. Afterwards Vera's mother thanked me for all I had done for Vera, her only daughter. I felt upset. I had learned how easily small inhuman acts or even thoughtless omissions can accumulate until the idea that one is doing one's best for the patient becomes a travesty.

Vera Protts's abortion was unusual only because she died. Of the ward's thirty-seven beds, at least thirty were always taken up with complications following illegal abortion. Only a small minority of women who had illegal abortions were admitted to hospital. Many suffered no complications and some who did dared not call the doctor in case he told the police. In practice the police showed no interest unless there were special circumstances, as in the case of Vera Protts.

Many of the women who found themselves in hospital were at risk of dying, but if treated promptly they usually recovered quickly. As soon as they were fit they were discharged, and another bleeding, exhausted woman would occupy the bed. There were seldom any empty beds. General practitioners spent much of their time trying to find beds for abortion cases.

All that changed with the 1967 Abortion Act. By then it had become clear that, whatever one thought of abortion – and everyone in the medical profession disliked it – huge numbers of women would always continue to obtain it. And there would always be willing abortionists. Moralising might make the moralists feel better, but it helped no one else. Anyone who saw those gynaecological wards knows the terrible state of affairs they revealed. I find it appalling that so many people in the present generation wish to return to that situation.

We did not deal only with spontaneous or illegal abortions. We also did them ourselves, or some of us did. When I started in my gynaecological house job, Isabel (Issy) Bishop, one of the two women consultants for whom I was to work, said: 'I shall rely on you to do the evil deeds.' She meant that all the other members of the team apart from the consultants were Roman Catholics and refused to do abortions. Most of the nurses were Catholic, too. But Issy and Lois Hurter both did abortions when they thought they were needed.

They did not act illegally. Then, as now, abortions could be carried out if the health of the mother was deemed by at least two doctors to be endangered. Our cases were all seriously ill but the Abortion Act of 1967 largely codified and made more respectable what many gynaecologists had long done in practice. Dugald Baird (later Sir Dugald), Professor of Obstetrics and Gynaecology in Aberdeen, had done large numbers of abortions on women who felt they could not cope with a new baby. A man of vision and daring, he believed it was part of his job to keep down the population of Aberdeen. Many others approved in principle, knowing what the alternative was in terms of human life and distress.

All the same, there was unpleasantness. Sometimes doctors, nurses or police made trouble. Some areas of the country were dominated by gynaecologists who refused to perform abortions or who pretended that they did them and then made difficulties. No one likes doing abortions, but most of those who do them regard them as the lesser of two evils.

Another area in which I felt a lack of humanity was psychiatry. The subject itself was ranked low, perhaps bottom in the hierarchy of specialties. General surgery and general medicine were at the top. Next came obstetrics and gynaecology, then smaller surgical specialties such as ear, nose and throat, eyes, orthopaedics and plastic surgery, the lesser medical specialties such as dermatology and gastrology, and non-clinical subjects such as haematology and chemical pathology. Last came psychiatry. No subject was more despised by medical students and their teachers, not even venereal disease.

Psychiatry itself, like other specialties, was dominated by hierarchies. Consultants in London teaching hospitals were held in infinitely higher esteem than those in mental hospitals or, lower still, in prison psychiatry, mental deficiency, alcoholism or drug addiction. These distinctions became important when addiction came into the public eye in the 1960s.

At St James' we saw many psychiatric patients but effectively had no psychiatrist. Once a week a doctor named Dr Batt would come from Springfield Mental Hospital to see patients referred to him. Dr Kahan, my boss, warned me: 'You will find that Batt is helpful only if you want to get rid of the patient, in which case he'll arrange for him to be taken to the bin. In any case, it's much better to do your own psychiatry. You'll learn a lot and it will be better for the patients.'

Kahan was a talented if untrained psychiatrist. I learned much from him, including the first principle of all psychiatry, indeed of all medicine, which is: 'Listen, and don't condemn.'

The second priority at St Thomas's, after the care of patients, was the teaching of students. In a way the whole hospital was organised for this purpose. Many patients enjoyed being the centre of attention and regarded as 'interesting', or were glad to be of use in training doctors. Some were old hands, often kept on because of their rare diseases and their outgoing personalities. Their regular visits to the hospital were an important part of their lives. They were also paid a few shillings for coming to examinations or agreeing to be demonstrated in lectures.

Some of the teaching was old-fashioned and irrelevant. It was also, by today's standards, sexist. Women patients were often addressed as 'Sweetie', 'Mother' or 'Grandma'. Doctors at all levels seemed to assume that women patients were stupid, mysterious, or both. These attitudes extended into what we were taught.

But some of the teaching was brilliant. To this day I don't know how the teachers managed to get into our heads so clearly what to do and what not to do and when. I found this particularly impressive when it came to orthopaedics and emergencies. The Professor of Surgery was a friendly orthopaedic surgeon called Professor Perkins. Without much visible effort on either side, he instilled into us enough of the principles of orthopaedics to be invaluable in future years. 'Active movements!' he would call out in a cheerful voice, or 'Collar and cuff!' Later, when I had to take such decisions myself, I was seldom indecisive. Unlike some colleagues who had trained elsewhere, I always seemed to know what to do in orthopaedics, including when to X-ray and when to call for specialist help. Perkins's teaching played an important part in building my later confidence as a doctor, though I did not fully appreciate him at the time.

The third priority at St Thomas's was research, of which there was a great deal. Some of our teachers clearly preferred it to looking after patients or teaching students, even though it was continually emphasised that research came second to the patients' welfare.

It was shocking and sometimes amusing when our elders fell from grace in this respect. For instance, there was Professor Sharpey-Shafer, the clever and eccentric Professor of Medicine. I learned much from him that was later valuable, but he had some unattractive habits. He used to walk down the ward using his rather grubby thumb to turn down the lower lip of each patient. He was looking at the mucosal membrane lining the mouth and demonstrating it to us, but he would do this without washing or even wiping his thumb, which was always stained with chemicals and tobacco and had probably come unwashed from his laboratory.

Even more shocking was Sharpey-Shafer's custom of asking patients scheduled for minor operations whether he could put a 'small tube' into a vein during the operation. He explained that he wanted to find out about their blood, and patients always agreed, being only too willing to help the hospital. What Sharpey-Shafer failed to explain was that the 'small tube' was a cardiac catheter, and that he would be pushing it up the vein until it reached the heart. This procedure was new, with a risk of death he didn't mention. On at least one occasion he dropped the cardiac catheter on to the theatre floor during an operation, looked round to see if anyone had noticed, and then inserted it into the patient's arm and pushed it along to the heart. One of his favourite sayings was, 'There is no better sterilising agent than circulating blood.'

Some of the research at St Thomas's seemed daft to us. For example, Ian Donald, an obstetrician who was later a pioneer in ultrasound techniques, had invented a machine to save newborn lives. The machine was so complicated that he was allowed to experiment only with babies who were already dead or dying. Not surprisingly, his failure rate was 100 per cent. Another young enthusiast had invented a machine for measuring flatus, or fart.

One type of research we did not see at St Thomas's was what Peter and I called 'tomato research'. We named it this after an expensive study which showed that dropping a tomato on to a hard surface does more damage than dropping it on to a soft surface, and that dropping it repeatedly does more damage than dropping it only once. Tomato research did go on at other hospitals. One study done at the Maudsley Hospital demonstrated with formidable arguments and statistics that schizophrenics whose families were prepared to look after them spent less time in hospital than schizophrenics who had no families. A work of comparable profundity showed that the chief leisure interest of teenage boys was girls, while the chief leisure interest of teenage girls was boys. Yet another study showed convincingly that children aged ten are bigger than children aged eight.

Fortunately there is not much tomato research in medicine. The exception is psychiatry, which seems to thrive on it.

*

The last priority at St Thomas's was the amusement of those who worked and studied in the hospital. This may sound a terrible thing to say, but it is actually important. Jokes kept us going through the fatigue and anxiety, and through the unhappiness of seeing on the post-mortem slab a patient with whom one has built up a relationship. Amusing stories quickly made the rounds.

For instance, one man frequently arrived in Casualty saying that there were snakes in his rectum. An enthusiastic young casualty officer had the idea of anaesthetising this patient briefly and then telling him that the snakes had been removed. To strengthen his argument, when the patient came round, he showed him a jar full of slow-worms that he had brought in for the purpose. 'There! I've removed your snakes. They won't trouble you any more.' He had reckoned without the strength and tenacity of paranoid delusions. The patient demanded that the snakes be put back at once, and he became so disturbed that the young doctor felt obliged to pretend to do what he asked.

Another man walked into Casualty complaining that every time he blew his nose his hair stood on end. He was immediately referred to a psychiatrist, who asked him to blow his nose. The patient's hair stood on end. He had a sinus or passage which led from the inside of his nose to the area under the skin of his scalp.

Another patient who gave us a good laugh was a lady who walked in and demanded some sleeping pills. 'Do you always have trouble in sleeping?' asked the young doctor. 'Oh, not at night', she replied, 'only in the afternoon.' I would deal with her differently today. I think she must have been quite disturbed and uttering a cry for help, but in our ignorance we did not recognise it.

Often what amused us also taught valuable lessons. One student had to make a diagnosis and suggest a remedy for a young woman with a baby. Her complaint was that the baby cried all the time. 'Is the baby breast fed?' asked the student.

She nodded and he told her to go into the cubicle and get undressed so that he could examine her breasts. After examining her, he proudly pronounced his opinion. 'You haven't got any milk! That's why your baby cries all the time. You must give him a bottle.' It is exciting to reach so conclusive a diagnosis so early in one's medical career.

The woman looked at him scornfully. 'I'm not his mummy,' she told him. 'I'm his auntie.'

The student who amused us most was Michael O'Donnell, who

wrote the annual Christmas show and put on variety performances. The show brought him to the notice of influential people in the media, furthering his subsequent career as a commentator on the medical and social scene.

In the first decade after the Second World War, idealism was far more widespread than it is today. We did things because we felt it would have been wrong not to do them. There was a selflessness and dedication, and perhaps also a lack of realism – qualities that seem now to be rare.

Chapter 4

Practice

When I had been a house physician for four days, I was left alone to look after four medical wards over the weekend. I was also on call for medical emergencies anywhere else in the hospital. I was terrified. That weekend is a blur of anxiety and activity.

A young doctor has to learn fast. By the end of the weekend I was exhausted but triumphant. No one had died who should not have died. I hadn't done anything too idiotic. I had gained some confidence. I had learned that if there is no one to call, you have to decide what to do, and then do it.

One problem did not solve itself that weekend, however. She was a patient in my own ward, Lily, sixteen years old, married, seven months pregnant, and dying of bronchiectasis, a lung disease. Furthermore, she was terrified of having the baby – indeed, more frightened of that than of dying. I had been told that if she died, as she might at any minute, I was to do a post-mortem Caesarean section instantly. There was a knife waiting in the cupboard near her bed. I would have done the Caesar unhesitatingly, even though it seemed wicked to be thinking about such things while Lily was still alive.

On Sunday afternoon I thought she was going to die. At lunch I happened to sit next to Mr Rigg, the senior obstetric registrar. He was much older than I was and, I assumed, wiser. Foolishly, I mentioned my problem to him. What I did not know was that Mr Rigg was an ardent Roman Catholic with unusually rigid views about the sacredness of human life. Later I learned that he hadn't been told about Lily because everyone except me knew he might cause problems.

Mr Rigg seemed deeply interested and offered to come to the ward to see Lily. He examined her briefly, then took me into the ward office and told me that since Lily was obviously dying, every effort must be made to save the child. He would take her to the theatre and do a Caesar. He realised that it would kill Lily, but since she was dying anyway this was unimportant compared with saving the child.

I became frightened. This was my first encounter with obstetrics guided by religious fervour. But Mr Rigg could not carry out his proposals without my consent, or rather, without Dr Kahan's consent, delegated for the weekend to me. I went to telephone Kahan. He was kind and understanding, though I sensed that his first thought was to curse me as an idiot. He said he would be at the hospital in twenty minutes, and he came along with the consultant obstetrician, Issy Bishop. He had telephoned her as soon as he had finished talking with me. I gather that they told Mr Rigg to mind his own business. Then all of us except Rigg went to the ward to see Lily. They ordered some minor alterations in treatment, and went home. Before he left, Kahan turned to me and said: 'I hope you are wiser for that experience.'

Lily survived labour, and the baby weighed nearly six pounds. Remarkably, Lily's health improved dramatically once she had had the baby. Three weeks later she went home. I never learned whether Mr Rigg knew the outcome of this case.

Of course, some patients did die, and then as now there was disagreement about how much pain-killer to give and when. I found myself in agreement with Dr Kahan, who believed that dying patients should be kept as comfortable as possible and free from pain. That should be the priority, rather than worrying about things like overdose or poisoning. Today some doctors and nurses even worry that a dying patient may become addicted to the drugs and, because of this, refuse to administer them. This shows how far the popular hysteria about drugs and addiction has gone. To deprive a dying person of comfort and keep him in pain because of ideology seems to me both inhumane and unprofessional. We gave morphine and heroin freely, ultimately in the form of the 'Brompton cocktail', a mixture of heroin, cocaine, gin and honey. This gave many patients a good death.

The trouble was that many nurses disagreed, especially those who believed strongly that prolonging life was more important than the relief of suffering. The disagreement often came to a head over the question of giving drugs to a patient who was asleep. Many nurses refused to do this, preferring to wait until the patient woke in pain and asked for the next dose. Kahan believed that the next dose should be given before the pain started again. Much as the nurses liked Kahan and thought he was a good doctor, he could not get them to obey him in this. Sometimes I had to get up in the night myself to give an injection to a sleeping patient.

Then as now, young doctors in hospital worked long hours. In teaching hospitals they were on continuous duty for twenty-four hours a day, seven days a week, with perhaps one free weekend a month and occasionally an evening during the week. It was rare to get more than two or three hours' sleep at a stretch. One Monday morning after working almost continuously for three nights and days, I fell asleep in the operating theatre while assisting at an operation and nodded off over the patient's leg.

But this way of working taught us the importance of continuity of care. We saw our patients at every stage throughout their illnesses. If a patient was seriously ill we stayed with him, even if it was time for a period off duty. We also stayed with those who had infectious diseases like tuberculosis, still common in those days. We knew that we might catch it, and three students in my year did so, but I never heard anyone complain about this; and it would have been unthinkable to refuse to work with the patients. We had chosen to be doctors and accepted the hazards. When I read now about doctors refusing to treat patients with Aids or demanding that they all be put on to an island, I feel a sense of despair. Why did they become doctors if not to heal and comfort *all* patients?

Nearly all the patients were grateful for our efforts. We weren't frightened of complaints, and I don't think we took seriously the possibility of being sued. I doubt that we even knew the term 'defensive medicine', though occasionally we might order an X-ray or blood test just in case there should be any trouble.

In the evenings I used to walk round the wards on my 'social round', when I had more time for each patient than during the morning and early evening rounds. I could chat with patients about all sorts of things and loved to hear about their lives and families, how they lived and what they had done in the past. I also discovered that I had the ability to explain complicated scientific and medical matters in simple words. I considered this very important.

During those years I saw doctors both good and bad. Some were preoccupied with their status, such as the young obstetrician who took endless trouble to acquire the number plate GYN 1 for his brand-new Rolls-Royce. I even met some who enjoyed sitting on committees. But I never encountered doctors who neglected their patients in the pursuit of political power or who used their patients as political pawns. I suppose this may be because all the doctors I met were busy seeing patients, which is what good doctors normally do. Only much later did I realise that 'political' doctors existed.

I don't think I ever met a doctor who was really uncaring. Everyone put the patients first. And while some of the young doctors were deeply religious, few made moral judgements about their patients. I remember no patients being turned away, castigated or even criticised for personal acts or a way of life that had contributed to their illnesses. Doctors and nurses were more likely to be short-tempered with a manipulative hysteric than with a drunk or a drug addict. No one was criticised because he had, for example, caught syphilis or tried to commit suicide, despite the very real danger of syphilis and the fact that suicide was then illegal.

Peter and I had young children and I had intended to work part-time for a few years, giving them as much attention as possible at least until they were settled at school. At that time neither of us was ambitious: we were more concerned with leading a satisfying life.

In the late summer of 1955 the whole pattern of our lives changed. I had just finished my appointment in midwifery and gynaecology. I was six weeks pregnant with my fourth child and was about to take the examination for the Diploma in Obstetrics. Peter was a psychiatric registrar at St Ebba's Hospital, a big mental hospital for acute cases in Epsom.

Then Britain suffered what proved to be its last epidemic of poliomyelitis. Peter was one of its victims, and nearly died. He was almost totally paralysed, and although he made a good recovery over the next year, the illness restricted his movements cruelly and permanently.

One effect of his illness was that he suddenly became ambitious, developing a purposefulness he had lacked before. He concentrated his mind, starting during the long months when he was a patient in hospital, first at Tooting and then at St Thomas's. He had always been exceptionally able, but I was amazed to see the way in which he chose to develop his talents. Still almost totally paralysed, he was confined to a wheelchair when he took the first part of the Diploma in Psychological Medicine, for which he studied while waiting for his physiotherapy.

This was a difficult period for us both. Fearing that Peter would never work fully again, I became more serious about my own career.

I did not think I could compete in the open market as long as I had young children, but I wanted to be prepared for anything. I stayed on in hospital life.

When he had recovered as fully as he ever would, Peter rose rapidly through the ranks of psychiatry. Before long he was senior registrar to William Sargant at Thomas's. Then, in 1961, he was appointed as Physician in Psychological Medicine to the Westminster Hospital. This was a secure, permanent and prestigious post, involving seven sessions per week.

In 1959, just before my fifth child was born, I had stopped working in hospital. Since by then it seemed that Peter would be able to follow a normal career, I felt I could relax and have time with our children. For the next ten years I had a small general practice and also worked in other people's. I did baby clinics and worked for the Family Planning Association. I also did a lot of medical and straight journalism, which I enjoyed enormously. I was interested in psychiatry, studied it, learned a lot from Peter, went on courses and picked it up wherever I could. I was never able to take the examination for the Diploma in Psychological Medicine, later the Membership of the Royal College of Psychiatrists, because I couldn't work for the required two years in mental hospitals. During my later troubles this was held against me, but I don't think my clinical skills were diminished because I did not have the right letters after my name.

Consultant work in the NHS is divided into sessions, each a nominal half day of three and a half hours. At that time there were eleven sessions in a working week. Some consultants did evening sessions and so had more time during the day. It is not always realised that hospital consultants are responsible for their patients for twenty-four hours a day every day, and that they have rotas to cover for each other. Most work tremendously hard. Much hospital work is done by junior doctors, but there is always a consultant on call in each specialty, at least in theory. This responsibility puts a burden on a conscientious doctor. Some suffer severely as a result.

Like St Thomas's, the Westminster had previously had only one consultant psychiatrist on its staff. He was Gerald Garmany, who was well known as one of the cleverest and most articulate psychiatrists in London. Peter expected working with him to be stimulating and enjoyable. Unfortunately, Garmany was past his prime, and Peter had to do most of the work. After a few years Garmany was persuaded to retire and Peter became head of the department, which was enlarging rapidly. Within a few years, because of mergers with other hospitals, it had increased from two consultant psychiatrists to more than sixty.

Once the Royal College of Psychiatrists was founded, psychiatry expanded throughout the NHS, though more in quantity than in quality. The quality of doctors tends to be a problem in specialties where little is known and there are wide differences of opinion, especially if the subject is of low status in the profession. At medical school some of our teachers used the phrase, 'no better than a psychiatrist'. Or they would boast: 'I never refer a patient to a psychiatrist!' Peter and I were among the few students who were interested in the subject; no one else in our year took it up.

For many years psychiatry in the Health Service was in turmoil. For years there had been conflict between the 'analytically orientated' and 'physically orientated' schools. The analytically orientated side, the psychoanalysts, became organised and powerful after the First World War. By the time the NHS began, the British PsychoAnalytical Society was powerful. Psychoanalysis had attracted the attention and support of many intellectuals who were much more able than most psychiatrists.

In contrast, traditional psychiatrists were descended from the former 'alienists', who worked in mental hospitals and were concerned with the mentally ill (or 'lunatics' as they were called) when they were a nuisance to others rather than because they were suffering in themselves. Advances in traditional psychiatry were most prominent at the Maudsley Hospital, then dominated by Professor Aubrey Lewis, a man of fine intellect and wide-ranging imagination but with little practical interest in improving the lot of patients. I don't know when the phrase 'the dead hand of the Maudsley' was invented but it has described the situation for a long time.

Partly in protest at this William Sargant, who had originally trained as a physician, left the Maudsley to pursue his personal belief that mental illness is a form of physical illness. He moved to St Thomas's and dominated psychiatry there with his strong belief in physical treatments such as ECT ('shock treatment') and in the operation of pre-frontal leucotomy. He was in the van of those who welcomed the new 'psychotropic' drugs.

Sargant, the son of a missionary, was something of a missionary himself. He had a powerful personality and believed passionately in his theories and techniques. He was sure that the future of psychiatry lay in getting rid of analysts and analysis and making psychiatry part of general medicine. He was in a strong position to carry out his plans. The Maudsley, under Professor Aubrey Lewis, did little to guide the new NHS. The British PsychoAnalytical Society had decided, after much discussion, to stay out of the NHS except for one clinic, the Tavistock, and one hospital, the Cassel at Richmond, which were staffed by analysts. These institutions provided psychotherapy and gave some training to young psychiatrists. I was told that the annual drug bill of the Cassel hospital was £5, for aspirin.

The decision of the British PsychoAnalytical Society not to join the NHS led to a decline in the power and influence of psychoanalysis. An influential backwater with little real power, it never came to dominate the psychiatric scene as it did in America. Instead the mainstream of British psychiatry, like that of medicine and surgery, lay within the NHS and for a long time little of any importance happened outside. Virtually all psychoanalysis was private, while British psychiatry became much more oriented towards physical treatment, a field in which it led the world for some time.

In an attempt to raise the status of psychiatry plans were made to convert the old Royal Medico-Psychological Society into the Royal College of Psychiatrists. It was argued that this would improve standards in the practice of psychiatry. Today this argument seems hollow. The idea that creating a Royal College would raise standards seems naive, particularly in a specialty riven with strife and attracting mediocre adherents. It was recently disclosed that the only subject in those discussions that aroused passion was the question of whether the college should have a mace!

Peter had never intended to do private practice, and neither had I. In the spirit of the age we assumed that everything could be done better on the NHS. We had a touching faith in the Health Service and were ignorant about some of the shortcomings already apparent to the discerning.

Peter began private practice in 1961 because Will Sargant, looking towards retirement, offered him six months' free use of his consulting room. At the end of that time his appointment book was full for several months ahead. Unexpectedly, he had found it interesting, and he was clearly successful. So Peter rented his own consulting room in the same house as Will Sargant. After several years he was so busy that he found it difficult to run his practice as well as doing his work at the Westminster Hospital. When our youngest child, Adam, was five years old and the oldest, Simon, about to go up to Oxford, we decided to sell our house in Dulwich and buy a lease on a house in the Harley Street area. Here we could 'live over the shop'. No time would be wasted in commuting, and I could help in the practice. We found a beautiful Adam house in Devonshire Place, the elegant street at the top of Wimpole Street, and for £40,000, which we had trouble raising, we bought the lease of 940 years.

Even after Peter and I divorced (in 1969) we continued in partnership. In 1979 I married again but continued to see patients referred to me by Peter as well as my other patients.

With vigilance and hard work we managed to cope with most emergencies and look after even violent psychiatric patients. I found the work with acutely ill patients interesting and exciting, but it was also exhausting. Apart from this, my special interest was in mothers, children and adolescents. At the time there were scarcely any women psychiatrists in private practice in central London. The only one I knew of in the Harley Street area was widely thought to be incompetent. It is not surprising that many general practitioners welcomed me, if only because I could save them time.

There were also few men psychiatrists who inspired confidence. The foundation of the college did nothing to prevent psychiatry's downhill course both inside the NHS and out. Much of our practice in the early years grew from patients who had not done well under previous psychiatrists.

This situation has, if anything, worsened. Recently Peter and I were asked to find a good psychiatrist for a relative. We had great difficulty thinking of one to recommend.

In treating people who are anxious, depressed or otherwise mentally disturbed it is essential to listen and not condemn. This should apply to all patients. Perhaps it should be written on every doctor's desk, especially in these days of medical moralism when patients are increasingly classified by merit. The old classification, in which 'physical' disease was held to be superior to 'mental', is still with us, but an additional classification is developing in which sympathy for patients depends on how far they are believed to have caused their disorder themselves. Even the President of the Royal College of Physicians has suggested that medical service should reflect this. Smoking, drinking and drug taking are joining wrist-slashing and overdoses in the self-inflicted category. I believe that this philosophy is creating another group of second-class patients whom doctors feel justified in not treating as well as they treat others.

Such attitudes led to disaster in one of my early psychotherapy cases. Joan, aged twenty-two, was slowly emerging from many years of anorexia nervosa when she had a setback, a row with her mother. She became hysterical, broke into the bathroom cupboard with a jemmy and swallowed a large quantity of sleeping tablets. Then she announced what she had done. This was a typical hysterical reaction and an indication that she had made a suicidal gesture rather than an attempt to kill herself. She was taken to the casualty department of the local hospital, where the nurse on duty was unsympathetic to a self-inflicted condition. At the time Joan seemed to be normal, so, to 'teach her a lesson', the nurse told her that she would have to wait at the end of the queue. When all the other patients had been dealt with, the doctor would see her. She made it clear that she thought Joan was wasting her time and that of the doctor.

While Joan was waiting casualties were brought in after a serious accident. The doctor was occupied for a long time. By the time the department was quiet again, Joan was becoming sleepy. At this point the doctor or nurse decided that she should have her stomach pumped out, which should have been done immediately she arrived. By the time the tube was passed, she was nearly unconscious. She vomited and inhaled the vomit. Six hours later, she died.

At the inquest, witnesses from the hospital skated over the times at which hospital procedures had been performed. The coroner did not press them or enquire further but concentrated on the jemmy: 'No mother can be expected to keep drugs so safely that they cannot be reached by a determined adult daughter with a jemmy,' he said. Clearly he, too, thought that Joan was a second-class patient.

The National Health Service had a problem with private practice. After discussion and argument it was decided to allow those who worked in the NHS to practise privately under certain conditions. Since that time, passions have run high on the subject. Not even the huge profits made by drug companies have aroused so much envy and hostility.

People who are hostile to private practice forget that until this century nearly all medical practice was private, and that good doctoring existed before state medicine. What matters is the quality of the doctor and of his training. The lazy, inefficient doctor in the hospital may even be the greedy exploitative doctor in his private practice, whereas the good doctor is equally responsible in both.

The biggest advantages of private practice are that the doctor has

time for his patient and the patient has the security of always seeing
the same doctor. This is particularly important in psychiatry, which
requires much time if it is to be done well. This is one reason why
psychiatry, perhaps more than any other specialty, flourishes in private
practice, even when the psychiatrist is incompetent.

Those who view private medicine as a money-making racket are
often unaware of the doctor's expenses. He has to pay for the room or
rooms that he uses for private practice, either in his hospital or outside,
for a receptionist and for any secretarial help. Some doctors, especially
outside London, are able to use their own homes, perhaps with their
wives as receptionists, but this is seldom feasible in London. Here a
new consultant trying to break into private medicine is likely to rent
a room in the 'rabbit warren' at the top of Harley Street. Houses there
are large and contain many rooms, most of which have been divided.
The landlords are the Crown Commissioners. Unlike the Howard de
Walden Estate, which owns the rest of the area, they allow doctors to
rent consulting rooms by the session or half day. At the time of writing,
rents there start at about £25 per half day per week, which includes use
of the waiting room and the services of a receptionist but no telephone
or secretarial help. Over the week, as many as sixty or eighty doctors
may work in a single house. Each morning cleaners and receptionists
change the nameplates.

A doctor who can afford something better usually moves to the
Howard de Walden Estate, which grants the licences to doctors it
deems suitable. The 'long streets', the lower part of Harley Street
and the whole of Wimpole Street and Devonshire Place, are regarded
as more prestigious and rents are more expensive than in the 'cross
streets' between them: Queen Anne, Weymouth, New Cavendish and
Devonshire Streets.

The Howard de Walden Estate has strict rules. Before they
are granted licences to practise on the estate, doctors have to be
approved, though the vetting is not arduous. The Estate issues its
own licences, usually to only one doctor for each consulting room,
and seldom permits doctors to share rooms. Even if he works there for
only one or two sessions per week, a doctor has to pay the whole rent.
He also provides his own furniture. At present a small but handsome
suite, including room for a secretary, costs about £14,000–£15,000 per
year, including service charges. A full-time secretary, together with
other expenses in running such a practice, costs at least the same again.
Garage space is likely to cost a further £4,000–£5,000 per year. Taking
account of holidays, the doctor who gives up two NHS sessions for

private practice has to earn at least £1,000 per week and probably more in private fees before he can cover his costs and compensate for his loss of NHS earnings and pension.

In short, private practice is not simply a licence to print money. It is often hard work for little return, and is especially arduous because the private doctor seldom has back-up from other doctors in the way that he has at a hospital. He has to do all the work himself and take all the responsibility. He also has to cope with the envy he will arouse in his NHS colleagues.

Harley Street is an address, not a qualification. Some people think that any doctor working there must be distinguished and successful, but this is not the case. Many eminent doctors do work in the area, but it also contains many mediocre doctors and some charlatans. Paradoxically, it is easier for a charlatan to make good there than it is for an honest NHS consultant: the latter is likely to spend most of his time at his hospital. Also, the consultant who abides by medical ethics and GMC rules accepts only patients referred to him by general practitioners. The charlatan takes them wherever he can find them.

Success in private practice demands qualities that are not necessary in hospital or general practice. First, the patient must like the doctor, or at least have confidence in him. This is not the case in the NHS. Having been brought up in the idealism of the early Health Service, I am saddened when I hear people talking about some doctors' behaviour. When a woman doctor was struck off the Medical Register for refusing to care for patients and for being rude to colleagues, a common reaction amongst my patients was: 'What's different about her? That's how most doctors behave.'

Some incompetent doctors do well in Harley Street simply because the patients find them congenial and have no means of judging them. When Peter and I were building up our practice we were aware of a number of such doctors in psychiatry. Some of our patients had been to them for years, and had finally become disillusioned with them or simply wanted to try someone new. More often, their general practitioners were aware of the situation and had heard of Peter's growing reputation. A few 'miracles' travel far on the grapevine; these are not difficult for a competent doctor to perform on patients who have been treated ineffectively or inappropriately.

It is descriptive, not arrogant, to refer to 'miracles'. The point is not that we were clever to perform them but that one should never write off a patient as hopeless. Even the most unpromising patient may change. I have seen this happen so many times that I have taught myself never to give up. The failure is one's own, not the patient's, or at least one must consider it as such. If a patient is 'uncooperative', the doctor has failed to make a suitable rapport with him. This realisation became especially important to me when I became interested in drug addicts. I believe that many of the shortcomings in that specialty come from the arrogance of doctors who wish to impose their will not only on their patients but on other doctors as well.

Chapter 5

Harley Street and Devonshire Place

Practising psychiatry enables one to meet a wide variety of people and get to know them far better – and in a different way – than in ordinary life. It satisfies curiosity, without which it cannot be practised well. One has to ask questions that one could not ask in social or family life, and most patients are keen to tell. A new patient is always stimulating and challenging. One can meet people for the first time, let them talk, or guide the talk, for an hour or more, and produce a noticeable improvement in their feelings and outlook. The improvement may come simply from the patient being taken seriously, especially when he did not expect it, or through the astonishment of revelation. Taking psychiatric histories involves finding out things patients hardly know themselves.

I used to wonder whether psychiatrists see such an extraordinary variety of people because psychiatric problems tend to develop in unusual people, or because the more unusual aspects of ordinary people emerge during psychiatric treatment. I now know that both are true. Also, in ordinary life the people one knows well tend to be friends, colleagues and family. In psychiatry, one is privileged to get to know all who come.

The official 'patient' is often a child or adolescent and the 'real' patient, or the person who should be the patient, is the parent. Sometimes the sick group is not a true family but an office or other professional group. People can be driven to breakdown by their superiors at work, especially if their careers depend on them. One successful London publisher, now dead, drove his managing editors mad one by one, then sent them off for psychiatric treatment.

The stigma often attached to psychiatric treatment can create real difficulties, with fear of exposure militating against successful treatment. This is particularly difficult if the patient is in public life. It may be acceptable for a pop star or an actor to have psychiatric treatment, but not the chairman of a bank, a cabinet minister or a member of the royal family. Not all public figures are so squeamish. For a long time, whenever I read about a certain cabinet minister or saw him on television, I remembered that I first met him raving mad and almost naked, chasing his boyfriend round the clinic.

Some people develop psychiatric difficulties because they are eccentric or unusual, and their true personality is unacceptable to parents, school or workplace. But a general psychiatrist probably sees many more people who are unable to be themselves enough to enjoy life or develop skills in living. One sees this especially in families. Children tend to do what is expected of them, and if this is different from what they really want to do, they may balance the situation by developing an illness or symptoms.

As in teaching and in life generally, helping people develop their potential is one of the most important aims in psychiatry. When I assess a new patient I ask myself, what is this person's potential? How can he or she best develop? How far is this illness or these symptoms holding him back? These questions arise most obviously in adolescents, but they are true of all patients. When I asked an experienced and successful psychiatrist what he considered his strongest professional asset, he replied: 'As a patient walks into the room, I know immediately what he's like when he is normal.'

It is not unusual for people who normally function well to react to stress by becoming psychotic, even though they are not inherently schizophrenic or manic depressive. Sometimes this tendency runs in families. I treated three members of a famous family, father, son and daughter, who all reacted in this way when life was difficult. Circumstances that might make other people anxious or depressed made them go mad, with hallucinations and paranoid delusions. They then needed urgent treatment, and would revert to normal within a few weeks. Having learned to recognise the pattern they could see the symptoms early and prevent development of the full syndrome.

Treating acutely psychotic patients oneself rather than delegating the job to others requires enormous application. Although in the right circumstances the patient benefits enormously, I do not do this any more. It is an occupation for a younger doctor; the anxiety and stress are more than I wish to deal with. I am also now too scared. In the new climate of 'blame the doctor', and of personal vendettas in the medical profession, I fear getting into trouble for treating such a patient. I never knew a case go wrong but one result of the troubles that befell me is that I learned the potential danger that lies in helping people. If one does not do exactly what the doctors with power dictate, one runs the risk of getting into serious trouble. This is true even, or one might say especially, when one has helped the patient more than one ever could by following those dictates.

One young girl I treated was Anne-Marie, a young fashion student. She had been normal until about a month before, when she had become convinced that she was about to be married. No man was in evidence, but Anne-Marie went to shops buying her trousseau and trying on wedding dresses, then had invitations printed and sent them to friends and relatives. The whole business got out of hand because her mother, unwisely but perhaps understandably, went along with her, feeling that it was important not to antagonise her.

After six weeks' treatment, Anne-Marie was still lying in bed demanding to go home to make arrangements for her wedding. I began to fear that she might turn into a chronic schizophrenic. Then one day, suddenly, she began to talk rationally about what had happened.

In time I discovered the cause of Anne-Marie's illness. She had been going secretly to a doctor in Harley Street who supplied her with amphetamines. (This was before the days when drugs were widely accessible and a constant danger to young people.) 'Amphetamine psychosis', which later I came to know well, was still rare, at least in Harley Street. It is indistinguishable from acute schizophrenia, but after the attack the patient returns to normality and remains normal so long as no further amphetamines are taken.

I decided to telephone the doctor. This posed a tricky ethical problem but I felt that if one of my patients had an adverse reaction to drugs prescribed by me, I would want to know and indeed would be annoyed if a doctor deliberately concealed the fact from me. He was ruder than any doctor had ever been to me. 'Mind your own f— business,' he shouted down the line. 'Keep away from my patients!'

It was clear that he disregarded the fact that Anne-Marie had been seeing him secretly without her GP's knowledge. I also thought he might be scared. He must have known he had behaved unethically in giving her large quantities of amphetamines.

Anne-Marie made a full recovery, though she did have one relapse. Eventually she admitted that she was again visiting the same doctor. Taking a deep breath, I telephoned him again. He denied that he was seeing her and was even more offensive than before. I left him in no doubt that if he continued to supply Anne-Marie with drugs, there would be big trouble for him. I don't think I have threatened a colleague before or since. But he stopped giving her drugs.

Inevitably, working privately and where we did, we treated a number of famous people and their children. These posed some interesting problems. A public figure will probably not mind if he is known to be having surgery for a hernia, but psychiatric treatment is different. If the patient requires admission to hospital, a psychiatric diagnosis must be kept secret at all costs. Sometimes an elaborate front must be set up. The story given out is usually medical or surgical, and the relevant physician or surgeon runs the gauntlet of reporters at the front door of the hospital. Meanwhile the psychiatrist walks in unnoticed through the back door.

Peter had some grand patients, and rumours abounded among journalists about some of them, or about people who they believed were his patients. When royalty was involved, the tension heightened still more. This aspect of our practice started when we still lived in Dulwich, and had no secretaries or other formal arrangements. We had to tell the children that if anyone from Buckingham Palace rang up, they were not to take it as a joke and should on no account make a joke in reply.

In some respects, the psychiatrist loses out when the patient is royal. It is the custom for doctors not to charge fees to royalty, the idea being that they acquire kudos from doing so. But the psychiatrist has to do his work secretly, often at inconvenient hours and at the expense of his other work. He loses money and gains nothing except the interest of the work.

When faced with a breakdown in one of their children, the rich and famous react in individual ways, but always against the background of their fame and riches. In our practice we have cared for the children of some of the world's wealthiest and most publicised people. One of these, nineteen years old, had a severe schizophrenic breakdown which began with her constantly hearing her father's voice on the car radio: perhaps sometimes she did hear it. Her father, one of the busiest of men, had a reputation for ruthlessness. I was slightly uneasy at the prospect of saying what I intended to say, and not allowing myself to be controlled by him. But when he arrived, he couldn't have been more cooperative. He volunteered to make himself free at any time, and showed genuine concern throughout his daughter's illness. Not all tycoons are so easy to deal with.

For some years, many Arabs came to us for psychiatric help. Some were rich and some were poor, even peasants. Paid for by their own medical services, they would be sent for treatment accompanied by a spouse and often children and other members of the family. Many had never left their homes before.

One of my most interesting encounters was with a princess from a Gulf state. She was in the Wellington, one of London's most expensive private hospitals, occupying many rooms with her relatives, servants and ladies-in-waiting. I was particularly interested in a group of pubescent girls who looked different from the rest and were all dressed alike in new dresses from Harrods. They had light brown skin, round faces and frizzy light brown hair, and they seemed to do all the menial tasks. I asked the interpreter about them and she said: 'Those girls are slaves from Nubia.' I had never knowingly met a slave before.

Given that psychotherapy is first a question of listening and not condemning, most psychological healing is done by people, often friends or relatives, who have had no training and may not even have heard the word 'psychotherapy'. They help because they have the gift of empathy, the ability to appreciate another person in his predicament. Some sufferers need only empathy for relief.

One of the most bizarre cases ever referred to our practice concerned a retired army officer who had amputated his own leg at the knee and nearly died. The local psychiatrist could find nothing wrong with him, and sent him to Peter.

It was an unusual case. Another eminent psychiatrist came to our house and he and Peter examined the patient together. At first they, too, could find nothing, apart from what he had done, to indicate abnormality. The patient was charming and urbane. He couldn't think what had come over him. He agreed it was an extraordinary thing to do. He had never done anything remotely like it before. He was sure that he never would again.

The man had done his amputation with a good deal of skill. Clearly he had studied the subject before putting it into practice, for when police searched his flat they found surgical textbooks in which amputation techniques were described in detail. Furthermore, before doing the operation, he had sent off an order to a firm of limb-fitters, giving the measurements of his leg and ordering an artificial leg to be sent to him. But why?

Peter decided to be more aggressive. He attacked him in a manner unusual in psychiatry and more like a cross-examination in a court of law. Eventually the man broke down and confessed to an extraordinary fantasy world. He believed that his real mission in life was to be a model for artificial legs and to have sexual relationships with amputees. Now that he was getting on in years, he felt it was time to put his fantasy into practice.

Peter and I both had sidelines which were separate from our general psychiatric practice. I wrote a number of books, and some patients would consult me after reading one of them. I was always careful about this, only seeing them if they were referred by general practitioners because accepting patients as a result of 'publicity' or 'self-advertising' is regarded as unethical by the General Medical Council and a serious breach of ethics. The GMC controls the Medical Register, which lists doctors who are permitted to practise in the United Kingdom. Sometimes it removes doctors' names from the register for the crime of advertising. If that happens, the person concerned is not allowed to practise as a doctor or to prescribe those drugs which may be prescribed only by a doctor.

As a writer, I was always aware of this danger. So when readers of my books or articles asked to consult me professionally I was always careful to say that I would see them only if they were referred by their general practitioners. Those who were not registered with a GP had to do so if they wished to consult me.

One psychiatrist I knew came to grief over this point. He used to write, as I did, for the now defunct BMA publication *Family Doctor*. Someone rang up and said he was so impressed with an article by the doctor that he wanted to consult him. His temporary secretary, who didn't know the rules, made an appointment. The call was a hoax. Someone complained to the General Medical Council and as a result they charged him with advertising, one of the sins within their jurisdiction. The unfortunate doctor went on trial and the details were widely reported. Eventually he managed to persuade the GMC that his story was true. He was cleared but suffered huge publicity and much anxiety. This was enough to alarm doctors who also wrote. It was at the height of the controversy about 'health education', in which there was dispute about whether information on health should be provided only at the discretion of doctors. It seems almost unbelievable today, when health matters receive so much attention in the media.

Seeing patients because they had been impressed by my articles, broadcasts or books was of course flattering. Unsurprisingly, there was often an affinity between me and these patients. One of them, who after an initial course of psychotherapy visited me occasionally for a number of years, I came to know particularly well. When she died of cancer, I felt I had lost a friend. A few weeks after her death, her teenage daughter came to see me. She wanted to meet the person who had helped her mother so much.

Another sideline of mine was a regular phone-in programme for Radio London, in which people telephoned about their personal problems. It was part of 'The Robbie Vincent Show', and I usually did the programme with Robbie Vincent as commentator. He had a remarkable gift for psychological insight. I worked with him on this programme for nine years, and by the end he could well have been the radio psychiatrist himself.

This work required techniques that were different from those of psychiatry. In the consulting room one tends to sit back and wait for the patient to talk. Long silences are part of the process and can be important. On the air there has to be constant talk. I was surprised to learn how much good work one could do in this unorthodox form of practice. Many people have serious problems, both practical and emotional, that they cannot tell to anyone. Sometimes the anonymity of the air enabled people to talk to me. Others were amazingly diffident, even about problems which clearly needed expert help. One woman rang up and said, in a quiet little voice, that her husband was creeping round the house after her with a knife. Did I think she should bother the doctor?

A further interest of mine was medico-legal work. I enjoyed this and always felt a moral obligation to go to court for a patient who needed my help. But the time involved was a problem for me. All too often I was told at short notice that, for instance, I would be needed in court next day. With difficulty and at inconvenience to many people, I would postpone all my appointments, many of them to the day after, which was then overbooked. After everything was arranged, I would then receive a telephone call to say that the case had been postponed by yet another day. Or I would travel to court, perhaps many miles, only to find that the case had collapsed.

Nevertheless, it is interesting work. One fascinating case was of a fraudster who seemed to have gone mad in a hotel just as he was developing a big scheme. The most interesting feature of the case was that the psychiatrist called in to deal with him had agreed to become a partner in the scheme! Clearly more interested in its potential millions than in treating the patient, he hadn't even bothered to diagnose him. I don't think the General Medical Council ever heard about that case.

Chapter 6

New Interests

In the autumn of 1979 our practice was busy, sometimes too busy, as it had been throughout much of the previous sixteen years. I had to complete my latest book by the end of the year. My professional life seemed stable. I enjoyed what I did and knew I did it well. I wasn't seeking change. If someone had told me I was about to see my practice and my whole life overturned, I would not have believed it. But that is precisely what was about to happen.

The change began with a letter from a general practitioner referring a patient to me, just one of hundreds that I had received in my years as a doctor. The doctor was Arthur Timmins, an elderly GP in Harrow. Dated 4 December 1979, the letter was written in a cramped hand on a small and scruffy printed sheet that served as both letterhead and certificate. This format was used by many single-handed general practitioners in the NHS. Under this was written in ink:

> This is to certify that Mr R. Whiting is suffering from opiate addiction and whilst under my care was co-operative and pleasant at all times. I should be grateful for your advice and treatment.

The doctor added that he hoped I would be more successful with Roger Whiting than he had been.

Dr Timmins had sent me patients before. It was standard practice for him to refer a patient in this way and for me to accept him. I put his letter in the patient's file.

It made no difference to me that Roger Whiting was addicted to heroin. He was someone who needed my help, and I thought only of helping him and doing good professional work. I knew many drug addicts were unreliable and unstable but I was not conditioned, like many doctors, to regard them as criminals and psychopaths. Perhaps naively, I took patients as they came and tried to decide what their problems were and then how to solve them.

Roger was not the first addict I had treated. Those I had seen in the past were mostly, like my other patients, young and middle-class. Most of these cases involved cannabis but a few were about hard drugs. One patient, the young heir to a famous fortune, had been cut off by his family because of his drug habits. A talented mathematician with a good academic record, he had become addicted to heroin.

Another was Lois, a glamorous sixteen-year-old from Chelsea. A publisher's daughter introduced her to heroin and the heir to an earldom taught her to inject it. When I first saw her she had been injecting intravenously for months. Eventually I got her admitted to Regent's Park Nursing Home, where she stopped being addicted to heroin and taking other drugs for the time being, and left after a few weeks to start a modelling course. I was to see her again, some twelve years later, when she was not only a long-term injecting addict but a prostitute and HIV-positive. I could not treat her because by that time I was in trouble myself. A few weeks later she was dead. The coroner could not decide whether she died from an overdose, committed suicide or was murdered.

Talking to addicts made me think about the nature of addiction, and it still does. A person is addicted if he suffers from unpleasant symptoms when deprived of a certain substance or activity. These 'withdrawal symptoms' differ according to the substance or activity to which the person is addicted and also, to some extent, according to his personality. The more unpleasant the withdrawal symptoms, the more the sufferer will crave the drug or whatever else he happens to be addicted to, and the more effort he will make to obtain or do it. Long abstinence usually diminishes the craving, especially if it is voluntary, but further indulgence soon brings it back. Apart from drugs (which include tobacco and alcohol), common addictions include work, violent exercise, gambling and sex. Many addictions are well concealed because the activities or substances are easily available and respectable in themselves. No one is likely to worry much about and may not even notice an addiction to tea or to reading novels, though the sudden unavailability of these may produce withdrawal symptoms as distressing as those of more obvious addictions. Addiction to certain chemical substances, including heroin, produces physical as well as mental withdrawal symptoms.

After talking with hundreds of addicts about their addiction, I find that I can understand it best if I compare it to the normal needs of human beings. Many addictions are indeed extensions of normal needs, and addiction can be regarded as the acquisition of an extra essential to life, at least in the addict's mind. This extra is then as important to the individual as, say, water is to all of us.

According to the definition above, we are all 'addicted' to water and we all suffer from 'withdrawal symptoms' if deprived of it. If totally deprived of it, we die, as can occur in some addictions. Under normal conditions we drink water automatically in whatever form we happen to like. We seldom even think about it. But if we are deprived of it, we become thirsty and uncomfortable. As the hours pass, we become increasingly preoccupied with it, then desperate and able to think of nothing else. Eventually we will do anything possible in order to obtain it, even sell the household silver or commit crimes. This, I believe, is how heroin addicts feel. As long as they have the drug, they can be as normal as anyone else and scarcely think about it. Deprived, they may become wild and violent, as is their popular image. The idea that they should just 'pull themselves together', 'say "no" to drugs' and be penalised if they do not, is absurd and shows no understanding.

The more the addictive substance or activity attracts disapproval and the more difficult it is to obtain, the more it becomes a 'problem' and the more isolated the addict feels. Addiction to sex is a problem only where there are no suitable partners or if there is venereal disease. Smoking is an addiction that meets increasing disapprobation in our society; mild and moderate addicts tend to give it up, while heavy smokers meet increasing difficulties. Opium and its derivatives (such as morphine and heroin) have undergone an even more radical change. At one time most people used them and came to no harm. Some people became addicted (a figure has been put at approximately 14–16 per cent) and, while they also came to no harm, for opiates are safe drugs, they sometimes attracted mild disapproval. Then opiates were outlawed and became caught up in public prejudice to the extent that they and those addicted to them came to be regarded with horror and disgust, treated as outlaws and forced to be criminals.

Opiates are the most powerful killers of pain, both physical and mental, known to man. But withdrawal from them creates its own pain, and anxiety and distress to a degree which most addicts find or anticipate as unbearable. The withdrawing addict also feels extremely ill, with diarrhoea and stomach cramps, itching and sleeplessness. Until he is ready to tackle the problem himself, and he is likely to need long and careful preparation for this, he will do anything to obtain the drug and relieve his suffering.

For me, Roger Whiting was the first of a new type of addict patient. He was twenty-nine, articulate, with a pleasant manner, and working-class. When he first came to see me he told me his story, a sad one. His mother had died of cancer when he was two. His father looked after him for two years, then remarried and lost interest. Roger's stepmother preferred her own children and he felt excluded. In his early teens he became part of a group taking heroin, and at the age of fourteen, under pressure from his peers, he tried it himself. Most people take weeks or months before they experience symptoms of withdrawal, the hallmark of addiction, but Roger became addicted immediately.

Since 1968, when the official drug clinics opened, he had attended his local clinic diligently, receiving regular supplies first of heroin, then of methadone. He seldom saw a doctor and no one tried to get him off drugs; the nurses or social workers handed him regular prescriptions. For years he was able to earn an honest living. He had completed an apprenticeship and qualified as an electrician, and could lead a normal life. He enjoyed his work and was good at it, but because he was an addict drugs were vital to his immediate well-being. He could not have studied or worked without them.

Suddenly, without warning, his clinic changed its policy. The social worker told him that in future he would receive no more injectable drugs but must make do with liquid oral methadone, the 'official preparation'. The doctor didn't bother to see him at all.

After fifteen years of injecting Roger knew what he could and could not manage to do. Liquid oral methadone had never helped him; he knew it would be impossible for him to lead a normal life.

And so it turned out. For a while he continued to attend the clinic but had to spend most of his time buying drugs on the black market. Because of this he lost his job and could support himself only by shop-lifting and dealing in drugs. In any case, he could not have earned by honest work the sums he now needed to pay for drugs. He felt he needed a regular prescription such as he had received for years. If he could have that he would give no trouble, could resume honest work and make a real effort eventually to give up drugs altogether. He would far prefer the life of an honest electrician.

I was to hear variations on this story hundreds of times during the following years. Sometimes they were undoubtedly exaggerated for my benefit, but I have seen the situation to be true so many times that I believe it.

I decided to try to help Roger Whiting. This meant prescribing clean drugs in diminishing doses and seeing him regularly to monitor his progress and help solve his many problems. On his part I expected him to accept the job he had been offered and do it conscientiously, to give up his illegal activities and, with my help, to build up his self-respect. He accepted my terms and seemed pleased.

Soon after I took on Roger, other addicts followed. One was an Australian money broker in the City who was terrified of losing his job through living on the black market. Another was a journalist who remained my patient until he was ready to give up drugs altogether.

It wasn't long before the telephone rang even more frequently and every post brought new letters. Many of those from doctors expressed anger at the treatment now being offered by the clinics. Others were from addicts begging me to accept them as patients. Nearly all told the same sad story: they had become addicted to heroin in adolescence, had led a normal, honest life when helped by the drug clinic, but were now chaotically criminal because of the change in clinic policy. Some had never attended a clinic, either because there was none in the area or because the writer had heard such unpleasant accounts of it that he did not wish to submit himself to it.

I quickly made two discoveries. One was that many addicts were of high intelligence, and could do skilled and difficult work if they could organise their lives so as not to be dominated by drugs. Yet this fact was apparently being ignored by the drug dependency establishment. One clinic refused to treat addicts *unless* they were unemployed. Others expected them to attend during working hours and refused to prescribe if they did not.

Yet my patients included a senior television producer in the BBC, a civil servant, two solicitors and several journalists. Another had made a fortune in property development and now owned many of the houses in my area. I also treated skilled tradesmen, writers, musicians and several pop stars.

My second discovery was that an addict will only give up drugs when he is ready to do so. He does not give up because others tell him to, though he may pretend. A doctor has little or no control over this, though doctors who feel a need to be in control of their patients will deny that this is so. This made nonsense of the current standard policy in the treatment of drug addiction which was either to insist on the addict giving up drugs immediately or else to put him on to a regime in which the dose was rapidly reduced so that, within a few weeks, he was 'drug-free'. I began to understand why it was that few addicts were presenting themselves for treatment at the official clinics, why most of those who did attend left the clinic before the 'treatment' was completed and why, of the few who completed the treatment, most relapsed within weeks or months, some sooner. I realised that I had stumbled on a substantial deficiency in the National Health Service. Something was terribly wrong in the official drug clinics.

When I saw how great the demand was, I realised at once that I had to limit my practice to a tiny proportion of those who applied. I accepted only those presenting evidence of employment. I felt sorry for the rest, but there was nothing more I could do for them except publicise their plight when I had the opportunity. I believe now that those efforts led to my persecution. Had I kept silent and simply treated patients, as other doctors did, I might never have got into trouble.

Hoping to understand the subject better, I read widely about drug addiction and its social and political background. But despite extensive reading I was not able to understand the current policies in the DDUs (NHS drug dependency units) or to discover why they had changed. I decided to try to learn from people who worked in the field. My first stop would be clinics, where I could see the treatment of drug addicts for myself.

During my years as a medical journalist, I had always been impressed by the way specialists welcomed other doctors who showed interest in what they did. I assumed that this would be the case in drug dependency. My first visit was to the drug clinic attached to a London teaching hospital. When I arrived, the consultant psychiatrist led me down a small corridor, took a bunch of keys from his pocket and unlocked the door at the end. This was the DDU, or drug clinic. It was the first time I had ever seen patients and staff so clearly relegated to second class. Drug dependency was completely cut off from the mainstream of the hospital. Even though I knew that consultant psychiatrists had originally insisted on the separation of the clinics from their own wards, I had not realised the extent of the separation. The security shocked me. I had never seen locked departments in hospitals or felt the need for such measures in my own practice, even with addicts. It is difficult to think of anything less conducive to a good doctor–patient relationship than a doctor with a bunch of keys.

At first I thought that the locks resulted from the prejudices of those working elsewhere in the hospital. Later I learned that the way they were treated frustrated some patients so deeply that they became violent. I heard many stories about doctors who had been assaulted. A reputation for a hard line in treatment or for insensitivity to patients, whether true or false, laid them open to attack.

The consultant at this hospital was different from the other teaching hospital consultants I had known. For one thing, he had not qualified in Britain. Few foreign graduates became consultants in teaching hospitals, and to achieve this would have required exceptional ability or personality. More surprising still, he had not passed the examination for membership of the Royal College of Physicians. Until recently success in this difficult examination (at one time its failure rate was 98 per cent) had been essential for psychiatrists seeking an appointment to a teaching hospital. Now it was easier because psychiatrists could do part of the examination in their own subject, but it was clear that there would not be enough MRCPs to staff the drug dependency clinics. In their eagerness to offload the junkies, the teaching hospital consultants had agreed to lower standards for colleagues who would relieve them of this burden.

I had looked forward to meeting Dr T., a prominent figure in drug dependency. I wanted to hear his views and discuss with him some of the problems that bothered me in drug dependency. At last, I thought, I would get straight answers.

There were also specific questions I wanted to ask. For instance, I hoped to discover why so many clinic doctors, in writing reports, would say that their addict patients were doing well on small doses of oral methadone when this was plainly not the case. Methadone is a synthetic opiate, to a large extent interchangeable with heroin. For reasons that are historical rather than scientific, it is often used in the treatment of heroin addiction, even by doctors who have a Home Office licence to prescribe heroin. During the early years of the present DDUs methadone was usually prescribed in injectable form. This policy actually created many addicts. When the policies changed, and in some clinics this happened without warning to patients and without consideration of their needs, the methadone was henceforth supplied in the form of 'linctus', a sweet yellow or green liquid, which many addicts refused to take. Most of them said it wasn't effective and some also complained that it made them sick or that it rotted their teeth. So why did all these doctors insist that they were 'doing well' on it? I could understand that doctors had an interest in making out that the current 'standard' treatment was successful but I did not expect the extent of the deception that some of them practised in order to conceal the true state of affairs.

At the time I also wondered why the clinic doctors, when they sent a report on an addict patient, almost never mentioned that, in addition to his clinic prescription for 'linctus', he had clear physical signs of injecting black market heroin. Yet almost invariably the patient would admit this freely and say that he felt obliged to do this in order to feel normal. The doctors' reports, while omitting this important information, were usually accompanied by many photocopied pages from the patients' notes containing detailed descriptions of apparently irrelevant physical examinations and laboratory tests such as serial normal blood pressures and analysis of urine for drugs, the latter being easily faked. I also thought it odd that while clinics had prescribed large doses of injectable drugs only a few years before, the doctors failed to mention this in their reports. Some clinics, when asked for a report, would omit to send pages from the notes relating to that particular phase of treatment.

Dr T. was polite, but talking to him made me even more confused than I had been before. He delivered expositions of his personal views with a verbal fluency that conveyed an air of wisdom, but I was accustomed to more clarity of content. I found it difficult to take part in the conversation because he continually changed the subject, and I could not get him to answer my questions. When he did answer, he did so with an evasive technique that I had hitherto observed in politicians being interviewed on television.

Dr T. had invited me to lunch in the consultants' dining room. Afterwards he announced that we would visit the psychiatric ward, where he had an in-patient, a pregnant woman who had been a heroin addict but whom he had weaned from drugs. When we arrived on the ward, the ward sister said that the patient was agitating to be allowed out for the afternoon to visit her disabled mother.

The patient was an attractive young woman, six months pregnant. She displayed that particular form of restlessness that one sees in an addict who is beginning to withdraw and is worried about the next fix. I felt sure that she wanted to go out to get drugs, though no one mentioned this possibility. Dr T. scarcely spoke to her but addressed his remarks to me, to the house physician or to the sister. He gave a summary of the case as he saw it and emphasised again how the patient had been weaned from drugs while she was in the ward. I wasn't so sure. The notes contained no reference to her having been examined for injection marks since she came in. Meanwhile Dr T. was speaking, almost joking. 'And since Dr Dally is so keen on looking for injection marks, let's have a look at her arm!'

He rolled up the sleeve of her dressing gown and revealed a large, inflamed 'track mark', pigmented and open, the clear signs of injection both long-standing and recent. It was obvious to me that she was not drug-free. Dr T. merely shrugged his shoulders. Clearly he did not intend to discuss it. It is hard to believe that he was surprised by what he had seen, but as far as he was concerned, the patient was drug-free because she had completed his course of treatment. Still talking to the sister rather than to the patient, he said: 'If she wants to go out this afternoon she can, but if she goes, she can't come back.'

This was my first experience of a senior doctor openly disregarding evidence which failed to support what he wished to believe. I had seen it happen unconsciously with Dr Prunty in the metabolic ward, but never so blatantly.

From there we went downstairs and through the locked door that led to the Drug Dependency Unit. The afternoon clinic was heavily booked. I was not surprised by this as I had heard that the clinics were overburdened by addicts requesting their help. Articles in the press often called for more clinics to deal with the enormous workload. I looked forward to seeing how so many patients could be accommodated.

None of the patients had arrived so Dr T. passed the time by talking to me and his staff about the treatment of drug addiction. He emphasised the importance of reducing the dose of prescribed drugs rapidly, and of never giving injectable drugs or taking account of what the patient said. He also stressed that treatment must be 'the same for everyone', regardless of the severity or length of the addiction. I did not understand why this should be so but could not get him to explain.

Dr T.'s discourse took a long time. At 3 p.m. there were still no patients, though they had been summoned for 2 p.m. At 3.30 Dr T. was running out of things to say. I was beginning to feel tired. At 3.40 there were still no patients. Dr T. looked at his watch. 'Well, I'm going home,' he said. And off he went.

This was my first attempt to see a DDU in action. I decided that Dr. T.'s clinic was probably atypical, particularly as I had heard so much about it from disgruntled ex-patients. I resolved to visit others.

At the time I was in correspondence with a woman DDU consultant, Dr N., about several ex-patients of hers. She had a reputation for being more liberal than many of her colleagues, so I thought I would try to make friends. I have always found women doctors to be amenable to an interested approach. I needed to ring Dr N. about one of her patients and, at the end of the call, I invited her to lunch.

The lunch was not a success. Dr N., many years my junior, seemed nervous. I got the impression that she was afraid to be associated with me, and I had a curious feeling that she would be reporting on the proceedings to someone else. When I tried to discover the reasoning behind the new clinic policies, she gave me no straight answers. What I remember most strongly was my feeling that she was not being straightforward, and also her statement: 'In drug dependency the most important thing is not to step out of line.' I hadn't heard that phrase in connection with medical practice before.

Dr N. invited me to visit one of her lunchtime clinics, which I did. Here, all the patients who were booked actually turned up. I soon discovered why. All had been referred by the court after being convicted of offences in connection with drugs. If they could get themselves accepted as in-patients for detoxification, they could go to hospital instead of prison.

At this clinic patients were not seen in private by the doctor. The entire clinic staff was there: Dr N., her registrar, a GP 'clinical assistant', the sister, a staff nurse, a psychologist, a social worker and the clinic secretary. Patients came either individually or in couples, and Dr N. asked most of the questions. Were they sure that they wanted to come off drugs? Yes, they were sure. Wasn't it just to avoid going to prison? Oh no, certainly not. Would they behave themselves in hospital? Yes, of course. Did they realise that if they were caught with drugs while in the hospital, they would be discharged immediately? Yes, they realised. Yes, they were eager for help. Yes, they would keep all the rules.

I learned the real situation later from other patients who had been through this system. Once in the hospital, you could get all the drugs you wanted: they circulated freely and the staff neither noticed nor cared. If you weren't caught and could tolerate the hospital, you were eventually discharged as 'drug-free' regardless of what you were actually taking. If you were caught with drugs or couldn't stand the hospital regime, it didn't matter because by that time the court had forgotten about you. Thus the addicts got off their charges, the clinic could claim success for their treatment and the court didn't have to do anything. It suited everyone.

I also paid a visit to a clinic run by an old friend, Dr Ghul Dhanani, who worked under Dr Pamela Aylett, the consultant who ran the DDU at the Westminster Hospital. I had known Ghul since she first came to England from Pakistan many years before, and regarded her as an intelligent, caring and sensitive doctor who made good relationships with the most difficult patients. If any doctor could attract and help addicts under the prevailing system, I thought, it would be Ghul.

The Westminster DDU was in the basement of a house in Vincent Square. It was open, with no visible locks or keys. The afternoon clinic was fully booked, though not with so many patients. As I would expect, Ghul allowed more time for each patient.

But not one of them kept the appointment. Eventually a non-addict patient arrived asking for Ghul. While she was away she left me to browse through the patients' case notes. They were brief and mostly unhelpful. I couldn't understand what was going on in this strange submedical world.

What I did now understand was why so many addicts were begging me to help them: the new policies were driving patients away from the DDUs. Addicts were not treated according to normal rules of medical ethics. Doctors were either not sympathetic or were scared to use their own judgement.

Meanwhile I continued trying to read up the subject, but this was largely fruitless. With most medical conditions one can go to a library and learn not only what the treatment is but the reasoning behind it. This was not possible in drug dependency. Many of the 'scientific' papers published in the previous eight years or so were irrelevant; many were so unclear as to be useless; and some were gobbledegook. No articles had evaluated the work of the clinics, but they frequently contained pronouncements about the wickedness of 'private doctors'.

One famous article, by R.L. Hartnoll and M.C. Micheson [1], was said to be the basis for the clinics' decision to change their policies and cut off addicts from their long-standing injectables. I learned that no one was more surprised about this than the authors of the article: if

[1] R.L. Hartnoll and M.C. Micheson, 'Evaluation of Heroin Maintenance in Controlled Trial', *Archives of General Psychiatry* (1980), 37, pp. 877–84.

it indicated anything, it was the opposite. There seemed to be no valid reason behind the decision, no attempt to understand the addicts or to interest doctors in other branches of medicine. The subject was kept tightly controlled by 'specialists'. General practitioners were positively deterred from becoming involved.

At about this time, some of these consultants wrote a letter to *The Times* suggesting that general practitioners who wished to treat addicts should do so only under the direct control of the local drug dependency consultant. This remarkable suggestion went against all the traditions of British medicine. General practitioners have always been their own masters, deciding when to refer a patient to a specialist and whether or not to take his advice. Now it was being suggested that, for drug dependency, this principle should be abandoned.

The suggestion was too much for the authorities and the profession; possibly enough people saw it as a power-seeking ploy. At any rate, it was ignored. A Home Office official said to me later: 'It went down like a lead balloon.'

Having got nowhere in my attempt to understand what was going on in the drug dependency world, I decided to go one step further. I got in touch with Dr Philip Connell and invited him to lunch.

Dr Connell, consultant in charge of drug dependency at the Maudsley Hospital, was a member of virtually every powerful committee in the field and the chairman of many of them. Unlike many prominent people in this field, he had done some original work on dependency. He was the person who first described amphetamine psychosis, the schizoid madness I had first seen in my patient Anne-Marie.

Connell accepted my invitation and arrived at my house as arranged. He greeted me genially, though I thought I detected a patronising manner. We walked round the corner to a nearby Italian restaurant.

During lunch I told Dr Connell about the patients being referred to me, about what I had seen, and how I felt that something was wrong in drug dependency. He seemed interested in what I was saying, but I realised that I was right about his patronising manner when he said: 'I used to think these things when I was young and idealistic.'

Since I was fifty-five at the time, I didn't take this as a compliment.

He continued: 'Your thinking has followed the same path that mine did.' Dr Connell seemed to be implying that my ideas were immature and irrelevant. He left me in no doubt that he did not take what I had said seriously, but without saying why.

As the weeks passed, I began to be aware that something sinister was going on in the field of drug dependency. The reason I had taken so long to understand this was because it had not occurred to me that virtually an entire specialty in medicine could be so detached from the mainstream that it could deceive the rest of the profession. The truth was, of course, that few doctors cared. Few were interested in addiction and were only too glad to hand the problem over to doctors they wished neither to meet nor to talk to. These 'drug dependency' doctors had taken over and, unchecked by the practice or common sense of their colleagues, had become a sort of 'mafia', acting in their own interests, largely concerned with power and prestige, including positions on important committees. They distorted the facts to suit themselves, carried out little or no serious research, and insisted that only they knew how to treat addicts while at the same time providing a service which probably would not have been tolerated in any other branch of medicine. Few addicts did tolerate it. Meanwhile the doctors were also demanding more public money in order to provide more of the same and encouraging the media to uphold the common prejudices about drug users.

Once I saw how things had gone wrong, it would have been impossible for me not to become involved. I saw injustice often amounting to cruelty against patients who had no redress. I could not turn away.

I was in a good position to help many of these patients. Doctors who protest publicly know that their promotion may be blocked and their careers ruined. As a private practitioner, I did not have to worry about promotion. And I was still naive enough to think that a doctor who did good work in a neglected field might be praised – or at worst ignored. I thought myself invulnerable to danger, and I don't think I was alone in this. Some of the idealism of the early days of the Health Service remained in me and in many of my generation.

There was one place where I felt I might find some common sense and have an open discussion on the subject. Ironically, this was not with 'drug doctors' but in the organisation that was charged with policing them. It was the Home Office.

In Britain, any doctor who sees a patient whom he knows or suspects is dependent on controlled drugs is required by law to notify the patient to the Home Office. This regulation is not taken seriously by many. For instance, doctors seldom notify addicts unless they actually prescribe drugs for them. Most don't even know of the law, and nothing is done to enlighten them. And if they do comply,

it is at their own expense. For other conditions requiring notification
– measles, tuberculosis and so on – the notifying doctor is paid a small
fee. For notifying an addict he is paid nothing.

None of this suggests that the Home Office or anyone else is
keen to obtain accurate figures about drug addiction. The Home
Office says that it probably knows of no more than about one addict
in five. Knowledgeable people say the figure is more like one in ten
or twenty.

In the late seventies and early eighties the work of the Home
Office Drugs Branch was growing rapidly. The increase in addiction,
chiefly heroin addiction, was so great that it could not fail to come to
their notice. This branch of the Home Office is concerned largely with
keeping the 'Addicts' Index' (popularly known as 'the Register') and
with helping and policing doctors who prescribe for addicts. It employs
a number of Drug Inspectors who inspect the prescriptions handed in
at pharmacies and make sure that they comply with the law and with
the spirit of current policies. Much of their work is duplicated by the
Drugs Squad (Controlled Drugs branch) at New Scotland Yard.

At that time the Home Office inspectors made visits every year or
two to doctors working in the field. They discussed the work, dealt with
anything they felt needed to be improved, and issued any warnings they
felt were needed. The more humane and responsible inspectors took
the opportunity to learn what they could and also increase and impart
their knowledge of the drug scene.

Under the Misuse of Drugs Act (1967), the Home Office also
had powers to call before tribunals any doctor who it believed was
prescribing irresponsibly. The tribunal could remove a doctor's right
to prescribe controlled drugs. This machinery had been used only
three times in fifteen years, and the General Medical Council, the
disciplinary body for the medical profession, had always refused to
prosecute doctors for this, advocating the doctor's right to prescribe
what he thought best for the patient.

Many people think that the General Medical Council, generally
known as the GMC, is part of the British Medical Association (BMA)
or even of the Home Office. This is not so. The BMA is an association
and something like a trade union. Any doctor can join. The General
Medical Council is a statutory body, a committee of the Privy Council,
with special powers, particularly concerning medical education and the
disciplining of doctors. The Council (then the 'General Council of
Medical Education and Registration') was founded in 1858 as part of
the medical profession's attempts to organise itself into a profession, to

raise standards and to gain more power. It is the keeper and compiler of the Medical Register.

Until the early 1980s, the GMC had a benign attitude towards doctors who treated addicts as well as towards many other matters. This was to change with a vengeance. Over the years, and especially after Sir John Richardson (later Lord Richardson) retired as president, the Council became more a prosecuting than a fact-finding body. Some defendants began to feel that the GMC was out to get them, so they hired eminent defence barristers. The GMC responded by hiring Old Bailey-type prosecutors with the aim of getting 'convictions'. Costs for both the GMC and the medical defence organisations increased enormously. There was disapproval and discontent, but little that anyone could do.

Once the drug dependency 'mafia' became influential, the Council began to use its powers to impose the new orthodoxy in the treatment of drug addiction. The Home Office was encouraged to hold more tribunals and, when the doctor was found guilty, as he almost always was, he would be summoned by the GMC. As long as it could get hold of the papers from the Home Office, it had a ready-made case. Furthermore, DDU consultants began to get power in the GMC.

Nothing was said publicly about any of this.

When my trickle of addicts became a flood, I thought I should make my position clear to the authorities and rang the Home Office. I knew that their officers sometimes descended on hapless doctors and made disturbing threats. They had done this to a friend of mine who had tried to be kind to an addict and I didn't want them to do it to me. Moreover, I was undecided about whether to continue to work with drug addicts. Their need was obvious and overwhelming, but I realised that it was a dangerous scene and wasn't sure how far I wished to become involved.

At this time the Chief Inspector of Drugs at the Home Office was H. B. ('Bing') Spear, a Cornishman who had worked in the Drugs Branch since 1952 and undoubtedly had a greater knowledge and a better overall view of the drug situation in Britain than anyone else. He had watched the heroin problem develop and seen the folly, ambitions and political manoeuvres that led to the setting up of the clinics, which he regarded as bad for everyone. 'We didn't need clinics,' he was fond of saying. 'We needed a thousand doctors willing to look after one addict each.' He continued to hold and express these views despite his position at the heart of the establishment.

When I rang the Home Office Drugs Branch, the result was unexpected. I was immediately put through to Bing Spear himself. 'I was waiting for you to ring,' he said. 'I thought you might need some help.'

I had been, and remained, scrupulous about notifying every addict I saw. During the last few weeks the numbers had increased exponentially. Clearly he was aware of this.

Bing suggested that he and his colleague, John Lawson, should come round to see me. John Lawson was Senior Home Office Inspector of Drugs for London and the Southeast.

A few days later the two men came to my house and stayed about an hour and a half. It was a friendly chat with two congenial people – among the first I had met in my pursuit of enlightenment about the drug scene. Bing's vision and grasp of the subject were remarkable. I was puzzled by his dusky appearance and yellowish skin, but later learned that he had had regular kidney dialysis for the past eight years.

Early in our acquaintance I noticed that Bing inspired great loyalty among his staff and admiration everywhere. Everyone whom I regarded as even remotely enlightened seemed to think that, but for him, the situation in drug addiction would collapse totally to the mercies of the drug dependency 'mafia'. Several people prominent in the field at the time made remarks such as, 'God help us when Bing goes.' Everyone knew too that because of his precarious health, he might 'go' at any time. This was prophetic: it was while Bing was away having a heart operation, and shortly afterwards a kidney transplant, that the people who opposed my ideas worked up the case against me.

Bing saw that I was serious and honest in what I did, and also, I think, that I was strong and unlikely to bend with every influence. He was appalled at what was going on in the clinics and at the predicament of the addicts. In former days he had known most of the addicts personally and had learned, as I was learning, by listening to what they said. Many addicts still claimed personal friendship with him, and though quick to criticise or vilify doctors, police or others in authority, none ever said anything hostile or even critical about Bing. He often said that when he retired he was going to run an 'addicts' union' and really get the addicts organised. In fact, when it came to the point, he did not do this. But by that time things had changed and, like me, he was sickened by what was going on.

My initial interview was not all jollity and agreement. They gave me serious warnings, in particular of the danger of being persuaded to prescribe more drugs than an addict needed to stay normal, thus enabling him to sell some on the black market. I was already aware of this danger. Avoiding it altogether was impossible: to be totally safe, one must not prescribe at all. This is the practice of many doctors. Whatever pious comments emerge from the Department of Health and Social Security or the GMC, no doctor gets into trouble for neglecting addicts, from vilifying them or from causing them suffering. But refusing to prescribe causes many addicts to avoid the official services in favour of the black market. Some doctors hold the view that as long as they themselves do not prescribe the drugs that are sold illegally, it doesn't matter if an addict increases the black market through having to make money to pay for his drugs.

Bing Spear and John Lawson were experienced and honest, so neither held this view. In fact, Bing believed that it was desirable to have a 'grey market' in prescribed drugs, which would prevent the addicts from having to use the black market. Unfortunately others with power did not hold this view, or, if they did, they did not admit it publicly. Such clinic consultants as made their views known strengthened public prejudices fed by horror-stories in the tabloid press. In turn, the press managed to put about that if only more public money was available, all addicts could be successfully treated by present methods. In view of the obvious failure of the clinics as they then existed, it was plainly nonsense to say that the solution to the drug problem would be to spend more public money on more of the same. Yet I never knew a doctor try to refute this delusion, and many encouraged it.

I had never been a strong defender of private practice but I couldn't help noticing that many drug dependency doctors were paid salaries for clinical work yet scarcely ever saw a patient. This is exactly the kind of behaviour that drives patients, often reluctantly, to private doctors. I felt sorry for patients who had been nominally under a particular doctor's care for years but had rarely, and sometimes never, seen him. There is something corrupt about a doctor who merely writes out prescriptions and leaves the real work with the patients to nurses or social workers who have no power to change the prescription or to write another. Such practices shame the National Health Service. I don't think they would have been tolerated in any other field of medicine.

Bing was aware of these problems and longed to do something about them. He cautioned me about the pitfalls of taking up this work seriously, but at the same time he encouraged me. Without that encouragement I would not have had the nerve to continue to work with drug addicts once I became aware of the opposition, even hatred, that it aroused among those in power. It was from him that I first learned of the drug dependency 'mafia' among doctors: who its members were and how they worked. He threw this out to me as a sort of challenge.

Bing and I have remained friends. I also remained on friendly terms with John Lawson, though I didn't see him so often after he was transferred to Bristol – allegedly because he was too 'soft' on doctors whom the drug dependency mafia wished to attack. Certainly what happened later was consistent with that. Bing was also thought to be too soft but he was the boss, so the doctors were not in a position to remove him. Instead they acted swiftly and secretly when he was away.

Chapter 7

Treating Addicts: the War on Drugs

It soon seemed that every addict in London and outside was trying to become my patient. An infinite demand appeared to exist in the world outside my consulting room: hundreds or probably thousands of heroin addicts telephoned or called at the house. Some thought they had found a 'soft touch', an easy supply of drugs, but many knew better. What they had found at last, they said, was someone who regarded them as human beings, who treated them with respect and gave them back a dignity that most had lost. These patients spread the word. My addict practice grew so rapidly that it threatened to swamp our general psychiatric practice.

For a while the number of addict patients increased despite my strong efforts to curb it. Over the next eight years I saw more than five hundred addicts. My critics liked to make out that I treated many hundreds at the same time, but this was not so. The myth arose, I think, through the Home Office, which I was obliged to notify even if I had seen an addict no more than once and had not given him any treatment. The addict's name then remained in the Home Office 'Addicts' Index' linked with the name of the doctor until he was notified by another doctor.

All the same I had as many patients as I could reasonably cope with, up to a hundred and fifty at one time, seen on average every two to three weeks. This may not seem a large number compared with the numbers of patients treated by some doctors, but it was a strain and required long hours of work. Also, compared with the minimal hours worked by many clinics and the small number of patients they cared for, despite their often large supporting staff, it seemed to some people to be excessive. But although I was sometimes tired, I never felt I had more work than I could cope with.

The main reason my enemies exaggerated the number of patients I saw was that they liked to focus on the fees I earned. 'Money is at the root of all this hostility to you and that's what it's all about,' Bing Spear told me repeatedly. 'When your name comes up at any meeting, they get out their calculators and produce the huge sums they like to think you earn. And of course, they don't take into account the expenses of your premises and practice, paying the staff and so on. Since they get those free themselves, they like to calculate on the basis that you do, too.'

I had by now realised that the official clinics had nothing to offer the vast majority of addicts, who in turn had lost all confidence in them. I realised, too, that some of the clinic doctors, along with politicians, were distorting the addicts' situation and needs. I felt I must try to tackle the subject seriously, but it was impossible to help all who were in need. My chief problem was how to select for treatment those applicants whom I could best help and who seemed likely to fit in with the other activities of the house and practice. Reluctantly I had to be ruthless. It would be easy to be overwhelmed by hordes of desperate men and women, many genuinely seeking help but some out to exploit me.

I excluded anyone who looked dirty or unkempt, anyone who behaved aggressively or unpleasantly, and anyone to whom my secretaries took a dislike. This was not because I thought these people unworthy of help but because I knew I could not deal with them under existing circumstances. I only considered those addicts who sent a written letter of referral from a general practitioner. Sometimes this was no more than a letter saying something like 'This man has asked to be referred to you', or 'This is to introduce Miss So-and-So.' The more enthusiastic or caring the GP's letter, the more likely I was to accept the patient. A few were irresistible, such as the charming patient whose doctor wrote, 'I delivered this patient myself and know the family well. I shall be pleased to help in any way I can. He has had a poor deal from the clinic and deserves better.' But I tried to be fair, realising that often it was not the addict's fault if his doctor's letter was casual or hostile.

Third, although in our general psychiatric practice we were referred patients from all over the world, I decided to limit the addicts to those who lived in the London area or who could get there and back in a day. Later I limited this still further, to half a day. Even then it caused difficulties. The drug dependency clinics mostly had strict catchment areas. No one who lived outside the area would be accepted as a patient even if he lived close by or in an area where there was no clinic. Even in London there were areas not covered by a clinic; addicts who lived in them had nowhere to go for help. None of the clinic doctors with whom I spoke seemed to think this was important. But my critics were quick to make a fuss about my patients who lived more than a mile or two from my rooms, as though there was something immoral in this.

I also only accepted patients whom I liked or felt that I could work with. I knew that if I was to help addicts stabilise their lives and eventually become drug-free, I needed a close doctor–patient relationship of a kind long abandoned by the clinics. And so it turned out. Many addicts responded wonderfully to being treated with respect and being appreciated for their positive qualities. They had not experienced this before, and it was one of the most important aspects of my work with them, as was the maintenance dose of opiate I prescribed to help them become and remain stable until they could give up drugs altogether. Many were amazed to be treated in this way and attributed their ultimate success to it.

I think I had a semi-conscious bias towards those who were highly intelligent, as many of them were. I always felt that one problem in the clinics was that many of the patients were much more intelligent than the doctors. And the doctors, unable to acknowledge this, failed to see the loss of human potential and sometimes felt a need to denigrate and humiliate their patients.

I felt bad about rejecting so many addicts in dire need, especially those in whom I recognised potential or who had families to support, as many of them did. At the same time I recognised that it was inevitable. I felt I understood the dilemmas of surgeons on the battlefield who have to be ruthless in selecting those wounded whom they feel they can best help, regretfully rejecting others who, under other circumstances, they might also have been able to save.

Before accepting anyone I also demanded proof that the patient could afford to pay private fees. This usually meant seeing a series of pay-slips or the previous year's income tax returns. I had to be as sure as I could that the fees would not be paid from the sale of drugs prescribed by me. It also raised the question of employment. Many addicts found it impossible to work. Often this was not because they were lazy or high on drugs but because of the time they had to give to their addiction, to finding the drugs without which they felt ill and could not lead a normal life, and to raising the money to pay for these drugs. They could work only if they felt well. They felt well only if they had a regular supply of drugs. Obtaining these on the black market might take several hours each day, which was incompatible with working normal hours, and cost more than could be earned by most people in honest work. Even if an addict was lucky enough to attend a clinic, prescriptions were usually for only a day at a time and had to be dispensed by a named pharmacy. Getting to that pharmacy in opening hours was impossible within most jobs. So the addict soon lost his job if he had one.

I soon realised that whether or not an addict was in employment was also important from my own point of view. A private doctor has to charge fees and an unemployed patient may have to sell part of his 'script' in order to pay those fees. Thus the doctor may, inadvertently and in theory, be encouraging the black market. Some drug dependency doctors liked to make much of this, while ignoring much greater harm done by the addicts they forced on to the black market through their policies. For this reason I became increasingly careful about ensuring that all my addict patients earned enough to pay my fees, or else had parents or others who were willing to pay for them. Although many were in a Catch-22 situation in that they could not work without legal drugs and could not get legal drugs until they worked, it became too dangerous to accept them as patients on the grounds that they might then be able to work. Often reluctantly and while recognising their predicament, I had to turn them away.

I became increasingly conscious that few members of the medical profession, including the specialists in the subject, cared about the addicts. The emphasis was on keeping in line with officialdom, imposing set policies and in general keeping the subject tidy. It is easy to impose a standard plan, prescribe according to it, ignore what is happening to the patient, and then claim, after the allotted time, that the patient is drug-free or even 'cured'. This was one reason why so many of the patients disliked the clinics and why so many said they liked me. The basis of my treatment policy was to find the human being in each addict and help him or her to develop individuality, self-respect and self-confidence. It was clear that unless these qualities were fostered there was no hope of helping an addict to give up drugs.

With a new patient I would make all suitable examinations and investigations and then, if he needed drugs, prescribe the minimum dose I thought he could manage on, and for the minimum time. My aim was always to help the addict become free of the need to take drugs, though not at the cost of his stability. It was of prime importance for him to straighten out his life, deal with his work, family and personal problems, and most had to do this before they could reduce their dose of drugs or give them up. Each regime was tailored to the individual, and I saw each patient once every week at first, sometimes less frequently later on. I got to know all the addicts well, and I think they knew that I regarded them as individuals and that I was interested in their personalities and their lives.

Sometimes the reduction of dose would take months or years. Someone who has been injecting drugs for twenty years or more is unlikely to be able to stop through a prearranged routine or system. Giving up needs preparation and hard work. It seems only common sense to say this, but popular prejudice dictates otherwise. Drug addiction attracts extraordinary contempt and moralising from many different quarters.

As I found out more about what went on in the NHS clinics, I felt it was also my duty, whenever I had the opportunity, to write and speak in public about what I had seen and heard. I believe that this, more than the way I tried to help my patients, led to the organised persecution from which I was to suffer. When members of entrenched establishments are criticised openly and their shortcomings revealed, they feel threatened. They are then at their most ruthless and unscrupulous.

Many of the drug clinics insisted on making contracts with their patients. As a condition of treatment, the addict agreed, often in writing, to reduce his dose of drugs at a specified rate, regardless of his need or ability to do so, undertaking to become drug-free within so many months, usually two or three or six. He had to promise this even if he had been addicted for twenty or thirty years. Many had numerous failed treatments behind them and knew that this one would fail as well. I soon learned that for many addicts, these contracts were ineffective and dishonest and encouraged speciousness in doctor–patient relationships.

I too made agreements with my patients, but of a different kind and different for each person. These took into account individual factors, including what the addict felt he could achieve. My aim was always that the patient should become drug-free eventually, even those addicts who were convinced that this would never be possible. As time passed I was pleased at the number who, though they had once felt they would be addicts for ever, changed their minds once their lives were stable and secure. They balanced those who seemed likely to succeed at the beginning yet proved to be intractable. Meanwhile, the addict would lead a productive, legal life on the smallest dose that kept him normal. (I say 'him' only because two out of three were men.)

The average age of the addicts I treated was thirty-three years for men and thirty-one for women. The average age at which they had become addicted was seventeen, so they had been addicted on average some fifteen years. Nearly all had had treatment in at least one NHS clinic, and many had attended several or the same one many times. One patient had had twenty-seven similar courses of treatment. He came to me disgusted because, although he was desperate for help, the clinic was offering him yet another. It never ceased to astonish me that they repeated the same failed treatment on the same addicts over and over again.

All the patients were contemptuous of the methods of the clinics and of most of the doctors who ran them, though they often respected certain members of staff, including nurses and social workers as well as doctors. They complained most of the doctors' authoritarian attitudes, of rigid methods of treatment, of lack of understanding of addiction, and of the absence of privacy or opportunity for discussion with the doctor. Many said that there was no useful doctor–patient relationship at all.

The essence of my treatment was that the patients would attend regularly at times agreed by both of us and receive whatever attention and treatment seemed indicated. This might include encouragement and moral support or more intensive exploration and psychotherapy. I regarded it as important to help the patients gain in self-respect and to behave accordingly. This was one of the hardest aspects of the work because they were so used to being treated as scum. If you are unpleasant to people or regard them as degraded, they behave unpleasantly and in degraded ways. As part of my attempt to improve their image of themselves, I expected them to look tidy and clean and to behave with consideration towards other patients in the waiting room, which was shared by three doctors, and towards my two secretaries. I told each new patient that anyone who was offensive to others in the house would be discharged immediately, and on the rare occasions when they transgressed in this I carried out my threat.

I also told them that under no circumstances were they to visit the West End of London – or any other place where illegal drugs were bought and sold – without previous discussion with me. If they needed to go, for example to shop or to take their children to a pantomime, it had to be with my agreement. And on no account were they to carry drugs when they went there. If they were picked up by the police in the West End, with or without drugs, or if they were seen there by me or one of my secretaries, I would discharge them from my care immediately.

This may sound draconian but I knew that the situation demanded it. I was liable to get into serious trouble if my patients were caught selling drugs prescribed by me. Many policemen believed that addicts should not get legal drugs at all and did everything they could to make trouble for those who did. Moreover, many police in London had already been corrupted by the drug situation. Some planted drugs on innocent people, sold confiscated drugs, or arrested known addicts on trumped-up charges. At first these were only suspicions, supported by the stories addicts told me. But during the time I treated addicts, a number of London policemen were found guilty and jailed for such offences, some of them the very policemen I had been told about. Since this type of corruption was always a possibility, I emphasised to my patients that if they avoided dangerous places, they were likely to avoid dangerous policemen. Most of them complied, but over the years I discharged at least a dozen patients who disobeyed and were seen or arrested in the West End.

I saw the addict patients weekly at first and sometimes more frequently. They could stay for as short or long a time as they wished. Some stayed only a few minutes, though often appreciated a longer talk when they came to know and trust me. Others required longer psychotherapeutic sessions, an hour or more. Gradually I learned roughly what each patient would need and could make their appointments accordingly. I came to know them all, some extremely well, and often their families too. Many patients were highly sensitive, skilled and thoughtful people who were acutely aware of the potential they had lost by becoming involved with drugs.

They also knew that the popular ideas about drug addicts were untrue. In their contempt for politicians and doctors who perpetuated these myths, the addicts were often articulate, incisive and witty. I was always delighted when one of them was promoted in his job or had exceptional success in his business or family. One addict made a million and a half pounds in a property deal. Another had a daughter who was accepted for law school. Another won a prize for the orchids he had grown and gave me a ticket to see them at the Royal Horticultural Show. Some gave me pictures they had painted and I began a collection of photographs depicting the very normal lives they were able to lead once they were stabilised. Most, however, had ordinary, unglamorous jobs which they did with increased zest and security when their drug needs no longer dominated their lives.

Some brought their children to see me and I encouraged this, partly to see that they were well cared for. It was also a safeguard for addict mothers against social workers and judges, some of whom believed that having an addict mother was grounds for removing a child from his or her home. On a number of occasions I wrote court reports which helped to halt these proceedings. For older children I kept a drawer full of presents, from which each child could choose one at every visit. Needless to say, this made me popular with them. Some of them brought me presents, often things they had made at school, or toys they had grown out of so that I could given them to other children. I was often able to help in family or medical problems.

I regarded my relationship with the addicts' children as particularly important because some general practitioners extended their dislike of addicts to their families, either giving them a second-class service or refusing to treat them at all. This was another example of the deplorable condition to which the treatment of drug addiction (or drug 'abuse', as doctors and officials liked to call it) had come in Britain.

Nearly all the addicts received prescriptions for drugs from me. These were mostly for methadone, the synthetic opioid which, for dubious reasons, had come to be regarded as a respectable treatment for heroin addiction. This treatment maintains the addiction and in some ways makes it worse, as it is often more difficult for an addict to relinquish methadone than heroin. But there was no choice in this. Since 1967 doctors outside clinics had been forbidden to prescribe heroin, and clinic doctors no longer did so. My idea was to prescribe as little as possible and to reduce the dose as fast as possible, but only within the capacity of the individual patient. Reducing the dose if the patient feels he cannot cope leads almost inevitably back to the black market and to the failure of treatment.

Deciding the initial dose was always difficult. Most addicts, unless strongly motivated to reduce their drug need, try to get as much as possible from the doctor and regard anything above their needs for normality as a 'treat', to be enjoyed with self-indulgence. It requires skill on the part of the doctor and also much time with an individual patient to assess the amount needed; and even then, mistakes are made. This is one reason why clinic doctors imposed rigid regimes and refused to discuss the treatment with the patient, leaving decisions to be taken by a committee behind the scenes. These doctors seldom had time to get to know the patient well, and often did not even see him. When they did, it was often a young doctor in training whom the addict had never seen before and would never see again. As a result, the idea had grown up in NHS circles that the dose and the rate of reduction should be fixed and immutable, decided by a committee and not even within the ability of the interviewer to alter. Otherwise, it was said, the whole interview would be taken up with argument about dosage. This was untrue but a convenient cover for lack of skill and interest on the part of the doctor.

I quickly learned that, provided the doctor was experienced and competent, addicts responded best to individual treatment. Nonetheless, I could sympathise with clinic workers. When an inexperienced or incompetent doctor was in charge, few addicts could resist exploiting the situation. Clinic doctors were not necessarily the most competent or clinically skilled, and some felt threatened by addicts, especially those brighter than they. So, under the existing system, deplorable as it was, they had to make rules to protect themselves.

During the early days, clinic doctors prescribed huge doses of drugs, usually in injectable form. Some doctors, for reasons I have been unable to discover, encouraged their addict patients to inject rather than take their drugs by mouth. Some even insisted on their doing so. This is a difficult area to explore because, although most of those who were responsible for this are still alive, they tend to falsify their memories and descriptions, and sometimes their clinical records as well. My policy was to prescribe liquid oral methadone wherever possible and to encourage injectors to switch to this. Those who could not manage without injecting received ampoules, as few as seemed possible.

At that time virtually all doctors were inexperienced in the management of drug addiction and, through no fault of their own, were deceived by addicts asking for more drugs than they needed for stability. When the doctors realised what had happened, they felt demeaned and tended to go to the other extreme. Many were now saying that no addict ever needed injectables and that none needed more than 40 millilitres of liquid oral methadone to remain stable. I knew this was untrue. It was just one more reason why few long-term addicts attended clinics.

Of course, I wished to avoid a situation in which I was prescribing a far higher dose than was usual in the clinics. I tried to assess the situation by reading the scientific literature on the subject but this, as I had already found, was negligible. British research into drug dependency had been conspicuous in neglecting the treatment of addicts and what to prescribe for them. In desperation I turned to earlier American literature, which was more helpful. In the end I decided not to prescribe more than 180 milligrams per day to any patient. In practice over the years, few patients received more than 80 milligrams, even fewer got more than 100 milligrams, and none as much as 180 milligrams. On the whole these rules worked well in my practice.

All this fuss was really due to the obsession of the authorities in the 'war on drugs' with the *supply* of drugs, while they ignored the equally important question of *demand*. Token efforts have been made towards tackling demand, but in general the policy was, and has remained up to the time of writing, to concentrate on the illegal smuggling and selling. Even this can be ignored if it is politically inconvenient, for anyone who studies the subject can see that the 'war on drugs' is a war only in fantasy. Politicians boast when illegal drugs are seized in ever-increasing quantities, as though this means they are winning the 'war'. They turn a blind eye to the main sources of supply because it is politically inconvenient to interfere with suppliers such as Colombia and Panama and it is difficult to influence in any effective way what happens in, for example, Pakistan, Afghanistan or Thailand. At the same time the demand for drugs, which is the basis of the whole problem, is largely ignored. Under present policies in the West, addiction spreads by pyramid-selling. Many addicts can survive only by creating more addicts to whom they can sell drugs to make enough money to pay for their own. Those in turn create other addicts, and so it goes on. If the results were not so tragic, it would be a laughable example of how those in authority exploit public prejudice in whatever ways suit them.

Fees were sometimes a source of difficulty and embarrassment. In private practice they have to be charged, if only for the doctor's survival. Yet many of the addicts were not the sort of people who would normally seek private medicine. Like many others in Britain, they only 'went private' when the NHS had failed them or they felt it was likely to do so. I tried to get funding from the Department of Health to run a clinic at cost price in a cheaper area, rather along the lines of the original family planning clinics. Needless to say, the request was turned down.

Our fees in the practice were slightly below the average for the area in 1980: £50 for an initial visit and £30 for follow-up visits. If the addict was stable and trustworthy and needed little attention, he needed to be seen only every three to four weeks, which meant an average weekly cost of £8–£10, but if he needed a lot of attention I often waived the fee. However, this caused difficulties. As the Home Office inspectors pointed out, if an addict could not afford my fee, he couldn't afford the chemist's either; and the chemist would insist on being paid even if I didn't. This must mean that the addict would sell drugs in order to raise the money, which put me in an awkward situation. The patient had to buy his drugs on private prescription and this might cost a further £15–£20 per week, sometimes more. I never discharged a patient who could not pay the fees, but I tried not to accept those who were unlikely to be able to keep them up.

Although fees in general doubled due to inflation during the time I treated addicts, I never raised mine. They remained pegged to the level they had been in 1979.

The subject of fees created enormous tension and hostility among the doctors of the drug dependency establishment. Some people seem unable to imagine that anyone who works for fees can possibly do a good or even an honest job, or can be motivated other than by greed. The doctors who are most vociferous on this subject are often those who, assured of a monthly salary cheque, see no need to earn it by giving good service to the patients for whose benefit they are employed. Several such doctors were influential in organising the persecution of me that was soon to come.

In 1981 I decided to start a new organisation, the Association of Independent Doctors in Addiction (AIDA). The 'independent' in the title meant independent of hospitals and drug clinics. Bing Spear was enthusiastic, said it had long been needed and offered help. This backing from the heart of the Home Office was useful. I persuaded some medical journals to insert notices about the new organisation and received several hundred replies from all over the world. Many of these were from general practitioners who were appalled at the way their patients were treated when they referred them to clinics and, often, at the power structures and rigid policies of these clinics and their remoteness from patients' needs. Some of the replies were from doctors like myself who were trying to help addicts and to treat them in a humane and effective way and who wished to meet and discuss with others of like mind. These doctors became the core of our membership. We have met ever since about every six weeks, at first at the Home Office and then, after the drug dependency 'mafia' had protested successfully about this, at my house.

I was also taking an interest in wider issues concerning drugs in society. I felt this was important. I could see what a devastating effect the current policies were having on drug users as patients and I wanted to try to understand how this had come about.

There was increasing tension in the country and excitement in the press about illegal drugs. Addiction was growing, particularly in the United States where the problem of drugs was worsening. Addicts were increasingly visible on the streets of New York and other large towns. As if to compete with the deteriorating situation in America, the DDUs in Britain had abandoned their previously humane policies, particularly of allowing drugs to long-term addicts who felt unable to give them up. An increasingly harsh belief was spreading among doctors that they should help only those who could give up drugs quickly. Some clinics also imposed special regimes such as compulsory group therapy in normal working hours so that attendance at a clinic was impossible while holding down a job. Accordingly, the clinics were losing, discharging and sometimes persecuting addicts who did not fit in with their increasingly rigid schedules. They were encouraged indirectly by the press with headlines about the perils and wickedness of drugs and drug-taking. The new policies were causing a great deal of resentment and suffering among addicts and their families. They were also causing a lot of crime, which the authorities tried to conceal by arguing that most addicts had convictions before they became addicts so that depriving them of a legal supply of drugs made no difference to their criminality. I thought these arguments were specious and knew that research had shown them to be untrue. It was upsetting to see the inhumanity with which some members of my profession were treating their patients and driving them away.

All this was in line with an increasingly repressive regime in the United States, from which the British government clearly took its cues. Interest now lay not in helping the addicts but in the 'war on drugs', fortified by international operations with helicopters and the picturesque adjuncts of publicity stunts. British government ministers were seen participating in these and expressing their determination to 'beat this evil' or to 'conquer this wicked trade', while it was increasingly obvious that there was no chance of doing so. Yet in line with this political and publicity campaign, treatment for addicts, where it was available, was becoming increasingly a question of instant abstention and appeals to moral fibre. I could see how dispiriting and dehumanising this was to people who were being reduced to the level of 'dirty junkies' and were then attacked and despised for it. I was depressed to see drug addicts treated in this way, for I knew that underneath they had as much potential as anyone else.

Until the present century opium derivatives, or opiates, could be bought freely, like aspirin today. Sold in grocers' shops, often displayed on the counter like sweets, they were popular household drugs. Most people used them, often for the pain which was common in an age without anaesthetics or modern dentistry. Opiates were given to crying babies and unhappy adults. Many people became addicted, but because the drugs were freely available addiction did not have the serious social consequences that it has today. Many prominent and successful people were addicts. Secret addiction was common and, as with alcohol or tranquillisers today, many people did not even realise that they were addicted. People also took opium when they were upset or facing a stressful event, rather as they might now take a drink or a Valium tablet.

In spite of this widespread use, the percentage of people who became addicted was probably no higher than under present prohibition policies. We do not know what proportion of the population is prone to addiction, but guesses in the region of 10–20 per cent are common. Moreover, most who become addicted give up the drug when their circumstances change. This happened after the Vietnam War, when 90 per cent of American servicemen became addicted while in Asia; of these, 90 per cent gave up taking the drug on returning home. In this, as well as in the way the habit spreads socially, addiction to opiates is similar to smoking. Most smokers can give up if they try seriously, but some suffer greatly while doing so and a few are unable to stop.

Demands for controls on the sale of opiates began to be heard from the mid-nineteenth century onwards, and eventually they could only be obtained from pharmacies with a doctor's prescription. These restrictions arose only partly from fears about the dangers of the drug. They also stemmed from fear of the growing urban working class, which used opium extensively, and from racial anxiety. Americans were scared by the large number of Chinese who settled on the West Coast after building the railways. Similar xenophobic anxiety associated with drugs existed in Britain and is graphically described in Dickens's last, unfinished, book *The Mysteries of Edwin Drood*.

Probably even more important in the development of fears about drugs was pressure from the newly organised medical and pharmaceutical professions, which were trying to extend their power. In 1893, pressure of public opinion and a motion in the House of Commons led to the establishment of a Royal Commission to investigate opium. It reported that opium was generally used in moderation and led 'to no evident ill-effects'. Today we know this to be true. The idea that opiates, including heroin, kill or 'screw you up' is false. Apart from addiction, almost all the evils of opiates come from their being illegal. Yet governments and so-called experts are unwilling to admit this.

Fashions and feelings in the medical establishment vary, and views tend to be based on feeling rather than on evidence. The following account of the effects of a drug comes from the *Textbook of Medicine* by Sir Clifford Allbutt and Sir Humphry Rolleston, edition of 1909. 'The sufferer is tremulous and loses his self command; he is subject to fits of agitation and depression. He loses colour and has a haggard appearance . . . As with other agents, a renewed dose of the poison gives temporary relief, but at the cost of future misery.' The drug to which the authors refer is coffee.

Early in the twentieth century the United States began to press for total prohibition of both opiates and alcohol. During the First World War the use of alcohol and opiates among Allied troops became a problem and after the war the United States strengthened its efforts to outlaw both. It has often been shown and then forgotten that it is impossible effectively to prohibit something people are determined to have. But the United States tried to persuade Britain and other countries to follow its policy. Early in the 1920s the British Home Office, then keen on prohibition, made moves to bring criminal sanctions against addicts and the doctors who prescribed for them. The Ministry of Health asked the medical profession for formal advice, and in 1925 a government committee was set up to decide whether doctors should be allowed to prescribe narcotics to addicts. The committee consisted entirely of doctors and was chaired by Sir Humphry Rolleston, president of the Royal College of Physicians. All members of the committee were doctors.

The committee reported early in 1926. Its conclusions were uncannily like my own, for which I was to be persecuted more than half a century later.

The committee favoured 'the gradual withdrawal method' in the treatment of addicts, emphasising the importance of first 'stabilising' the addict. This later fell out of favour and all efforts were directed towards rapid withdrawal of drugs. The committee also recognised 'two classes of persons, to whom the indefinitely prolonged administration of morphine or heroin may be necessary'. They were, first, those 'in whom a complete withdrawal of morphine or heroin produces serious symptoms which cannot be treated satisfactorily under the ordinary conditions of private (i.e. general) practice', and, second, those 'who are capable of leading a fairly normal and useful life so long as they take a certain quantity, usually small, of their drug of addiction, but not otherwise'. Furthermore, 'When . . . every effort possible in the circumstances has been made, and made unsuccessfully, to bring the patient to a condition in which he is independent of the drug, it may . . . become justifiable in certain cases to order regularly the minimum dose which has been found necessary, either in order to avoid serious withdrawal symptoms, or to keep the patient in a condition in which he can lead a useful life.' The report emphasised that it might be possible for the patient to give up at a later date, and added a remark about stable addicts: 'In all such cases the main object must be to keep the supply of the drug within the limits of what is strictly necessary.'

The government accepted the Rolleston report. This method of treating recalcitrant addicts became known as 'the British system' and was successful for many years, during which time there were few problems with opiates in Britain.

When I read the Rolleston report for the first time, I realised that it was almost exactly what I, and many others, had come to believe but which doctors were being increasingly persecuted for practising. The description of patients in the report was almost exactly of those patients whose existence was being denied by the clinic doctors and who were now flocking to me and other doctors who recognised their plight. They had been forgotten, or their existence denied, in current official thinking.

There was, however, one important difference – social class. The Rolleston committee was referring to middle-class addicts in the days when taking drugs had been primarily a middle-class occupation. It was when young, working-class people started to take drugs in the 1950s and 1960s that moral panic flared up.

In the United States prescribing opiates for addicts remained illegal. Refusing to go along with the Americans, British doctors insisted on humane treatment of drug users. Medical views became part of government policy-making and have remained so to this day. Many observers believe that Rolleston would be a useful guide for most countries with heroin problems, and that, if American medical and legal policies had been based on these ideas, the world might have been spared decades of agony.

In 1933 the United States repealed its constitutional amendment prohibiting alcohol, but not before prohibition had contributed to the development of the Mafia, whose activities have plagued America ever since. The American government's dealings with the Mafia over the invasion of Europe also helped to re-establish the selling of heroin illegally after the war. The illegal drugs trade, now one of the biggest industries in America, dominated whole economies and threatened even large nations with its corrupting influences. Yet all that Western nations did was make more noise about the 'war on drugs', the war they could not win.

Throughout this century the United States has been keen to persuade other nations to follow its example and ban the use of heroin totally, even for the dying. Britain has always resisted this, though not always consistently. It seems to have depended on where the doctors currently with power in the field perceived their interests to lie. Later these doctors were not of the stature of Rolleston and his committee.

The situation changed in the 1960s when young people in the industrialised world began to use drugs for recreation and emotional support. This meant the growth of a black market in smuggled heroin. In Britain, where prescribing for addicts was legal, a few doctors began to prescribe drugs for the new 'addicts', and some of these drugs were sold and addiction spread. For a while no one realised what was happening. When the facts emerged, there was a scandal and 'the British system' was blamed, along with the doctors. A new committee, under Lord Brain, whitewashed the situation, though was realistic about 'stable addicts', who were later to be persecuted.

When it was obvious that the Brain committee had been ineffective, it was reconvened. By this time certain doctor-politicians saw that they could use public hysteria about drugs as a way to personal advancement; these people had a powerful influence on the committee. When the committee reported, in 1965, it did not recommend the obvious easy steps to control a handful of doctors, nor did it encourage general practitioners to care for the few hundred new drug users. Instead, it recommended a change in the law, giving the psychiatrists unprecedented power. This was a political move that appealed to the government, who accepted it. The law was duly changed and the problem was centralised into new clinics or DDUs.

The public paid the bill and seemed satisfied. The rest of the medical profession ignored the existence of drug addiction. Under the Misuse of Drugs Act (1967), heroin and cocaine could be prescribed only by doctors who held special licences. In practice this meant doctors who had been given appointments in newly created clinics which were now to be opened all over the country.

It was the beginning of a new kind of doctor, a psychiatrist specialising in 'drug abuse'. Other psychiatrists were thankful not to have to deal with addicts. Some of these drug dependency doctors were eager to extend their power and gain prestige, and some achieved powerful positions. The new drug clinics needed to attract patients, and they prescribed liberally. In the process they even created new addicts. The doctors did this unwittingly because neither they nor anyone else knew much about the new addicts. The clinic doctors realised that nothing was going to make their patients give up drugs quickly, and so they gave priority to stabilising their working and social lives. They began to prescribe methadone, a synthetic opiate, in place of heroin. This was because it lasted longer and needed to be taken only once a day, compared with three or four times a day in the case of heroin. Since most addicts preferred injectable to oral methadone, it became the custom to prescribe it.

This regime did much to help long-term addicts become stable. Maintenance drugs were prescribed for 'stabilised addicts' and diminishing doses for other patients, following the lines of the Rolleston report. Some long-term addicts were told that their maintenance doses would be available on the NHS for the rest of their lives.

But addicts exploited doctors and persuaded them to prescribe huge doses. People who worked in the clinics discovered that many addicts were neither responsible nor pleasant. Non-medical workers in the clinics resented the role of the doctor, who was the only one who could prescribe; they thought that non-prescribing methods of treatment should be given more prominence. Doctors in the clinics disliked having to write so many prescriptions and wished to delegate some of their work to their non-medical colleagues. Moralists gained influence, spreading the idea that addicts should be forced to give up their habits and behave like everyone else, and the uncritical acceptance of this idea enabled the clinic consultants to extend their power.

Meanwhile addiction was spreading and each year the number of new addicts increased. These were easier to treat than long-term addicts, and soon there were enough of them to fill the clinics. Little or no research was done on the effect of the clinics' policies. Experience and expertise had built up, but some doctors have always preferred to talk about their years of experience, which invariably support their current beliefs or prejudices, to studying dispassionately what was really happening.

One thing seemed certain. Clinic doctors knew that most addicts could behave normally only if they were given drugs. Reflecting this, in 1975 the *Columbia Encyclopedia* informed its readers that addiction to 'narcotics' is not harmful so long as the drug is regularly supplied, and that the black market is more dangerous than the drug. But by that time most doctors in the field had either forgotten this or had other aims. These well-worn ideas now contradicted both government policy and the new philosophy of the clinics. The change to a harsher regime occurred only slowly. As late as 1982 the Advisory Council for the Misuse of Drugs, in its report *Treatment and Rehabilitation*, stated: 'The majority are relatively stable individuals who have more in common with the general population than with any essentially pathological sub-group.'

Ambitious medical politicians were already pushing the other way, increasingly ignoring the needs, and the very existence, of long-term addicts. Some of them became unwilling to prescribe for addicts at all. As a result, almost all addicts who could not manage without drugs were turned into criminals and most of them left the clinics, whose workers could now assert that they did not exist. In the words of one of these: 'Clinics have become much nicer places to work in.' This 'improvement' was achieved by effectively ignoring the patients who most needed help.

Some addicts had found independent doctors willing to help them. These doctors were not permitted to prescribe heroin but they could prescribe other opiates, including methadone.

The doctors with power in drug dependency reacted angrily to this development, which they viewed as competitive and threatening. They said that the independent doctors didn't know how to treat addiction. They wrote letters to the press, published articles against them and tried to get them into trouble with the authorities.

The result was a situation of 'Doctors at War', which continues to this day. The clinic doctors gained a decisive victory when they won over the General Medical Council. Previously the GMC had kept out of the controversy, upholding doctors' clinical freedom to prescribe as they saw fit. But doctors powerful in the drug dependency establishment had connections with the GMC, which now came forward to discipline critics of the new regime.

Meanwhile, hostility towards drug addicts increased among both the general public and the medical profession. With few people concerned about addicts or their rights, new laws eroded their civil liberties and threatened the rights of everyone else. The Drug Trafficking Offences Act (1986) enabled courts to confiscate money and goods accumulated in the five years before conviction for a drug trafficking offence. Using the commendable desire to put traffickers out of business as a pretext, these laws undermined the presumption of innocence. This fundamental change in British law went through Parliament, with much of it undebated, because it was perceived as being directed primarily against drug dealers. Some provisions of the new Act appeared in the Criminal Justice Act.

Few groups have been used more shamefully and cynically by both politicians and the medical profession than the long-term addicts, many of whom can be totally stable, and all of whom are more stable if they have suitable help.

The earlier medical writers accepted unquestioningly the idea of the moderately stable addict, the consumer of drugs who could exist without apparent personal or physical deterioration for years on the same level dose of the drug. It was accepted that among victims of this condition were people of the highest qualities, morally and intellectually.

This has been forgotten. When it came to light, a sensible and humane policy might have been developed, encouraging doctors to deal with it, pool information and build up skill. It would have been absorbed into a GP's general knowledge, along with other 'new' conditions. Instead it was seized on by media, politicians and politically minded doctors. Some of these decided that there was no such thing as a long-term or stable addict, or that they were so few that they could be ignored. There was persistent refusal to discuss the matter and there was criticism and persecution of 'dissident' doctors. The forces of law and order joined in persecuting addicts and the doctors who tried to help them.

Some of the myths I uncovered about the use and 'abuse' of drugs were strange and so entrenched in modern, post-industrial society that even thoughtful and educated people were deceived by them. I also saw that much was being done to perpetuate and promote these myths and nothing to dispel them. Vested interests, financial, political or personal, much stronger than logic or facts, were playing on people's feelings and fantasies. At the time I didn't know how powerful these interests were. At first the situation seemed to be not a political struggle but an unsolved intellectual puzzle. Accustomed to good and honest doctors, I thought it was largely a question of finding and presenting the truth. I was wrong.

There were many questions. Corruption of language is probably inevitable where there are strong reasons for suppressing truth. Since George Orwell described Newspeak in his book *Nineteen Eighty-Four* we have been aware of how language can be changed to make it impossible not only to arrive at the truth but also to rule out all other modes of thought. Drugspeak works in the same way. Thus the simple and easily understood phrase 'illegal drug user' is not used in Drugspeak, which refers to 'drug abuser', 'drug misuser', or even 'problem drug user'. These terms are judgemental and can mean whatever the speaker wishes them to mean. 'Abuse' and 'misuse' imply that something is morally wrong and that it should stop. Drugspeakers are contemptuous and patronising towards those who are dependent on illegal drugs.

The phrase 'drug abuse' seems to have originated in the United States during the early part of the century when the non-medical use of certain intoxicants led to increasing moral indignation and public concern. Before that drug-taking, including opium-taking, was regarded as merely an unfortunate habit. The term 'abuse' was probably first used to express disapproval of the use of cocaine by Southern blacks, the condemnation being more of the people who take the drugs than of the drugs themselves.

The World Health Organization has struggled with the concept and terminology of 'drug abuse' and 'drug dependency'. Often the definitions merely state that something is bad without clarifying what the something is, without specifying the criteria on which the negative judgement is based, and without stating the assumptions from which the value is derived. The WHO has tried to classify drug abuse according to motive, but this was unsatisfactory and also tended to attack the user rather than the use of drugs. For example, the committee said that the frequent intravenous use of cocaine 'appeals to persons with psychopathic tendencies, which are often unmasked by the drug'. Similarly, the hallucinogens 'possess a particular attraction for certain psychologically and socially maladjusted persons who have difficulty in conforming to usual social norms. These include "arty" people such as struggling writers, painters, and musicians; frustrated nonconformists; and curious, thrill-seeking adolescents and young adults.'[1]

[1] See Eddy et al., Drug Dependence Bulletin of the World Health Organization (1965) 23, pp. 721–2.

The legal definition of 'drug abuse' is even less satisfactory. Legislators are often reluctant to ask doctors or scientists to help in drawing up legislation, so they sometimes make silly mistakes. One example is the labelling of cocaine as a 'narcotic' by the 1914 Harrison Narcotic Act. In fact it is the opposite. A narcotic diminishes activity in the brain, whereas cocaine increases it and so is classified as a stimulant. This is how it came to be included in legislation designed to stamp out opiates.

Britain adopted America's confusion over the term 'drug abuse' only in recent years, when the drug policies changed and a new drug dependency establishment used confusion as a political tool. Indeed, the situation is now so confused that probably clarity can be restored only by a genuine desire for truth together with abolition of the moralistic weasel word 'abuse' – or at least its restriction to individuals who, like uncontrolled alcoholics, use drugs intemperately and in a manner which makes them incapable of living normal lives.

The phrase 'drug abuse' is now used widely in Britain and is even part of the official language of the civil service. For some years government publications have referred to 'drug abuse' without defining it. Clearly we are all expected to make the same moral judgement. There is even a government committee called the 'Advisory Council on the Misuse of Drugs' and a government-funded organisation called SCODA, the Standing Conference on Drug Abuse. Yet I could find no references to 'drug abuse' or 'drug misuse' in the official literature of fifteen years earlier. In those days government publications referred unequivocally to 'drug addiction'. Even now more thoughtful writers tend to use the morally neutral term 'drug dependency' whereas some of them, mainly doctors, still use the old term 'addiction', as do the Drug Inspectors at the Home Office who control what they call the 'Addicts' Index'. So it seems that some sort of division exists between those who use words of moral condemnation and those who do not.

I found that doctors who worked in drug clinics or DDUs were particularly keen to use moralistic words and to propagate them. The word 'addiction' was regarded as anathema by people who complained about 'medical models' of disease and who wanted to see the power of doctors diminished, and also by doctors who were in charge but wished to delegate their work to workers without medical qualifications. During the previous fifteen years this conflict between 'medical' and 'non-medical' workers in what were now known as the 'caring' professions had also become both fashionable and acrimonious, especially in psychiatry, where a number of conflicts raged about who should prescribe drugs.

In seeking answers to my questions, I came to the conclusion that in general the term 'abuse' or 'misuse' tended to be used to describe deviation from what the speaker thought was acceptable practice. Further, I realised that to lawyers, the word 'abuse' means illegal use and so is something that demands legal intervention, whereas to doctors 'abuse' means non-medical use, requiring treatment, or control, by doctors. Thus each group was using the concept to enhance its domain. This explained why the terms 'abuse' and 'misuse' were not used in relation to the moderate use of far more dangerous substances. For instance, in the case of alcohol, the term 'abuse' seemed to be applied only when drinking exceeded the bounds of social acceptability. A single dose of an illegal drug, even one as harmless as cannabis, was more likely to be seen as 'abuse' than a heavy bout of drinking or smoking.

Drugspeak refers to 'flexibility' in treatment when it actually means a choice between a narrow range of options, all of which are unacceptable to the vast majority of addicts. Drugspeak is fond of the phrase 'multidisciplinary approach', which usually means 'treatment by committee'.

Another word with special meaning in Drugspeak is 'consensus', meaning 'the view of the powerful doctors of the drug dependency establishment'. For years they were fond of insisting that there was consensus in the field when in reality there was not. I believe that my criticism of the concept of consensus was one of the reasons why I was attacked with such bitterness. Margaret Thatcher has a rather different concept of 'consensus' which is nevertheless relevant here: 'To me, consensus seems to be the process of abandoning all beliefs, principles, values and policies . . . It is the process of avoiding the very issues that have got to be solved merely to get people to come to an agreement on the way ahead.' Though used in another context, this is an excellent description of what happens in the field of drug dependency.

Drugspeak has turned the word 'maintenance' into a dirty word implying the prescription of illegal drugs on demand, whereas the original meaning was, in line with the traditional 'British system', the prescription of drugs to those who cannot lead normal lives without them. This method of management was suggested by the doctors on the Rolleston committee in 1926 but it did not suit the new drug dependency establishment. It was one of the biggest issues behind the repeated cases they constructed against me.

Interestingly, in 1988 the Royal College of Psychiatrists produced an official report on drug dependency called 'Drug Scenes'. It was a typical product of Drugspeak. In it 'maintenance', one of the biggest issues of the day, was discussed only briefly and superficially and not even mentioned in the index. Moreover, the index contained a remarkable entry: 'AIDS – excuse for promiscuous prescribing'.

Another term expressing a popular myth which the so-called experts make no attempt to dispel is 'drug-crazed', though they do not, on the whole, use the term themselves. When someone does something bizarre, particularly if it is violent, the media often suggest that the perpetrator was 'drug-crazed', and maybe even that drug addiction or heroin was the cause. In fact heroin has the opposite effect. Violent or bizarre behaviour may be caused occasionally by LSD (which is little used nowadays and is not addictive), sometimes by amphetamines and, most frequently, by alcohol. The only time a heroin user is likely to become violent is not when he is under the influence of heroin but when he cannot get it.

Another popular word in Drugspeak has been 'specialty', which suggests that dealing with drug dependent people requires the special skills of a whole branch of psychiatry. This is nonsense. What is needed, as with most medical disorders, is a little experience gained in the normal course of medical study and practice. No one knows how to treat drug addiction and there is little specialised knowledge such as one would expect to find in a 'specialty' or 'sub-specialty'. Pretending otherwise is an imposition of orthodoxy and a form of empire-building for those who claim to have this expertise.

Psychiatry's problems were not solved by the foundation of its Royal College. Faced with the inadequacy of many of its practitioners, the failure of many of its methods, wide divergencies of opinion about the origins and treatment of almost every psychiatric condition, and the self-importance of many of its ceremonies, it has tried to extend its power by affirmation rather than by demonstration or quality. Making the subject of drug dependency a 'sub-specialty' has been a means of doing this, thereby asserting claim to expertise and driving the general practitioner out of the field. The GP is likely to agree readily that he is not 'qualified' in the field of drugs and that the subject is better left to doctors of superior training and knowledge. Yet in reality the GP, properly informed and supported, is probably the best person to deal with 95 per cent of addicts. But Drugspeak, by insisting that drug users can only be helped by 'experts', denies the GP even the minimum information that would help him and undermines his self-confidence. There have been a number of official pronouncements to the effect that general practitioners should take more part in treating drug users, but in practice these have either been attempts to gain control of the general practitioner, or else have subtly carried the opposite message in order to scare him from the scene. In this way the field is controlled by the 'experts', typified by a 'great man' who widens his power by sitting on committees and advising the government and is ultimately honoured for so doing.

Meanwhile addicts are being driven even further from official help. No one knows how to prevent illegal drug use. In the light of that fact, the idea that only 'experts' should be involved is specious and as foolish as if there were special 'experts' to treat pimples or the common cold. It is not surprising that reaction to critics and seekers of the truth is vigorous and even vicious.

Chapter 8

The First Hearing

'The "mafia" is out to destroy you. They hate your guts.'

'Be very careful. They feel threatened by you and they are hard men.'

'Watch out! They want power and are vindictive and dangerous.'

'We shall get rid of doctors who don't toe the line. We are going to pick them off one by one.'

'How can we *stop* this frightful woman from practising?'

I had been a doctor for over thirty years without getting into trouble. But now something different was about to happen. There were threats, lots of them.

The warnings came from different sources – patients, a social worker, a psychiatrist friend who worked in a drug clinic, a nurse from another clinic, policemen, journalists. The doctors who ran the current system of drug dependency treatment were often rude to me in letters and telephone calls and at professional meetings. Vituperative articles in the popular and medical press inveighed against private doctors; one of the tabloids even referred to me as though I was a criminal. Books and articles misrepresented what I did. Unpleasant untruths were spread about me. My solicitor said that some were undoubtedly defamatory, but I didn't want to sue. Always optimistic, I believed that truth would prevail in the end.

The most powerful warning came from Bing Spear. He said that members of the drug dependency establishment were 'out to get' me and were already discussing how to do it. His ideas about drugs and addicts were similar to my own, and sometimes I felt he used me to get over messages to others. As a civil servant he could not speak out as freely as I could. But for him I would have given up treating addicts long before the 'mafia' got me.

In the Home Office car park after a meeting, one of Bing's medical colleagues said to me: 'Bing is over the moon about you. He thinks you're the best thing that has happened in drug addiction for years.'

It was shortly after this that the drug dependency establishment persuaded the Home Office to ban the meetings of our organisation AIDA from their premises. Meeting there had given us a respectability that was unacceptable in some quarters.

I did not take the warnings as seriously as I should have. Like Kafka's Joseph K., I had done nothing wrong. I had always tried to act in the best interests of my patients, and to me this, backed by common sense and professional skill, was the most important criterion. I felt that I was doing work that was badly needed and that a few people in high places were on my side. I even received a personal invitation from Margaret Thatcher to go to Downing Street to talk about the drug problem early in 1983.

On the appointed day, my husband Philip drove me to Downing Street. It was raining and the traffic was so heavy that I became convinced we would be late. I felt an anxiety that I tried to suppress as absurd. After all, at Somerville Margaret had knocked on my door many times trying to sell me tickets, for God's sake. How could I possibly feel anxious about meeting her? All the same, I knew this was rationalisation.

I wasn't looking forward to the meeting, though I knew it would be interesting. I had never felt that Margaret was a kindred spirit or compatible with me. I didn't vote Conservative. However, I did hope that I would be able to persuade her that her government was wrong in its drugs policies, that its official advisers were, at best, misguided, and that the minister in charge (whom I didn't intend to mention unless she asked) was making an ass of himself over it.

There was no need to ring the bell at Number 10. The front door opened as I approached. The interior was more ordinary than I had expected, and smaller. It seemed to be just a standard, well-kept Georgian house like so many in Britain. The staircase swept up in a welcoming fashion and on its walls were portraits of past prime ministers, which Margaret later showed me.

I was shown into a waiting room, where I found Dr Pamela Mason, a senior doctor in the Drugs Section of the Department of Health and Social Security. I had met her before and had not felt I had much in common with her. I had been told that she supported the policies of which I was critical, and I guessed that she had been summoned to 'observe' my conversation with Margaret, and perhaps to report on it. Dr Mason and I exchanged a few pleasantries and were silent until a young man came in and asked us both to go with him.

We were shown into Margaret's 'sitting room' which was comfortably furnished with chairs and sofas on which were many scatter cushions. Margaret came forward eagerly and greeted me warmly, calling me 'Ann' as I knew she would, and said how pleased she was to see me. (I remembered an absurd incident some years before when she attended a Gaudy at Somerville. She swept through the college hall calling out, 'Hello, Alison, hello, Nina, hello, Ann,' on her way to the Senior Common Room, to which the rest of us were not invited. One former student from our year clasped her hands together, raised her eyes to heaven and said, 'Isn't she *wonderful*! She remembers all our names! I feel so *honoured*!' My thought had been that, since there had been so few of us, it would have been churlish of her to appear to have forgotten them. It was also an example of the 'halo effect' that glows over people in high places.) 'Hello, Margaret,' I replied. No one at Somerville had called her 'Maggie'.

As we greeted each other, my first impression was that she had improved. She seemed to be more sympathetic than she had been as a student and was easier to talk to. I wondered how far this was genuine and how far it had been engineered by her advisers. She now had the knack of making me feel, in spite of myself, that she was genuinely pleased to see me and interested in what I had to say. So of course I liked her better than before, when she had seemed alien and remote. But unlike the old days, she seemed formidable. This brought out the same quality in me.

Dr Mason sat discreetly at a table behind me and remained silent. The young man sat down ready to take notes. Margaret indicated that I should sit on the sofa, then fussed around, rather unnecessarily I thought, making sure that the cushions were arranged to my liking. Then she sat down on a chair opposite me and said she wanted to know everything I had to say about drugs.

I talked, and she questioned me, for more than an hour. I was impressed by her concentration, her apparent swift if somewhat startled grasp of what I was saying, and the questions she asked. I explained my view of the growing crisis in illegal drugs and the way in which it was being mishandled by politicians and the medical profession. I described the long-term addicts who were now forced to survive by selling drugs

to new 'recruits'. I explained how this had increased enormously since
the London clinics had changed their policies and I described some of
the inhumane practices that existed in the clinics and something of what
this meant in terms of suffering and wasted potential. I pointed out that
the drug crisis was largely unnecessary, brought about by prejudice and
exploitation, and that the terrible effects of illegal drugs were largely
due to illegality rather than their inherent properties.

I was not surprised to find that Margaret herself held many of
the popular prejudices about heroin. But she listened attentively to
all that I had to say, and at the end she said enthusiastically: 'Thank
you for coming. You have opened up a *whole new world* to me. I had
no idea that that is how things are. Thank you very much.'

I was pleased. I knew that if she looked, she would find that what
I had told her was true. I noticed that Dr Mason looked a bit sour as
we stepped into the street. But I hoped the interview might lead to
something good.

It didn't. Later I felt it might have had just the opposite effect. I
have often wondered whether the first direct attack on me occurred
because I met with Mrs Thatcher. It was about this time, perhaps even
directly as a result, that work must have started to construct the case
that was to get me into trouble.

More important than the feeling of having friends in high places was
the knowledge that most of my addict patients were doing well under
my care. Their general health and well-being improved phenomenally.
They were markedly better nourished. Their rashes and infections had
cleared and did not recur. Hardly any would be picked out in a crowd
as addicts. They had jobs, families and a zest for life that is absent when
the whole day is spent looking for drugs and committing crimes to pay
for them. Had I not come into their lives, these classic long-term addicts
– who no longer officially existed – would be feeding the black market
and creating more addicts. Or else be in prison or dead. I could help
give them self-respect and the satisfaction of contributing to society
rather than preying on it. I was literally saving lives.

I also knew that, once they had obtained stability and confidence,
many were able to give up drugs altogether, which they could not do
while living on the black market or under the system then operating
in the NHS clinics. I felt that I only needed a chance to demonstrate
my methods and the whole world, or at least that part of it interested
in problems of drug dependency, would understand.

Amazing as it now seems to me, I also had an innocent faith in the justice of medico-legal procedures. As in that favourite novel of my childhood, *The Citadel*, I believed sincerely that if a doctor was honest, thoughtful and open in what he or she did, and if he could justify his actions, no harm would come to him, even if he was not fully conventional in his ideas. After all, many unconventional treatments eventually become established practice. Even though I knew that the GMC had started to strike off doctors for prescribing to addicts, it seemed to me that they were only attacking those doctors who were ignorant, greedy or dishonest. Since I was none of these things, I assumed I was safe.

I wasn't completely naive. I did realise that some members of the drug dependency 'mafia' were not only hostile to people like me but openly hypocritical, prone to slanting evidence, ignoring truths and generally fixing things for personal advantage. But at the time I did not appreciate how dishonest these doctors were, or how powerful. Now I see that I was a real threat to them.

The warnings suggested that I keep quiet and stay out of trouble. Several doctors who shared my beliefs kept their heads down, treated their patients and said nothing in public. Even so, many were chased from the field by threats or by legal action. But I find it difficult not to answer when questioned, not to lecture when invited and not to write when I feel strongly about something.

The patient who got me into trouble, Brian Sigsworth, was a prime example of how present drugs policies waste human potential and make competent people destructive. He was an able member of society whom society turned into a criminal. He cost the taxpayer many thousands of pounds and in the end he died in squalid circumstances without achieving anything.

Brian was referred to me in May 1981 by the same Dr Timmins who had started my interest in drug addiction more than a year before. He wrote a letter telling me that Brian was a long-standing heroin addict whom he himself had tried to treat without success. He was now on Diconal, a synthetic opiate, which Dr Timmins had been giving him.

Dr Timmins did not wish to continue to prescribe – I later heard that he was under threat from the Home Office – and asked me to take on Brian's treatment. As always, I put the letter into the patient's file and routinely checked his record with the Home Office Drugs Branch. The answer came back that he was known to the Home Office, which meant that his name was in the 'Addicts' Index'. He had first been notified to the Home Office in 1976 from Brixton prison. Thus I knew that he had a criminal record, but since nearly all long-term addicts have been in prison, this was no more than something which demanded caution.

Before I met the patient I also received a telephone call from a Dr Finlayson who looked after the students at the polytechnic in Coventry where Brian was studying. He was 'holding the fort' for Dr Timmins. Dr Finlayson had been prescribing liquid oral methadone but knew that Brian could not manage on this and was buying injectable drugs on the black market. The doctor expressed delight that I was going to take over the treatment of Brian's drug addiction and assured me that he would help all he could.

Brian arrived, untidy but clean. He was big, somewhat overweight and muscular with curly hair, a ready smile and quick, witty responses. I saw immediately that he was highly intelligent, like many addicts – they are, after all, survivors of persecution in a society where everything is against them. His history was irresistible to someone interested in the processes that develop and wreck human ability. I felt immediately that here was a man of good potential who could probably be helped.

Brian was born in London. He was illegitimate and never knew his father; his mother had died of cancer two years before. An unsatisfactory pupil, despite his high intelligence, he played truant, didn't even learn to read or write, and was expelled from his secondary school for refusing to be caned.

Soon after that he discovered 'purple hearts', the popular name for Drinamyl, a compound drug containing both amphetamine and barbiturate. After a few years of taking this drug, Brian gave some to a friend in exchange for heroin. 'That was the greatest,' he told me. 'After that, I never looked back.'

Heroin had dominated his life for seventeen years. He had exploited the 'drug doctors' of the sixties, having been a patient of Lady Frankau, and later of Dr Petro, both well known for their treatment of drug addicts, from whom he received prescriptions for enormous quantities of drugs – as much as 70 grains (4200 milligrams) per day. This was about fifty times more than any doctor would be likely to prescribe in 1981.

What concerned me about Brian was his criminal record. I asked him about it and learned that it was extensive. He had been to prison many times, though always, it seems, for crimes committed to obtain money with which to buy drugs.

After being expelled from school he got into trouble and was sent to a school for young offenders, then to Borstal. Here a teacher took an interest and taught him to read and write. He was sixteen years old. Immediately he became excited about books and was soon as hooked on reading as he was on heroin. A year later he passed his O level in English.

His need for heroin, however, meant that after his release he inevitably returned to crime to pay for drugs. He studied for and passed A levels while serving a prison sentence, and during another, longer, spell in prison read for an arts degree at the Open University. He liked English literature and sociology best. After his release he continued his studies and was now beginning a degree course at Coventry Polytechnic. The subject he had chosen for his thesis was, suitably, 'Aspects of Deviant Youth'. Though studying in Coventry he spent most of his time in London, where he lived with a girlfriend.

Brian seemed happy with his life apart from his drug problem. He had found what he wanted to do. Academic life attracted him but he thought he would prefer to use his experience and training in something more practical such as social work or working with handicapped children. He was enthusiastic and had many ideas about social work. Like most long-term addicts, he also envisaged a time when he would come off drugs. He made this his objective before he married his girlfriend. He felt sure that he could do it in the end but, again, like most long-term addicts and like St Augustine's wish for chastity, not yet.

I felt that Brian was the sort of addict who most needed my help. Unable to benefit from the clinic system, he was forced to lead a criminal life. Yet he had many interests elsewhere and was strongly motivated to develop them.

I was sufficiently worried about Brian's criminal record to make a special phone call to the Home Office about him. The routine information available to doctors from the clerks was limited and sometimes inaccurate. Indeed, one clerk was sacked for answering all doctors' queries with the single response, 'We have no knowledge of this person.'

I spoke to Ian Heaton, a Drugs Inspector whom I knew. He fetched Brian Sigsworth's file and discussed the details. Of course Ian was not a doctor and I was not asking for his permission to treat Brian or for advice about how to do this. One has to be clear about this because the GMC can be unpleasant to doctors who seek guidance from non-doctors, even officials who know more about the subject than the doctor does. The problem I discussed with Ian was not one of clinical judgement but of criminality. He told me that Brian had a 'bad police record' but it seemed that everything he had told me was true. Ian confirmed that Brian had no convictions for deceiving doctors or for forging prescriptions, which was important because addicts who do such things are dangerous to their doctors. Ian agreed that Brian deserved a humane chance to make something of his life.

I was also concerned about the time he spent in Coventry, as I tried to accept only patients who lived permanently in London. On the other hand, Coventry was less than two hours away. Brian made the journey frequently to be with his girlfriend, and Dr Finlayson in Coventry was anxious to help. Moreover, Ian Heaton had confirmed that there were no facilities for treating him in Coventry. It seemed, and Ian agreed, that it would be uncharitable to reject him on the grounds of distance. Before I accepted Brian I told him that living far away would be no excuse for not keeping appointments, and that I must see him weekly at first until I got to know him better. He accepted my conditions.

Looking back on this, it seems absurd that I was so concerned with these details and that they were a serious consideration. A patient was in great need – his whole future at stake – and I was worried about whether his journey to see me would get me into trouble. It seemed crazy. It still does.

During the next eighteen months I came to know Brian well. He seemed to be getting on with his work and was clearly enjoying it. Then Bing Spear rang one day to say that he had been arrested by the Coventry police and charged with supplying drugs to another person. He was in jail on remand.

I didn't know the circumstances so I could make no judgement. I hoped that Brian hadn't been selling drugs and exploiting his relationship with me to do so: I couldn't be certain but I felt this was unlikely. I had also heard that the Coventry police were particularly quick to seek convictions for small breaches in the law.

I learned later that Brian had lent some drugs to an addict friend who was suffering from withdrawal. He insisted that he had not sold the drugs, and a friend in the Home Office found that the assertion of lending rather than selling had not been disproved. The police had simply found the other addict in possession of drugs which they traced to Brian and which I was presumed, not proved, to have prescribed. But it was enough to make trouble for me.

A newspaper cutting in the local Coventry newspaper provided the excuse. I don't know whether someone sent it to the General Medical Council or whether a member happened to see it, but this is of little importance. I first knew there was trouble when I received a recorded delivery letter from the General Medical Council. It was written in stilted, formal language of a kind that happily is seldom seen nowadays. I came to associate such language exclusively with the GMC. The important parts read:

. . . the Council has received from the Solicitor to the Council information which appears to raise a question whether, as a registered medical practitioner, you have committed serious professional misconduct within the meaning of section 7(1) of the Medical Act 1978. . . .

In the information it is alleged that, between 11th June, 1981, or earlier, and about 25th November, 1981, you abused your position as a medical practitioner by issuing to Mr. Brian Sigsworth a number of prescriptions for dipipanone hydrochloride with cyclizine and methylphenidate otherwise than in the course of bona fide treatment. . . .

. . . it will be the duty of that [Preliminary Proceedings] Committee to consider the information and any explanation furnished by you, and to determine whether the case shall be referred to the Professional Conduct Committee of the Council for inquiry into a charge against you.

. . . I am accordingly to invite you to submit to the Council at your earliest convenience any explanation which you may have to offer. . . .

P. L. Towers, Registrar

My first thought on receiving the letter was that there had been some mistake. No one in his right mind, I thought, could say that I had abused my position as a doctor. The suggestion that I might have acted 'otherwise than in the course of bona fide treatment' or 'committed serious professional misconduct' seemed absurd. Of course I could make mistakes like anyone else, but not bona fide? I felt sure that no one could take this seriously. I had done my best to supervise Brian and I had acted responsibly. No one could expect me to follow him every minute or to know exactly what he did when he was out of my sight.

Naively, I even thought this might be a good opportunity to get across to the Council that the disgraceful situation in the field of drug dependency was damaging the integrity of the medical profession. I was aware that the GMC was out of touch with reality and needed to be brought up to date. When members understood what was happening, they would doubtless be pleased to know.

In the shock of receiving the letter I failed to notice something that was to play a large part in what happened later. No one had complained about me and no one ever did. I had always understood that there had to be a complaint before the GMC could act against a doctor. This is not so. People often ask me, 'Who made the complaint against you?' and are mystified by the answer, 'No one.' I think that this misconception, which is widespread, is part of the GMC's mystique, which it encourages – or at least does nothing to counter. In a situation where common sense or public outrage suggests that the GMC should act, it often does not do so and manages to give the impression that it cannot do so because no one has complained. The reality is different.

The Council can act on what it calls 'information received'. It can so organise this 'information' as to charge with serious professional misconduct any doctor it wishes. The GMC does not have to say where the information comes from. It may even decide that it wishes to receive certain information and then arrange, and even pay, for that information to be delivered. It can instruct a solicitor to find and deliver the information. The Council solicitors may, and do, employ others, such as ex-policemen, to seek out the information that the GMC wishes to have. Later I learned that such things had happened in my case.

Conversely, the GMC can, and does, ignore anything it chooses, such as information or complaints against a particular doctor whom it does not wish to charge. However serious or numerous the complaints – and some of the complaints it has ignored have been multiple and grave – it can reply that the complaint is insufficient or not within its powers to investigate. One GMC member told me that he once asked the chairman of the Professional Conduct Committee what would happen if a serious complaint was made against him. The answer was 'Oh, we'd find a way round it. We wouldn't charge *you!*'

It is also not generally known that the GMC can act only when it thinks or chooses to think that there is prima-facie evidence of *serious* proffessional misconduct. Simple *professional misconduct* is insufficient.

This is why there have been some bizarre cases of 'serious professional misconduct'.

When I received the letter I was so far from thinking about danger that at first I did not even contact the Medical Defence Union (MDU), with whom I was insured. The matter seemed too trivial to bother them with. I thought I would write a full and careful reply which would give the GMC, perhaps for the first time, a picture of the unsavoury situation that had developed in drug dependency.

I had several weeks in which to write the reply, but I was also preparing to go to the United States on a publicity tour for my latest book, *Inventing Motherhood*, which was about to be published in America. My publishers had already booked me to go to Atlanta, Washington and New York, with phone-ins from coast to coast.

While thinking about all this, I telephoned Bing Spear and told him what had happened. He was alarmed. 'This is serious. You should get in touch with the MDU as soon as possible.' Bing, of course, knew far more about the ways of the medical establishment than I did. I took his advice and telephoned the MDU.

My secretary arranged for me to go and see Dr Kate Allsopp in her office. Kate, about ten years younger than I, was shortly to be promoted to Joint Deputy Secretary, second in command of the MDU. I realised immediately that she was highly intelligent and experienced. She also had an attractive, straightforward personality and a friendly manner that was reassuring to a doctor in trouble.

Like Bing, Kate took the news seriously and made some uncomplimentary remarks about the GMC and how it operates. This made me feel more nervous. I now saw that I needed a lawyer to draft the reply. My original idea of simply explaining the situation had been absurd.

I wanted John Calderan as my solicitor but Kate wouldn't countenance this. The MDU would only pay if I used Hempsons, their solicitors. This was MDU policy. And it was better, she said, to use the MDU solicitors because they did a lot of this kind of work. 'They know the GMC and how their minds work.'

Later I saw that this was imperfect reasoning.

'Moreover,' Kate continued, 'these cases tend to become expensive and I wouldn't like to think of you having to pay for it all yourself when you've paid fees to the MDU for so many years.'

I had to agree. Afterwards I discovered that the doctors were the only profession on whom such restrictions were placed and that an increasing body of opinion held, as I came to suspect during my case, that the relationship between the MDU, their solicitors and the GMC was altogether too cosy. Despite undoubted goodwill towards those they represented, the client may not always have felt that his best interests were served. Much has since been published on this subject, but at the time I don't think anyone had said this openly or acted on it.

Though disappointed at what Kate said, I was appeased to some extent because I liked her and felt confidence in her. And at that stage I certainly didn't want a rift with the MDU.

Kate arranged that while I was away in America, Charles Butcher of Hempsons would write a reply to the GMC's charges based on my own detailed account of my actions and of everything to do with Brian Sigsworth. The report would then go before the Preliminary Proceedings Committee of the GMC.

I felt confident. I assumed that the committee existed partly in order to weed out cases such as mine, where someone had got the wrong impression. What no one told me at the time was that when the GMC wish to prosecute a doctor, the Preliminary Proceedings Committee is simply a formality. I was later told that this is true in 'all drug cases, automatically'. Had I known that at the time, I would have been far more anxious. As it was, I went to America with no more than a faint sense of unease.

When I returned I found an impressive report by Charles Butcher. I thought that no one who read it could possibly decide to indict me. I also found that, because of my being a possible witness in another case, the MDU had felt obliged to stop using Hempsons in my case, and were sending me to Anthony Johnston of Beachcrofts, whom I found to be both sensitive and sympathetic.

I had been told that the meeting of the Preliminary Proceedings Committee was on 12 May, a Thursday. I still felt confident, but I wanted to make sure that everything was all right and didn't want to have to endure a weekend of doubt. I asked my secretary Anne Lingham to telephone the GMC. Presently she came back to me, almost in tears. 'I'm afraid it's gone against you,' she said. She also told me that the man she had spoken to at the GMC had seemed delighted to give her the bad news. Not for the first time, I had the feeling that something sinister was happening.

Brian Sigsworth had been sentenced to three years' imprisonment and sent to a secure prison on the Isle of Wight. Later another addict who had spent a year in that prison told me: 'Although it's supposed to be for violent or otherwise difficult offenders, they send a lot of harmless people there so that they can say how successful they are.'

I wondered how Brian was doing now that he was 'a criminal' again, and hoped this setback would not destroy the progress he had made. I had never seen anyone improve as a result of imprisonment, and the only question was whether it would harm his fragile new personality. Meanwhile I had my own troubles.

Most members of the General Medical Council are elected, though the democratic process works imperfectly. Only about one-third of doctors return their ballot papers; few have any means of judging the candidates except through the meagre information provided. It is widely believed that candidates whose names begin with early letters of the alphabet have more chance of being elected than those whose names come later. Those who vote tend to choose candidates sponsored by the British Medical Association, which means a high proportion of medical politicians and committee men.

The Council's traditions follow ideas expressed frankly by Lord Platt, president of the Royal College of Physicians from 1957 to 1962. He thought it 'important that the government of the profession should not be too democratic. It should . . . take its standards from the top, and clearly favour that small and not usually vocal minority whose professional standards, be it in practice or research, stand far above the average.'

The GMC has always tended to attract criticism. In 1880 the *British Medical Journal* announced that in future it would report the proceedings only 'with extreme brevity and after severe condensation'. 'A Council which meets at such great cost to the general funds of the profession to perform functions frequently so commonplace and trivial, by methods so dilatory and diffuse, becomes rapidly an object of suspicion and a source of irritation.'

The *BMJ* also referred to the 'enormous costliness of its proceedings, their slight value, and the tedious oratorical displays which for a long series of years have been considered *en règle*', and added that the GMC's proceedings 'seem to be regarded by the profession generally as intolerably prolix and protracted'. Some would say that this is as true today as when it was written.

In 1971, the GMC began to impose a yearly charge on every doctor who wished his name to remain on the Medical Register.

Doctors did not believe the Council would spend their money sensibly and many protested. But of course they paid, rather than run the risk of practising unregistered.

In the same year there was something of a mutiny, orchestrated by Dr Michael O'Donnell, the editor of *World Medicine*. He and some of his friends put themselves up for election in opposition to establishment candidates. They were elected and for the first time in the history of the GMC there was possibility of criticism from within as well as from without. Some of the rebels have remained on the Council, but a member told George Mikes: 'The ones who came in as rebels are now even stuffier than the traditionals.' Certainly they now have little visible influence on the GMC, though O'Donnell has continued to draw attention to the absurdities of the medical establishment.

In 1978 the old Disciplinary Committee was renamed the Professional Conduct Committee, in theory to emphasise its role in maintaining high standards. Cynics say that the real aim was to conceal its harassment of doctors. The Council's power to strike doctors off the Medical Register for 'serious professional misconduct' has been exercised in recent years through this committee.

The committee has always been able to strike off whom it wished. In 1971 a doctor was suspended because he had lived with his wife before they were married and, before that, she had been his patient. In 1982 I attended the trial of Dr Ali Khan, a general practitioner and respected local politician who had been asked by doctors and police to help deal with the drug problems near London airport. Without professional support or guidance, he was soon overwhelmed by the demand. It wasn't difficult for police and prosecutors to reveal minor errors and misjudgements, and Dr Khan was struck off the register.

There is of course no hint that members of the GMC might not be honourable people. But I knew personally one member who was widely believed to have embezzled £40,000. The other partners in the practice had what they believed to be proof of this but, after much discussion, decided not to prosecute.

Apart from Dr Michael O'Donnell, I knew several other GMC members, including one doctor I shall simply call 'Jay', a member of the establishment with a private subversive streak.

One complaint about the GMC is that members try cases among themselves, listening to what their colleagues say rather than judging on the evidence. Several people have told me that cases are often decided before the hearing starts. Michael O'Donnell has referred to this in the *British Medical Journal* as 'trial by gossip'.

Another criticism is that the GMC is often reluctant to give general guidance and then condemns those who lack the guidance. When I started treating opiate addicts I wanted to make sure I was not doing anything that might get me into trouble, so I consulted the 'blue book' which the GMC issues annually to guide doctors in ethical matters. It had little to say, and what it did say gave me no anxiety.

However, after hearing rumours that some members of the drug dependency establishment wanted me out of the way, I wrote to the Council in August 1982 asking for guidance about treating addicts in private practice. Mr R.C.B. Gray, then Deputy Registrar, replied that 'the Council has hitherto issued no specific guidance' on that subject. A few months later I was in trouble for breaking the non-existent rules.

One genuine change in the GMC, apparently dating from about five years before my clash with it, was its move away from an investigative function towards a more aggressive one. My solicitor friend John Calderan had appeared before the Council years before as a young solicitor and had found that it investigated impartially. When he saw how the GMC now conducted its cases, he was appalled.

To me, one of the most chilling pieces of information, given to me via several GMC members, was that becoming a member of the Professional Conduct Committee was highly prized within the GMC. It has long been my impression that an active desire to sit in judgement over others is a characteristic often found in the meanest people.

Keenness to judge was not always popular in the GMC. Sir James Paget, one of the most eminent nineteenth-century doctors, said he disliked his work on the Council more than any other area of his practice.[1] Sir Charles Newman wrote of Sir James:

It is hardly a matter to wonder at that so often, when, because he has achieved great eminence in medicine, a leader of the profession has been appointed to a place on the Council, the work has tended to distress him: it is hardly the kind of work a doctor would be likely to enjoy.[2]

[1] Paget, S., *Memoirs and Letters of Sir James Paget* (London, 1903), p. 281.
[2] Newman, Sir Charles, *The Evolution of Medical Education in the Nineteenth Century* (London, 1957).

I also discovered that some members of the GMC and its staff are extraordinarily vindictive against doctors they decide to persecute. One of them kept lists of doctors he wanted to 'get', including some whom the GMC had disciplined in the past but who, in his view, had been let off too lightly. This man worked hard to see these doctors back in front of the Professional Conduct Committee.

I was beginning to realise what a Kafka-esque world I had stirred into action. My friend of many years, the writer George Mikes, had access to much information about the GMC and, as an observer of the stranger forms of human behaviour, took a great interest in it. He told me, 'Some pretty grisly people sit on these committees and some of them love to throw their weight about. They enjoy the excuse to be nasty.' He identified some of the grisly ones but said that with luck there would not be more than one or two of them on my committee; the others, he hoped, might keep them in order. He also learned that there had already been a whispering campaign against me in the GMC, that several members had been spreading stories which he was sure were untrue. He hoped that others would be able to see this and that it would not build up prejudice that would preclude a fair trial. 'Fairness is in short supply,' he said.

This astonished me. At that time I found it hard to accept that a respectable professional body was being influenced against me with lies told by its own members.

Never having been involved in a big legal case before, I was amazed by the work that went into preparing it. Any detail that might conceivably be mentioned had to be gone over, worked on, and prepared for examination.

I had to write accounts of every aspect of my practice and patients. I had to ring round all my friends whom the GMC might think were highly respectable and ask whether they would be kind enough to provide me with a character reference. This was embarrassing, but no one refused to cooperate.

I also had meeting after meeting with my lawyers and spent many hours writing up detailed accounts of my history, family and patients, and of Brian Sigsworth and how I had managed his case. Even more detailed were the accounts of my practice and finances, and of Peter's finances. Every scribble on the case notes was scrutinised, every crossing out examined to see if it could possibly be construed that I had falsified evidence. Hour after hour I was submitted to questioning and 'devil's advocacy', as if I were being cross-examined. I saw how difficult it would be to deceive a sharp solicitor or counsel.

Since I had done nothing wrong, I had nothing to hide. I was, as always, optimistic. I believed that my lawyers and I could persuade any group of intelligent and unprejudiced people that I was right. This feeling was enhanced at the final conference with my senior counsel, Adrian Whitfield QC, a man of great charm and intelligence. Playing devil's advocate, he grilled me on just about everything. At the end of the meeting he leaned back and said in a voice that sounded full of confidence: 'Dr Dally, I don't think you'll have any trouble.'

However, he insisted that we were going to fight 'the battle, not the war'. I disagreed with this profoundly.

While we were preparing the case, an interesting debate on drug dependency took place in the popular and medical press. In February 1983 I had written an article in the *Sunday Times* entitled 'Have Drug Clinics Failed?'. The article led some people to question current methods of treating addicts. Shortly afterwards two patients brought me copies of a questionnaire which they said was being distributed to patients in the clinic run by Dr Thomas Bewley.

Dr Bewley qualified in Dublin and later studied psychiatry in England and the United States. Specialising in alcoholism and drug addiction, he was appointed consultant to Tooting Bec, a large mental hospital in South London. Bewley was a strong advocate of the clinic system, and when the DDUs were set up he was appointed not only to the Tooting Bec clinic but as consultant at St Thomas's. It was unusual for a psychiatrist with foreign qualifications to gain a consultant's post at a teaching hospital. For the next twenty years he gave long service to committees in the Royal College of Psychiatrists and elsewhere. After being dean of the college for some years and trying several times to become president, he was finally elected to that post. He had also tried on several occasions to get himself elected to the General Medical Council. His wife Beulah, also a doctor, was a member of the GMC.

Bewley had a strong dislike of private practice and made no attempt to hide it. His questionnaire, entitled 'Private Prescribing', started off with straight questions about how private doctors treat addicts. Since those being asked were all NHS rather than private patients, the answers were largely hearsay. My first thought was that it was a study of the fantasies of NHS addicts about private doctors, and I was rather amused by it.

As I read further I realised, however, that this was not a study of fantasies. The document continued with questions about fees, how much private doctors charged and how addicts paid them. The only question relating to the experience of the addict was: 'Have you ever been to a private doctor?', and 'If yes: was this in the past month?'

There is debate in medicine about the value of asking patients direct questions about the services they receive. But it was, so far as I knew, unknown to ask patients about treatment that *other* patients were receiving. Yet in June 1983, three weeks before my case began, an article by Bewley was published in the *British Medical Journal*. Written with his colleague at the Tooting Bec DDU, Dr Hamid Ghodse, it had a bold title: UNACCEPTABLE FACE OF PRIVATE PRACTICE: PRESCRIPTION OF CONTROLLED DRUGS TO ADDICTS. The article, based on the questionnaire, informed us that:

> Self administered questionnaires completed by 69 out of a hundred consecutive drug addicts attending two drug dependence clinics suggested that some private general practitioners were easily persuaded to prescribe controlled drugs. . . . The practice . . . may lead to a severe spread of addiction as occurred in the 1960s . . . If the General Medical Council or a tribunal set up in accordance with the Misuse of Drugs Act 1971 cannot stop the practice, then the present licensing system should be extended to include all controlled drugs.

Not all respondents answered every question; only half had ever visited a private doctor. But all their answers were used to the disadvantage of the private doctor.

I was not the only person who was surprised to read this article in the *British Medical Journal*, which is usually exceptionally careful about its statistics. It attracted criticism both in the correspondence columns of the *BMJ* and elsewhere. Two well-known research workers pointed out that the spread of addiction in Britain came largely from the illicit heroin market, and they backed this up with evidence.

Peter Dally was another who commented in a letter to the *BMJ*. He pointed out that the drug clinics, when run by general psychiatrists, seemed to be successful, but had now been taken over by 'a narrow, specialist staff who took a narrow, restricted view of their addicts'. He pointed out the inadequacies of the study and expressed a 'sense of outrage that a respectable journal like the *BMJ* can publish a misleading article such as this one. . . . The results quoted here are frankly ridiculous.'

I do not believe that that article, had it concerned any other branch of medicine, would have passed the stringent criteria of the *BMJ* editors and assessors. But the paper was quoted widely and used in the case against me at the GMC.

Eventually the day of the trial came, 5 July 1983. I walked with my lawyers, family and friends to the GMC building in Hallam Street, a short distance from my house. In a Georgian street behind the Royal Institute of British Architects, it stands out as a monstrosity of thirties architecture. The only congenial thing about the building was the pleasant manner of the old soldiers from the Corps of Commissionaires who looked after the doors.

After sitting for a while in the scruffy little back room made available to the 'defence', we were told that our case would not be heard that day so we all went home. I realised that it was not always possible to judge accurately the time that cases would take, but I had also been warned that the GMC likes people to be inconvenienced so I was not surprised when the same thing happened the next day. In the afternoon we returned. Eventually Adrian Whitfield was called out into the corridor, then came back and said, 'We're on.'

The council chamber, a large, high-ceilinged room, occupies most of the first and second floors of the building. Stained glass windows display past presidents as if they were saints. Press and public were crowded into a small gallery at one end of the chamber. It was stiflingly hot up there, as I knew from previous visits as a spectator. This was July and the atmosphere was, I heard, almost intolerable. But the GMC refused to open the gallery at the other end until the first one was crammed. Even the commissionaire in charge said that he found this unreasonable, and took pains to let everyone know that it wasn't his doing. Reporters familiar with the GMC said that this typified its attitude to outsiders.

My lawyers and I were assigned to a long table just inside the door. The committee sat to our left, an anonymous semicircle of solemn middle age. There were about eight of them. Those I remember most clearly were Dr Scott, a Scotswoman; Dr Ashworth, a northerner with half-moon glasses and a perpetual grin; and one man who repeatedly took off his shoes under the table – his name I never learned.

We sat at right angles to the chairman. This was the president of the Council, Sir John Walton. Flanking him were the deputy registrar and the legal assessor, a senior barrister who sits with the committee to advise on legal matters.

I thought Sir John looked more like an accountant than a
doctor: behind his small moustache, his face was impassive and
curiously lacking in expression. In fact he was Professor of Neurology
in Newcastle, an active medical politician and so successful an upholder
of *gravitas* that he was shortly to become president of the Royal Society
of Medicine for the year in which its new building was opened by the
Queen.

Facing the committee, in the middle of the chamber, a table
and chair comprised the witness stand. I sat at the end of our
table, near the committee. Adrian Whitfield, my senior counsel, sat
beside me with his junior. Anthony Johnston, my solicitor, and the
other lawyers sat further down. Opposite, at a similar table, sat the
'prosecutors'. The GMC likes to make out that it does not prosecute
and in theory it does not, but I cannot think how else to describe that
unsmiling array of lawyers and their helpers. One of them looked so
awful that Adrian whispered, 'I suppose I've got to endure sitting here
and staring at Ratface.' Another lawyer nicknamed him 'Uriah'.

'Presenting the facts', as the GMC describes its prosecutions,
was Timothy Preston QC. Any outside observer would be forgiven
for regarding Tim Preston as the Chief Prosecutor, which was what
he was well known for at the Old Bailey. He was thickset and had
a gruff manner. Adrian had told me that I should not underrate him:
he was clever and experienced, but he said that Preston would 'play it
straight'. This reassured me; Preston seemed to me to be a formidable
man but I felt ready to answer him. Before the proceedings began
I thought of him as someone who was intending simply to discover
the facts of my case. It did not occur to me that he might have been
instructed to put me in the worst possible light with a determination
to get a conviction.

The charges read out were similar to those in the original letter.
They sounded dreadful, so dreadful that again I found it hard to
take them seriously. How could they possibly find that I had acted
in bad faith? Everyone knew that a doctor cannot be responsible for
everything her patients do when she is not there.

After a few preliminaries, the case for the prosecution opened. I
learned for the first time that Brian Sigsworth had also been found
guilty of breaking into the surgery of Dr Finlayson, his doctor in
Coventry with whom I had cooperated. Of course I disapproved
strongly, but this meant it was likely to be uncertain whether the
drugs he gave his friend had been prescribed by me.

The prosecution's case began with Dr Timmins, who had referred

Brian to me. Preston said, 'It seems that Sigsworth was referred to the respondent in April 1981. I shall be calling Dr Timmins; it is a fact that he does not remember that referral, but it seems that he did so refer the patient to the respondent.'

The impression given to me by this statement, and to everyone I spoke to, was the opposite of what was said. Looking at the text, I think Preston must have skated over the first bit, 'It seems that Sigsworth was referred . . . ', then put slow and strong emphasis on the words, '*It is a fact that he does not remember that referral*'. The result was that we all thought he had said that Sigsworth had *not* been referred, which implied that I had taken him, 'unethically', off the street.

Preston read the report submitted by Butcher, my original solicitor, then announced that he believed that the committee should consider certain questions. These rested on the behaviour and supervision of the patient when he was not with the doctor (no one explained how a patient can be supervised when he isn't there, or how a doctor can do this), and on the fees charged. He suggested that prescriptions should not be given to third persons (without mentioning the care I took on the rare occasions when I had done this), and suggested that having to pay fees might provide an 'obvious temptation' to the patient to finance the enterprise, at least in part, by disposing of or selling some to third persons, particularly 'when, to the doctor's knowledge, the patient concerned is a man with a bad criminal record . . . including previous convictions for supplying controlled drugs'.

I found these remarks particularly offensive. He made it look as though I had handed out prescriptions without taking elementary precautions, which was not true. I had explored Sigsworth's record carefully, and Ian Heaton at the Home Office had told me that he had had no convictions for supplying drugs. I felt outraged at what I saw as a misrepresentation and was surprised that my counsel did not leap up to protest. It seemed that the trial was concerned with advocacy rather than fact-finding. The first witness for the prosecution was Brian Sigsworth himself. He had been brought up from prison on the Isle of Wight a day or two before. When the prison officers brought him into the council room he was wearing his own clothes but looked scruffy, angry and defiant, very different from the Brian I had known.

He refused either to take the oath or to affirm. He looked increasingly angry. Preston started to examine him. 'Is your name Brian Sigsworth?'

'I have nothing to say.'

This caused consternation. The legal assessor intervened. There was discussion among the lawyers. Sigsworth insisted: 'I said I would not give evidence against Dr Dally.'

'Does that mean that you are not prepared to give any evidence at all?'

'I will not give evidence against Dr Dally.'

More consternation. Everyone had to leave the chamber while the lawyers and the committee discussed the problem *in camera*. In the end the committee decided that Sigsworth might give unsworn oral evidence. He agreed to answer some questions about himself. He agreed that he had convictions for possessing illegal drugs, which, he pointed out, since he was an addict and had been in prison, was 'fairly obvious'. He denied that he had ever supplied drugs to others and said that the tablets found on his friend had been stolen from his bottle.

Brian could see what was happening. He did his best, and he seemed to be telling the truth. He gave me a long, friendly look and was taken away by the prison officers. I never saw him again.

Next came Dr Finlayson. He said he had treated about twenty addicts and insisted that Sigsworth was not like them. I don't know whether he meant to imply that he therefore was not an addict, but that was the impression he gave.

During this doctor's evidence another incident occurred which has remained in my mind. The president intervened to say that the dose I had given Sigsworth, sixteen tablets a day, was more than the maximum dose recommended by the British National Formulary, which put it at twelve tablets a day. Adrian Whitfield, with great astuteness, spotted that Sir John was reading from an edition of the British National Formulary which had not even been published at the time of the alleged offences. The edition then current had given a maximum of eighteen tablets a day, two more than I prescribed.

There were a number of such 'mistakes' during the trial, and all of them worked against me.

Then a journalist was called. We had once talked on the telephone about Diconal, the drug with which I had treated Brian, and he had written an article about it for a local newspaper. I had told him that Diconal was very dangerous if injected (it was meant to be taken orally) and that I prescribed it for only one or two cases both of which were exceptional. Then I was quoted as saying: 'They say that the high you get from injecting Diconal is better than anything else in the world.' This was a reason why I prescribed it so rarely. But now it was presented to give the impression that I had prescribed it knowing that the patients would inject it to get 'high'. I was amazed at the capacity of lawyers to twist the meaning of words.

Next morning the first witness was Dr Timmins. He admitted under cross-examination that the letter referring Sigsworth to me had been written by him. But by then, I felt, the damage was done. Throughout all the GMC proceedings, both then and later, it was my impression that once the prosecution had made a point it was accepted by the GMC, even when there was no evidence for it and even when it was later refuted. It was my impression, and that of other observers, that some members wanted to believe everything the prosecution said.

This was the problem with the next witness, the policeman who had arrested Brian. Preston had told the court emphatically that Brian had previous convictions for supplying drugs. We knew that he was mistaken. My counsel asked the policeman 'to confirm that in May 1981, Sigsworth had no convictions for supplying drugs'. In a flat voice the policeman confirmed that Brian had '*no* previous convictions for this offence'.

No one seemed to notice or care. I felt that the false picture of Brian as an inveterate drug dealer whom I supplied with drugs was now so firmly embedded that nothing could shake it.

Then it was my turn.

Adrian began by asking me about my background, education and qualifications, about the practice in Devonshire Place and its finances. Some of my letters and articles were handed to the President. I knew that these were a particular cause of the establishment's hostility towards me.

After further preliminaries were completed it was time to break for lunch. During the recess I was shocked to see Julie, one of my former addict patients, in the GMC building. An intelligent young mother with a long history of addiction, Julie had recently moved to Portsmouth, where I persuaded her to try to get on with the drug clinic. She hadn't got on well.

Julie said she had been approached by a stranger who asked her to come to London to give evidence to a committee concerning me. She got the impression that she was to be given the chance to say how dreadful the clinic was and how much better were my methods. She was delighted to have the opportunity to do this. But when she got there, she found that she had been brought to London to give evidence against me. She refused to do this and had left in anger.

I wondered what on earth had been going on. Who were these people who had been approaching my old patients?

After lunch the proceedings droned on. There was much emphasis on my reasons for accepting Brian as a patient. I had explained this many times, always saying how much care I had taken in doing so. The committee didn't seem to understand.

The pressmen in the gallery commented in dismay, overheard by friends of mine.

'What's this all about? She hasn't done anything wrong.'

'What are they going on about? There must have been some mistake to bring the case in the first place. They've never before charged a doctor for serious professional misconduct for prescribing in one case only.'

'Presumably they couldn't find any more. So what *are* they up to?'

When the evidence had all been presented, the committee had to reach its verdict. To find me guilty of serious professional misconduct they had to prove bad faith. No one had managed to show that I was in it for the money. Then it was suggested that I had been 'reckless' and recklessness could be taken to be bad faith. So how was 'recklessness' defined? Three times the committee retired, changing the definition of the charges. The audience in the gallery became increasingly bewildered, trooping in and out of the council chamber.

Eventually the president announced their decision. ' . . . the committee have accordingly judged you to be guilty of serious professional misconduct in relation to the facts found proved against you in the charge . . . ' an audible gasp of astonishment from both galleries.

Tense as I was, I heard 'They have taken into account the many references received and representations made on your behalf. They are prepared to believe that you will heed the warning conveyed to you by these proceedings and have determined in all the circumstances to admonish you and to conclude the case.'

I had been shaken by the ferocity of the prosecution's attack and the unwillingness or inability of the GMC to look at the drugs problem from any view other than that of the current drug dependency establishment. Now I began, slowly and incompletely, to understand what was happening to me.

My friend Jay helped to enlighten me. He told me that the drug dependency establishment was powerful in the GMC and had been campaigning against me there for a long time. It had been only a matter of time before some incident would occur on which the Council would feel it could bring a case against me. So it was not a question of just another case coming up for judgement. Jay also told me that since the case there had been a lot of gossip about it among members.

My friend George Mikes had been making discreet enquiries and said much the same. He felt concerned for my future and told me I was dealing with dangerous people.

What these friends told me rang true. I could see how it must have scared other doctors, including those who supported me, and I could also see that part of the intention was to destroy my credibility as a writer, commentator and witness in a court of law. They had not succeeded in this at the first attempt and were disappointed.

A few weeks later some friends who had watched the case from the public gallery attended a medical meeting in the north of England. There they met an old acquaintance who was a member of the committee which had condemned me. They asked him: 'Whatever were you doing attacking Ann Dally?'

His reply was extraordinary, 'Yes, it did seem rather odd but what else could one do?'

This answer revealed much about the British establishment. 'What else could I have done?' asks the man who would never stick up for anything on principle or even work out what is right or wrong. Yet this man held a responsible position. To me, the saddest thing of all was not that he acted as he did but that he admitted to it so blandly, as if everyone would assume that there was no alternative.

It seemed to me that something had gone seriously wrong with the GMC in relation to political cases. The machinery might be good for alcoholic doctors or those who neglected or seduced their patients. But using the disciplinary procedure to suppress differences of opinion was another matter. I felt shocked, even violated, in a way I never had before.

It so happened that the evening the case finished, 7 July, was the date of the first meeting of the association I was forming in the hope of encouraging addicts to organise for themselves a pressure group. I had hired a hall at Friends' House, Euston Road. It was after 6 pm when the case finished and, tired as I was, I went straight there from the GMC.

This meeting was part of my aim to encourage addicts to stand up for themselves and to educate others. I was convinced that this was the only way to improve their situation and to expose the scandals.

The meeting, which I chaired, was successful. The new organisation was established. I didn't want to be directly concerned with it, since I felt it was important for the addicts to discover that they could do things for themselves. Most of them had such low self-esteem that I knew it would take a long time, but I was more convinced than ever that this was necessary if the drug situation was to improve. The new group was called the Alba Association, which was the addicts' idea. They wanted a name that had no connection with drugs. 'Alba' was from Albemarle Street, where two of my sons had offered them free use of their office address for the group's correspondence.

As a result of my case I had a number of requests to write articles. A scribbler by nature, I took the opportunity to publicise my views. This, I learned later, angered the GMC still further.

There were many reactions to the case, both in the media and outside.

Margaret Thatcher wrote to me, pointing out that she could not comment on the issues but adding: 'I know that this must be a painful situation for you and your husband. I know too that the strength you have always shown will carry you through this difficult time. . . . I know that you sincerely believe in what you do.'

The Lancet published a long article by its legal correspondent, barrister Diana Brahams, accompanied by an editorial expressing '. . . doubts about the handling and outcome of [the] proceedings. . . . ' At the time, some journalists and other observers at the hearing expressed bewilderment at the decision of the committee. An impression of injustice was widespread; and speculation was heard about the motives behind the charge.'

Michael O'Donnell made similar remarks in the *British Medical Journal* of 1 October, referring to me as 'a sacrificial lamb':

I am convinced that everyone concerned at the GMC, clearly motivated by the best of intentions, acted conscientiously within the rules. Yet the impression left with observers who watched from the public gallery . . . is that a rigid and unimaginative medical establishment has impeached an idealistic doctor who had the cheek to question the party line on the management of drug addiction. . . .

Two happenings during the GMC 'trial' helped foster the impression created. . . . In the first place, some person associated with the GMC or its lawyers mentioned within the hearing of journalists and others in the public gallery that the prosecution was unlikely to succeed because of the wording of the charge. Soon after this, and after the GMC equivalents of the closing speeches for the defence and prosecution had been delivered, the legal assessor who sits alongside the chairman to advise him on legal procedure seemed to observers in the public gallery to reinterpret the meaning of the charge, at least in terms of the arguments that had by then been placed before the committee.

. . . I can equally understand why journalists . . . should conclude that this was a political trial in which the 'establishment' was out to 'get' Dr Dally because of her heretical views.

Medical tradition, with its emphasis on the importance of the individual, copes uneasily with the idea of 'making an example' of one to discourage others. Maybe that's why when doctors try it the attempt so often boomerangs. . . . I wonder if without the background political noise a case which in the end the GMC adjudged to amount to 'reckless' prescribing for one patient would have reached the council chamber for the full ritual of a 'public trial'.

The irony is that now the example has been made the message that has got through is not the intended warning but the suggestion that the GMC is still much as A J Cronin portrayed it in *The Citadel*, an authoritarian body that comes down heavily on those who challenge orthodox views.

In an apparently unprecedented move, the president of the GMC, Sir John Walton, replied in the correspondence columns on 29 October. He said that Dr Michael O'Donnell had 'given a totally false impression':

These decisions are not taken lightly or hastily – least of all vindictively. They are taken, often with great sadness, and indeed deep regret, after the most earnest and painstaking consideration of all the available facts, presented and heard according to strict rules of evidence . . .

The question in the case . . . was not the benefits or disadvantages of any particular methods of treating addicts. The facts alleged in the charge against Dr Dally were that . . . she had abused her position as a medical practitioner by issuing . . . a number of prescriptions . . . otherwise than in the course of *bona fide* treatment. That alone was the issue on which the professional conduct committee had to adjudicate. It was on that issue alone that all the material facts were found to have been proved to the committee's satisfaction, and it was those facts which, in the view of the committee, constituted serious professional misconduct.

'A silly, pompous letter,' said a friend of mine, himself an 'establishment' person who knew Sir John well.

'Sanctimonious claptrap,' said George Mikes.

Another protest came from Professor Arnold Trebach, who had watched the proceedings from the gallery. He wrote to Sir John Walton that he 'believed that an injustice had been done'. He discussed the proceedings in some detail and hoped that the Professional Conduct Committee would review the case. In replying, Sir John made the same points as in his letter to the *British Medical Journal* and added that the rules of the Privy Council 'do not provide for the review by the Professional Conduct Committee of a case which they have determined and concluded'.

In fact, far from considering review and revision, at least one member of the GMC expressed his view that Dr Dally deserved to be dealt with more harshly. It wasn't long before I heard that solicitors had been instructed to look for material which might be used to work up another case against me. This was to take three and a half years. Meanwhile, other doctors were being driven from the field.

Chapter 9

The Misguidelines

Early in 1984, a few months after my hearing, I became a member of a government committee. Someone had had the idea that the medical profession needed clinical guidelines for the treatment of drug misuse, and naturally a committee was formed to produce them.

I had reservations about taking part. The intention, I felt certain, was to use any guidelines to bolster orthodoxy, consolidate the power of the DDUs, and find new means of putting down opposition. In medicine, guidelines drawn up by the establishment are all too easily converted into regulations and a means of punishing dissenters. But I was still President of AIDA, the Association of Independent Doctors in Addiction, which was invited to send a representative. The members wanted our voice to be heard, and they elected me. Thus I began to make regular journeys to that outpost of the medical establishment, the Department of Health and Social Security at the Elephant and Castle.

I knew immediately I arrived that the stuffy skyscraper, later accused of making its inmates ill, was not my scene. As an avoider of committees, I was inexperienced in their procedures and the techniques for manipulating them. I disliked politicking and those who did it. But uncongenial as it was, I decided to continue.

The establishment case was fortified by an article in the *British Medical Journal* of 10 March 1984. It was clear to me that it set the tone for the Guidelines. Like many such articles it was long on 'experience' and short on information and logic. Although the Guidelines were in theory to encourage general practitioners to look after addicts, even stating that it was their duty to do so, this article suggested that addicts could only safely be treated in special 'multidisciplinary centres', which, as was well known, only the establishment could provide.

The combined experience of the special drug dependence clinics as put forward here requires serious consideration. Overprescribing is widely accepted as harmful. The single-handed doctor, whether general practitioner or consultant in the NHS or private practice, who has little or no experience of addicts is a vulnerable target for the drug-seeker. So have been consultants and juniors in special treatment clinics where the team approach is not used.

The committee met one day a month for most of the year. One substantial group was made up of psychiatrists, all known supporters of current policies and devoted to their 'consensus' view – which was really a consensus only because they were of like mind and disregarded those who did not agree. In fact there could be few medical subjects about which those working in the field were so divided. Yet none of this substantial minority of dissidents among DDU consultants had been invited to sit on the committee. One member began by proclaiming: 'The first essential in treating addicts is to make certain that no drugs can escape to the black market.'

This was tantamount, of course, to saying that drugs should not be prescribed at all. And considering that prescribed drugs form less than one-tenth of 1 per cent of the black market, I thought it showed a curious lack of proportion. But this sweeping statement set the tone for the discussions.

The other substantial group was made up of doctors representing the great institutions of the profession: the Royal Colleges, the British Medical Association, the General Medical Council, the NHS consultants, and so on. It wasn't difficult to see why they had been invited to join, even though they had no experience of treating drug dependency and couldn't possibly advise on clinical matters, which was what the committee was about. Admitting their lack of experience, they tended to defer to the drug dependency establishment, and thus increased the power of establishment views. Occasionally they revealed a sense of justice, but they seldom spotted injustices or anomalies for themselves.

One incident is engraved on my memory as typical of the proceedings. In a discussion of the many drafts produced for our attention I was worried about a sentence that read: 'Some pregnant women are afraid that the social services will remove their babies. They should be reassured.' I thought this was devious and raised it to the committee.

'How can you reassure someone about something that is likely to happen?'

No one had even noticed this. But I had experience of social workers removing or threatening to remove addicts' babies, often for no reason other than that they were addicted. Knowing this, many addict mothers went to great lengths to avoid the official services, even to the extent of depriving themselves of antenatal care.

The chairman laughed and said: 'Oh, that's easy. We're reassuring mothers about the care of the *foetus*. What happens afterwards doesn't concern us.'

This was one of the few occasions when I allowed anger to enter my voice. 'I think that's specious,' I said emphatically. 'I don't think the committee should go along with it.'

The committee agreed. It was one of the few occasions when the majority on the committee opposed the 'official' view. If I hadn't objected to this point, it would have been accepted without question. Now the wording was changed to something more honest if not more helpful. It was still obvious that the official policy did not care about mothers and babies and would deceive them if it was convenient.

A small minority who did protest consisted of a few 'outsiders' such as myself. It included several GPs and a few other doctors who had experience of treating addicts outside clinics. The group was not large enough to have much power in the committee. I thought it significant that none of these doctors, who were clearly there to give an appearance of 'balance', was in a position of power or even ran a drug dependency unit. One of them, my friend Dale Beckett, had done so in the past but was now retired. The committee had not invited people such as James Willis and John Marks, two DDU consultants who were critical of the orthodox view.

Our 'dissident' group also included a congenial general practitioner, Arthur Banks, a committed Christian and former medical missionary. He seemed shocked by what was going on. Sometimes Arthur protested openly about the nature of the discussion or the tactics used, and I believe he would have protested more had he not recently suffered a severe heart attack. There was also Dr Betty Tylden, another retired psychiatrist and very much an individualist. She criticised both the establishment and private practice but had little experience with addicts generally, being chiefly interested in pregnant addicts. Even though the group was not strong enough to counter the majority insistence on 'consensus', we sometimes made strong protests.

Some members of the committee showed distaste at my presence and were offensive to me. During the first few minutes of the first meeting one of them leaned towards me and said in a loud sneering voice: 'Dr Dally, it is true, isn't it, that you are not a *proper* psychiatrist?'

Another member said he objected to the presence of 'someone who has been found guilty of serious professional misconduct'. He was so angry that he seemed to spit out the words. Snide remarks were also made about private doctors, mostly implying that all were crooks. At one point someone, not me, criticised the clinics and implied that they were not doing a good job. One member shouted across the table: 'There is NOTHING wrong with the clinics except when these private doctors steal their patients!' The Home Office officials tried to calm him.

I studied with amazement some of the techniques used to 'guide' our discussions. For instance, it was clear that the document was going to apply to the treatment of all addicts, yet I found it impossible to discuss the problems of long-term addicts. Every time anyone mentioned them, and a few did, the subject was skilfully changed. It was emphasised repeatedly that 'treatment must be the same for everyone'.

Meanwhile, no one seemed concerned about why so few addicts, one in five at the most, were ever seen in a clinic – or why only 5 per cent or less were actually treated. It is commonly argued that one should only treat patients who ask for treatment, but doctors do not always know or care that a patient may fail to present himself because he has no faith in the doctor.

Several of our small group of 'dissidents', supported but not initiated by me, decided to refuse to sign the final report and to write a minority report. We had a good deal of discussion about this. Suddenly we became aware that a complicated procedural move had taken place behind our backs. Somehow we had been prevented from carrying out our intention of registering our protest. I didn't understand how this had happened. Someone who was accustomed to committee politics explained to me that a 'new situation' had been created so that no one on the committee would sign anything. It also meant that a minority report, such as we had intended to write, would be out of order. It was a clever move. I realised that, in the art of skulduggery, those who do not spend their lives sitting on committees are no match for those who do.

We turned to another matter.

*

Some members of the drug dependency establishment had long sought new regulations limiting the right to prescribe controlled drugs for addicts to specially licensed doctors. In practice this would mean that the doctors to get licences would be those working under a consultant at a drug clinic. Such a system would, of course, lead to an increase in the power of the DDU consultants. It would also introduce a new principle into British medicine, for the first time giving consultants power over other doctors working in their own surgeries and consulting rooms. It would be the first loss of the general practitioner's time-honoured right to be his own master in his own practice.

The committee voted in favour of this idea, but it was not adopted. The fact that it could even be discussed seriously was, I felt, an indication of the horror with which drug addicts were held, and of the way they can be used to erode other people's rights. It linked later with the Criminal Justice Bill which permitted confiscation of the assets of drug dealers unless they could prove that they had been obtained lawfully, and persuaded banks to disclose information about customers' accounts. This may seem due justice for drug dealers, but for the first time it introduced into British justice the principle of being guilty until proved innocent. People seldom think of human rights in connection with illegal drugs. They seldom think of doctors' freedom in relation to drug addicts. They assume that everything to do with drugs should be condemned by all possible means.

So the *Guidelines of Good Clinical Conduct in the Treatment of Drug Misuse* was published in the autumn of 1984. All patients were to be treated in much the same way, regardless of whether they had been addicted for weeks or for decades. No patient's treatment was to last longer than a few weeks or months, and all were to be drug-free by that time. The maximum initial dose of methadone to be prescribed was 80 milligrams, less than one-twentieth of what, only a few years before, the clinics themselves had advocated and prescribed.

Thus a large and important group of addicts was excluded from the Guidelines and not even discussed. Doctors were advised to refer long-term addicts to the clinics at a time when most clinics would not help them. Later, after my next appearance before the GMC and when the climate of opinion was beginning to change, there was publicity about this, but at that time everything was done to ignore the needs of the long-term addicts. They were only offered help if they were willing to accept the short standard detoxification treatment.

Later I became a critic of the Guidelines – or, as John Marks called the document, the 'Misguidelines'. Because of that I have often been asked why I signed it, made no criticism at the time, and did not produce a minority report. I have tried to describe what happened but it is not easy to explain. Many people do not think that such dishonesty can occur in a committee of professional people. Others do not wish to believe it even when they have witnessed it. One member of that DHSS committee clearly forgot what had happened despite having been present and, shortly before my appeal, criticised me in a letter to a newspaper for having signed it! My solicitors sent a letter threatening to sue for libel. The doctor had the grace or wisdom to apologise.

The Guidelines were supposed to be sent free to every doctor in the land, but there were delays and things went wrong. Many doctors complained that they had not received their copies. Of those who did, many found it unrealistic, arrogantly written and indigestible. Though purporting to encourage GPs to treat addicts, it actually tended to lessen any small interest they might have in the subject. They could see that the Guidelines were likely to become covert regulations to be used in disciplinary proceedings against any doctor who dared contravene them. Some of the more daring members of the committee had suggested that this would certainly be the effect even if it was not the purpose. Their comments had been ignored.

Although the Guidelines were used to set 'standards', no doctor was ever disciplined for ignoring what was perhaps the most important statement: that it is the duty of a GP to treat addicts both for their general health and for their addiction. In a survey of eighteen general practitioners in a London suburb which I organised a year later, not one was willing to help addicts and sixteen were positively hostile. Some even displayed notices in their surgeries saying that they did not treat addicts. Meanwhile on a number of occasions the Guidelines were used in disciplinary procedures against doctors who had tried to help addicts. At a Home Office tribunal against one GP at which I was an 'expert witness' the prosecution referred continually to the Guidelines in a way that suggested that any breach of them, however small, was a point against the accused. And in my own case, the next time I appeared before the GMC, the prosecutor spoke of the Guidelines as if they were regulations. Members of the Professional Conduct Committee gave the impression that they, too, regarded them as set rules.

After a while it was so obvious that the Guidelines pamphlet was nonsensical that even those who had welcomed and promoted it began to admit that it was 'out of date'. By that time many people were beginning to view the drugs problem more realistically.

Chapter 10

Thunderclouds

The publication of the Guidelines began a new era in drug dependency which was widely described, among those who knew what was going on, as a witch hunt. There was a huge increase in the number of Home Office tribunals and GMC prosecutions of doctors who had prescribed for addicts. While some seemed to be justified, some were simply vindictive. Only a few years before these had been almost unknown.

The GMC stated in its evidence to the House of Commons Select Committee on Home Affairs, published in 1985, that a doctor suspected of prescribing drugs that were then sold on could be charged with serious professional misconduct. There was increasing use of *agents provocateurs*, often policemen, to try to catch out those who failed to prevent this. Merely knowing that such things could happen was enough to deter most doctors; they were not inclined to take the risk. With few exceptions, clinic consultants were glad to join in the pursuit of dissidents. One of them admitted: 'The witch hunt appeals to the "pack feeling" of hunting. I'm afraid this is a common characteristic of doctors.'

Sadly, the Home Office, once a bastion of tolerance and humanity, was changing. Bing Spear was often in hospital, and his frequent absences gave an opportunity to harder and more traditional bureaucrats, some of whom clearly enjoyed policing doctors. The fact that a few doctors were crooks and others were misled, having been provided with no practicable guidance, only increased the zeal of some officials.

Meanwhile, drug use was increasing. The official DDUs had long waiting lists, mostly of new addicts, and were still spurned by the vast majority.

On 26 April 1984, I received a routine official visit from Home Office inspectors, my first since the question of the Guidelines had been prominent. In theory these interviews might be used in disciplinary proceedings, but until the Guidelines were published I felt this was very much in theory. Bing Spear and John Lawson, the inspectors who usually came to see me, were anxious not to make trouble but to save it; they were friendly, interested and anxious to impart their considerable expertise. I always listened carefully and tried to put their recommendations into practice, and I learned far more from them than from so-called specialists or from the medical literature. I tried not to say this to them because it embarrassed them. They were not supposed to be regarded as 'medical experts'.

On this visit, for the first time, Bing didn't come. He was ill. The inspectors were John Lawson and his colleague John Gerrard, who took notes. Lawson was friendly but seemed embarrassed. He told Gerrard not to start writing yet. Then he told me that the drug dependency establishment were still trying to make trouble for me and were now trying to get me charged before a Home Office tribunal. He said: 'You will be judged by the standards of the clinics and if found wanting you will be deprived of your right to prescribe controlled drugs. It will all depend on how much you conform to what the clinic doctors want.' He added, 'I advise you to pull in your horns. They're really out to get you. They want you out of the way.' Of course they did. I was revealing their hypocrisy.

Then the official interview started. Lawson explained that the Home Office would use it to decide whether I should be brought before a tribunal. Anything I said could be used in a tribunal and would be produced if the GMC 'decided to take action'. I remembered Bing's saying: 'The GMC are delighted to have their cases ready-made. It saves them from having to do the work.'

The interview began by questioning my procedures for examining, investigating and treating addicts. Then Lawson asked about three patients. I didn't know why he chose them because all were stable and there seemed to be no problems with any of them. Lawson said that the number of patients I treated was 'on the high side', but I replied that I had not seen any new patients that month. I also said that it was not the number of patients that caused problems but their quality. And, I added, I rejected many more than I accepted.

At the end of the interview, Lawson explained the tribunal machinery again and said that the matter would be submitted for a decision on whether my prescribing should be so referred. He added that I had not been singled out but was one of many doctors to be seen.

Some of the doctors seen by Home Office inspectors that spring had hostile interviews. Some were scared even if they didn't. Having seen what had happened to me and others, they decided to stop their addict practices immediately. Most of these were good doctors who had been appalled at the situation in the clinics and had tried to help in a small way. A few were suspended or struck off the register. It seemed to me that the few villains in the field continued as before. Meanwhile, long-term addicts were being driven on to the black market.

For a doctor to regard addiction as just another medical condition and do his best to alleviate the suffering was now to court disaster. Inevitably, some addicts tried to deceive their doctors. If they succeeded, the Guidelines provided a basis for the authorities to prosecute.

The technique of catching doctors was simple. Either they were framed, perhaps by police posing as addicts, or they were caught out on small mistakes. Minute examination of the work of any doctor (or solicitor or anyone else) would probably reveal things that, taken out of context, could be described as irresponsible.

The effect of these policies could be seen in six of my own patients or former patients. After the Guidelines were published I refused to prescribe injectable drugs for them, largely because I was afraid of the persecution I saw taking place. I did this with regret, knowing that these patients would buy and inject drugs from the black market, doubtless sharing needles in the process.

In the two years following publication of the Guidelines all these patients died from overdose after injecting black-market heroin. In the years I spent treating hundreds of addict patients, I never knew one die from drugs prescribed by me.

After my experience before the GMC, I was approached by others in trouble or by their lawyers. One of these was an old friend, Dr David Slovick, an experienced GP in Notting Hill. Like me, he had long been aware of the inhumane behaviour of many doctors towards addicts; in a small way, he had done his best to help them.

His attempts to help addicts brought him trouble. In 1985 he was summoned before a Home Office tribunal and charged with irresponsible prescribing. The prosecution had collected statements against him from DDU doctors who had never met him and almost certainly had no experience of general practice. In unctuous language clearly designed to please the prosecution, they criticised him for not following DDU clinic practices to the letter. I was sad that colleagues could write such things on so little evidence.

Unsurprisingly, David was banned from prescribing controlled drugs. The tribunal had taken care to see that the rest of his practice did not suffer, but this did not save him from further trouble. He had forgotten to ask for permission to prescribe phenobarbitone – a standard treatment but officially a controlled drug – to epileptics. On two occasions he did this without even thinking about it. As a result the police visited him. He rang me up shortly after and said: 'There has been a big stink. I'm so fed up with it all that I'm retiring. I can't take any more.'

Another doctor fared even worse. Dr Kobina Taylor was a Ghanaian who had once been an ambassador for his country and now worked as a GP in the Midlands. Like Dr Slovick, he had the misfortune to realise that drug addicts needed help that they were rarely getting. He was particularly affected by the suicide of a patient through lack of help.

Home Office inspectors visited him but offered no advice, even though they could easily have done so. When his surgery had become inundated with addicts, the inspectors came again and gave him a hostile interview. After that, two policemen visited him undercover, pretending to be an addict and his friend. They told Dr Taylor a sad story, which he believed, and he gave them a prescription. The pair arrested him on the spot for supplying illegal drugs. When he appeared in the magistrates' court, the police opposed bail on the grounds that he might continue to supply drugs.

Dr Taylor spent a month in jail. When tried in the Crown Court he was found not guilty. But the Home Office inspectors recommended that he be brought before a tribunal for irresponsible prescribing. His lawyers employed me as a witness.

I formed the opinion that Dr Taylor was an honest man. He did make mistakes, including technical irregularities in his prescriptions. The prosecution made much of these but they were written in a way that is common among general practitioners. Had the authorities not wished to prosecute him for other reasons, these minor transgressions would never have attracted attention. He was inexperienced in addicts' tricks, which the authorities could have warned him about but chose not to. Dr Taylor was also foolish, in that persecutory climate, not to do laboratory tests, nor did he carry out a full medical examination, which was against the Guidelines (but in line with common practice).

I was struck by irrelevant references in police and Home Office statements to lack of paint and peeling wallpaper in his surgery.

These had apparently been included to give a sleazy image rather than realistically describe a typical inner city surgery.

It was my opinion that Dr Taylor had been a victim of an impossible situation. A caring doctor, if not a very thoughtful one, he followed his own methods of practice and tried to do his best for his patients, as requested in the Guidelines. He was in some respects irresponsible, but all he needed was education in the care of drug addicts. Unfortunately, selected victims of the authorities were, to use the word of one Home Office inspector, being 'nailed'. Dr Taylor was one of them.

Had he, like so many of his colleagues, ignored the plight of his patients, broken the Hippocratic oath and treated them like dirt, he would not have got into trouble. The chairman of the committee that brought the Guidelines into being received the CBE the following year.

In a desire to avoid further trouble for myself after the case, I asked a prominent DDU consultant to see a potential patient of mine for a second opinion on dosage. The patient was taking huge amounts of opiate, far more than I was prepared to prescribe under present circumstances without substantial backing. He saw the patient and replied:

I cannot advise you what method of treatment you employ. He made it quite clear that he would die an addict and cannot see any possibility of coming off drugs and made it clear that he was not going to hospital as he would lose his pad [his house], his books, his interest in lilies and orchids and this was impossible and indeed to even raise such a point showed very little understanding.

I understand that there may be some concern because of the recent findings of the General Medical Council and as you know there is a working group to be set up to discuss guidelines for prescribing to addicts; individuals such as Mr B— will of course figure in such discussions.

This was a new experience for me: seeking a second opinion from a specialist only to be told that a committee would be discussing such cases next year! This specialist seemed not to care about the patient's fears of losing everything that was most important to him in life. All he cared about was the patient's inability to give up drugs altogether.

*

The year of the Guidelines, 1984, was also the year of the miners' strike. Britain was increasingly perceived as a divided nation. People worried about unemployment, the future of young people, and an increase in crime and violence. Drugs were seen as a symbol of deviance, a focus of evil and a threat to social unity. Public concern about drugs increased and sometimes amounted to hysteria. Almost every article or programme on drugs did all it could to denigrate the 'drug abuser'. It was the one subject on which politicians on both sides of the House seemed to agree.

In that climate, clinic doctors were easily able to maintain their position in the medical profession. Pretending that caring for drug addicts required their specialised expertise kept the field within the control of a few doctors with the same outlook. The success of their efforts became vividly clear to me when I heard one of the group give evidence to a House of Commons Select Committee. Other witnesses were greeted without ceremony and were asked quite serious questions. When the drug dependency doctor appeared, the change in attitude was remarkable. 'Oh, how *very* good of you to come! How nice to see you again.' I didn't know why they were behaving like this.

Although the evidence of this doctor conflicted seriously with that of other witnesses, no member of the committee drew attention to the fact or asked him a difficult question. Then it was thank you so much for coming, how good of you, etc., all over again. Everything this man said came out uncritically in the report.

Another performance I witnessed was even stranger. This was a speech given by Dr Thomas Bewley, newly elected president of the Royal College of Psychiatrists. One evening in the autumn of 1984 members and guests of the Medico-Legal Society filled the Barnes Hall of the Royal Society of Medicine to hear him speak on 'Overreaction to Drug Dependence'. Many members of the audience were lawyers who dealt with drug cases and were puzzled by the discrepancies between the stories they read in the papers and what they saw in the courts.

Dr Bewley dealt first with tobacco addiction, for he was well known as a vociferous anti-smoker. He then went on to discuss alcohol, cannabis and glue-sniffing, a small though growing problem among young teenagers at the time. Then his talk was over.

At first there was an astonished silence. Then a lawyer rose to her feet and asked: 'But what about heroin?'

Dr Bewley replied with a dismissive wave of his hand. 'It's too unimportant to mention,' he said, and refused to discuss the subject.

Throughout 1984 I had become increasingly aware of hostili

shown to me by some DDU consultants. More articles and letters in the medical press were aimed directly at me and AIDA. Addicts repeated remarks made about me in clinics. Those who were particularly against me often communicated about patients with little-disguised acrimony.

One curious incident at around this time made me wonder whether the campaign against me was reaching new depths. I was rung up by a general practitioner who asked me to visit a patient in the Priory Hospital in Roehampton and, if all went well, to take over his care. The case did not concern drugs or addiction.

The patient was a young scholar who had damaged his brain falling off a fire escape. He now had epileptic fits and many personal problems. We got on well and he begged me to take over his care, which I agreed to do. After seeing him I was writing my case notes in the corridor when a doctor whom I knew as one of the drug dependency 'mafia' came in, threw me a curt 'Good afternoon', and started whispering to the ward sister. I had the feeling they were talking about me.

I telephoned the GP and told him I would look after the patient if he still wished it. He was pleased.

Next day the patient rang up in a distressed state. 'They won't let you look after me because you aren't a proper psychiatrist,' he told me.

Later the GP left a message with my secretary to say that other arrangements had been made for the patient. I never heard from him again, though I did get a letter from the young man asking whether there was any way he could be my patient.

The powerful group of doctors who condemned me was somewhat amorphous, consisting largely of London drug clinic consultants supported by others from outside London. As far as I know, it was Bing Spear who first publicly identified the group, in an interview with the *New Statesman*. They had a number of connections with the Royal Colleges and the GMC, and were particularly influential because they had the confidence of David Mellor, then a minister at the Home Office. At the time Mellor was often on television telling us how he was 'determined to beat the evil' of drugs, or how he had helped destroy the drugs trade by visiting South America. He seemed to have no idea of the true situation.

A common obsession among DDU doctors was that their patients were theirs for ever – a form of property. On a number of occasions when I contacted them about a former patient who had been referred to me, they reacted angrily, implying that I had no right to see the patient or that the general practitioner had no right to refer him to me.

I was always scrupulous about this. If a patient was still attending a clinic or had recently done so, I would not accept him, even if the GP requested it. This was especially the case if the patient had attended a clinic where the consultant was openly hostile to private doctors in general or to me in particular. If the addict had attended a clinic in the past but was no longer doing so, I would write to the consultant for a report.

On two different occasions addicts were referred to me by their general practitioners and I saw them a few times. Suddenly, out of the blue, I received angry letters from DDU consultants saying that the patients had attended their clinics until very recently. Yet I had received no information about this from the Home Office, whom I, like the clinics, was legally obliged to notify.

In both these cases it turned out that the clinic doctors had never notified these patients to the Home Office. Yet even after this was discovered and it was clear that the error was theirs, they continued to write angry letters. I determined to take the greatest care to avoid disagreements with them.

My caution did not prevent me, however, from offending Dr Bewley. This was in the autumn of 1984, only two weeks after the Guidelines had been published.

The patients concerned, Jeremy and Tina, a prosperous young couple with a small child and a business, were ex-patients of Bewley's. Unable to follow the harsh new prescribing policies, they felt forced to use the black market. Dr Bewley seemed neither interested nor concerned. He would not alter the schedules so that they could cope, and when they asked to be referred to another doctor, he refused in a way that gave them the impression that they were not allowed to attend any doctor other than himself.

Jeremy's mother became so worried about his deterioration and upset by Bewley's attitude that she sent letters of complaint to both the Home Secretary and the Minister of Health. Their replies informed her that the couple were free to consult another doctor if they wished. So they informed Bewley that they no longer wished to be his patients and asked their general practitioner to refer them to a private doctor. She then referred them to me.

Knowing of Bewley's hostility to private medicine, I took extra care not to upset him. After failing to reach him by telephone, I asked in writing for reports on the couple. Weeks were to pass before any information arrived. I could not make the patients wait so long before starting treatment.

But Bewley was quick to begin complaints. After I had started treating Jeremy and Tina, he telephoned to say that he had discovered that I had not notified the patients to the Home Office. This was untrue. He went on to accuse me of being 'grossly irresponsible', referred to my previous trouble with the GMC, and said that he believed it his duty to refer the matter to them. But he still did not send the reports about the patients.

I knew I needed legal advice. Feeling disenchanted with the Medical Defence Union, I got in touch with my solicitor, John Calderan. He told me to send him the papers and a personal account of what had happened. 'Meanwhile, write him a stalling letter to tide us over till we've decided what we're going to do.'

I did this and again asked Bewley to send the reports. A week later, still not having received them, I wrote again to point out that I had behaved impeccably by any ethical standards and once more asked for the reports. John Calderan read the letter and said: 'With any luck that will shut him up.'

A week later I still had not got the reports. Eventually I received a letter enclosing reports from which some relevant information was missing. I was not surprised by this, in light of my earlier experiences of the DDUs. Bewley's accompanying remarks were more restrained than those in his previous letter, but I knew that he had already complained about me to the Home Office, who were, I had been told, ignoring the complaint.

Next day I received another letter from Bewley. He alleged that I had 'offered private treatment' to his patients without 'first finding out about the treatment they had received previously'. He believed, he said, that I had prevented them from continuing their treatment with him and that it was a question of 'serious professional misconduct'. And he informed me that he felt obliged to send the correspondence to the General Medical Council.

John Calderan took me to a QC who specialised in libel. He waved the bundle of papers at us and pronounced: 'This is defamatory without question!' Then he added more soberly, 'He'll plead privilege, of course.'

Privilege is one of the defences against an action for defamation. The letters Bewley wrote might be deemed to be privileged or partially privileged. This meant we had to prove malice.

'Nevertheless,' the QC went on, 'we may be able to stop him in his tracks.'

I wasn't keen to sue Bewley, however strong my case. Nevertheless I wanted to stop these attacks.

Most lawyers love to write skilful, belligerent letters, and John Calderan is no exception. The letter he wrote with counsel said in part:

You have repeatedly accused Dr Dally of gross irresponsibility, twice promptly within a few days of receiving her letter of 26th October asking for a report, but fully a fortnight before you actually provided such report. The thrust of your accusation . . . as you know, was wholly untrue: she had sought to contact you by telephone and had written to you. The fact is that the only reason why Dr Dally had to prescribe before receiving your report is that you did not send her that report, but instead were far more urgently concerned to accuse Dr Dally of irresponsible prescribing.

The facts disclose no rational basis for criticising Dr Dally's handling of this matter. They have been fully and courteously explained to you in correspondence by Dr Dally. In spite of this you have chosen to repeat these seriously damaging allegations in a quarter where injury to Dr Dally's reputation may be expected to be severe. You have not condescended to provide any particulars of your allegations or any evidence to support them. On the facts as related in this letter it is apparent that no such evidence exists, and that any such particulars would merely uncover the complete lack of substance in these allegations. We invite you to provide such particulars and evidence, or withdraw your accusations. Doubtless you would feel an apology to be appropriate.

Dr Dally has consulted us with a view to protecting her reputation: if unjustified attacks upon her persist, there is only one way in which this can be achieved and that is by litigation. You should be warned that unless your attack upon her reputation ceases, you will be sued. Your personal opposition to private practice is well known; if it leads you into libelling and harassing responsible and careful private practitioners on no rational grounds, the inference will readily be drawn that you are motivated by malice.

John was pleased. He said jovially: 'That'll give him something to think about!'

My letter to the General Medical Council, also drafted largely by the lawyers, covered much the same ground. It included a few more medical details and matters involving medical etiquette and ended by asking for guidance.

The following week I received a letter from the GMC informing me that the Council 'does not propose to take any action in relation to the matter raised by Dr Bewley'.

The letter also stated: 'The President is of the opinion that it was quite proper of Dr Bewley, if he formed the opinion in good faith that he had such evidence, to write to the Council as he did.'

John said: 'We know of course that the Council's idea of "good faith" is precisely what they choose it to mean.'

The GMC letter added, possibly ominously: ' . . . the circumstances of individual cases vary, and therefore any complaint received by the Council . . . would be considered on its own merits.'

'Does that mean the GMC can vary its rules to attack doctors they don't like?' asked my son Adam. He was beginning to get the flavour of medical politics.

Still, I was relieved. Dr Bewley's letters had caused me a good deal of anxiety. They had also cost me nearly £2000, which I had to pay myself. But at least the correspondence had provided instruction and amusement to a number of people.

By the beginning of 1985, people were beginning to gossip about Ann Dally's disagreement with the new president of the Royal College of Psychiatrists. On 20 January a piece appeared in the *Guardian*:

Something approaching civil war is waging amidst Britain's shrinks with confusing ramifications for the Bewley family. Dr Thomas Bewley, president of the Royal College of Psychiatrists, has been involved in something of a contretemps with Dr Ann Dally, another psychiatrist, though of a radically different school of thought from Dr Bewley. This led to Dr Bewley laying information before the General Medical Council, which might be thought something of an embarrassment to at least one member of this august body – Dr Bewley's wife, Dr Beulah Rosemary Bewley.

The GMC last week found in Dr Dally's favour – round one to her. But now two of her patients are reporting Dr Bewley himself to the GMC. Another one for Dr Bewley (wife, not husband) to sit out on the sidelines.

The *Guardian* was referring to Jeremy and Tina. The same day on which I received the letter from the GMC, they had made detailed formal complaints to the Council about the way they had been treated by Dr Bewley.

The GMC's reply to Jeremy and Tina arrived before the end of January. After predictable formalities it informed them that:

> Complaints about the regime of treatment which a doctor has prescribed in a particular case or similar matters involving a doctor's clinical judgment are not . . . considered to raise a question of serious professional misconduct . . . the council cannot undertake to intervene in response to your complaint.

One of the doctors at the Medical Defence Union was 'surprised to hear that matters of clinical judgement do not concern the GMC. Without too much difficulty I can lead you to a couple of practitioners who know to their cost that this is not always the case. I do wish the GMC would be a little more consistent.'

Dr Bewley's reply to my letter, written by his solicitors, did not arrive until mid-February. It assured us that he did not accuse me of 'inducing' the two patients to leave his programme, but that he 'was extremely distressed to learn that your client had prescribed for Mr and Mrs H— as she did.' He was particularly distressed, it seems, because I had participated in formulating the Guidelines, and Dr Bewley 'considered that your client had not complied with these guidelines although she had participated in their formulation'.

I was sad to hear of Dr Bewley's distress. It might have been avoided had the Guidelines concerned themselves with long-term addicts such as Jeremy and Tina rather than with treating every drug user alike and disciplining doctors who did not follow the rules.

My solicitors wrote a long reply saying that Dr Bewley's letter evaded the issue and failed to answer most of the points in our letter. But since the GMC had decided to ignore Dr Bewley's complaint about me, I could afford to be magnanimous. I felt sorry for him he was vulnerable, out of his depth at a time when he needed to give a dignified image as the new president of the Royal College. I found it rather sad that 'Britain's top psychiatrist' should behave in such a way.

This was not the only occasion when I felt I was being attacked behind the scenes. Soon after the Bewley affair, I was telephoned by Professor Priest, Professor of Psychiatry at St Mary's and Registrar of the Royal College of Psychiatrists. 'Dr Dally, we have had a complaint that you have been using your associateship of the college for your own advantage.'

I was so surprised that I didn't even ask what he meant. I simply said it wasn't true and told him a little of what had been going on.

'I receive you, loud and clear,' he replied. He asked me to write a fuller account of what I had been telling him. 'Don't send it to the college,' he said. 'It'll be safer in my locked drawer at St Mary's.'

I sent my explanation to him and received acknowledgement of its receipt. After that I heard no more and never solved the mystery of what lay behind the complaint.

After my interview with John Lawson in the spring of 1984, having no doubt that persecution was afoot, I wrote to the Home Office saying that I would make some changes in my practice and take on no more new addict patients. I also wrote a document which I gave to John Calderan describing the situation and my fears that the drug dependency 'mafia' or the GMC would attack me again.

I received a letter from Bing Spear saying that in view of the changes I was making in my practice, the Home Office would not initiate a tribunal or take other action.

My ceasing to take on new patients caused distress. Some GPs begged me to make exceptions, and I received heartfelt pleas from people who had been abandoned by clinics or whose doctors had stopped treating addicts. Eventually I discussed the situation with Bing, who said the Home Office would have no objection to my taking new patients.

So I continued, though with fewer patients. I had wanted to cut down anyway: I had worked too hard for some years, and longed to have more time for writing. By July I had made Mondays free, so that my weekends in the country were prolonged.

Later these changes were used against me by those trying to make out that I had gone back on my word.

Some time after this I heard that Lawson had been removed and sent to Bristol. The rumour was that he was regarded as too soft on the doctors, and a harder man was being brought in. More doctors, good and bad, were scared off and withdrew from the scene. I also heard that threats had been made to 'nail Harley Street to the wall'.

In the spring of 1985 I began having problems with a patient, a Turkish Cypriot whom I shall call Khalid.

Khalid had been my patient since 1982, when he was thirty-two years old. A tall, rather seedy-looking man with a soft voice and a gentle manner, he was a builder by trade. He always drove to my house

in his builder's van full of tools and covered with ladders. Sometimes
he employed as many as ten or twelve men, sometimes he worked on
his own or with his brother.

When referred to me in February 1982, he had been addicted
for eleven years. He had been treated without success in various
clinics and had nothing good to say about them. His wife was ten
years younger than himself. They had marital problems, and when I
first saw him he had left her and was living with his mother. But he
missed his children and hoped the family would get back together.

I didn't fully trust Khalid but I liked him and decided to take him
on. We agreed that he would have a daily dose of methadone, which
would be gradually reduced but not as rapidly as the clinics demanded.
On the whole he complied with this, in the typical slow manner of a
long-term addict. During his three years as my patient he reduced his
need for drugs by about half. I regarded this as a good result.

I got on well with Khalid – so well, in fact, that I recommended
him to my daughter and son-in-law who needed some work done on
their house. I very rarely did such a thing.

My troubles with Khalid arose when his wife began telephoning
me and saying that he was selling drugs. I had no evidence of this and
invited her to come and see me, but she refused. She also refused to
tell Khalid that she had telephoned or to allow me to do so. It seemed
to me that she was blaming her marital problems on his drug habit and
on me. Because I prescribed his drugs, she reasoned, her problems
would be solved if she could stop him coming to me.

When I enquired about her indirectly, Khalid told me that she was
trying to make trouble for him. I wanted to raise the issue directly but
respecting her confidence, felt unable to discuss her calls. I hoped they
would come and see me together so that I could help with the problems
in their relationship.

Many months after her first telephone call, in September 1985,
Khalid's wife sent me an unemployment slip to 'prove' that he wasn't
working. But it was more than a year old, and in any case it would
not be beyond Khalid to draw unemployment benefit while he was
also working, which was none of my business.

Mrs Khalid telephoned again and shouted at me: 'His addiction's
getting worse and it's all because of the drugs you prescribe. He's
selling drugs, too.'

Since his official dose was diminishing and he had recently requested
a further reduction, I thought this unlikely. Again I suggested that
she tell Khalid about her worries and about her calls to me, and

that they come and see me together. Again she refused. Eventually I received a solicitor's letter setting out what she had already said on the telephone.

At this point I became worried. I rang the Medical Defence Union. They advised me to discharge him immediately, and at Khalid's next appointment, at the beginning of October, I did. I still didn't tell him about his wife's calls but I showed him the letter from the solicitors. Khalid was angry. 'I know them, they're Turks,' he said. 'I'll soon sort them out and I'll be back.'

I told him that I would not be able to resume his treatment until things were sorted out with the solicitors. This also meant with his wife.

'I'll soon sort it out,' he assured me again.

'Meanwhile,' I said, 'go to your GP and see what help he can give you. I'll talk to him if he wishes.'

I was a little uneasy but not unduly worried. I wrote in the notes that I had discharged him but I put the notes on one side. I didn't want to write a discharge letter to the doctor only to find that Khalid and his wife returned in a week or two and I would then have to write another letter.

The next day Khalid went to his GP. The GP suggested that he go to a drug clinic. Khalid wasn't prepared to do this and took to the black market. Within a few weeks he had been arrested and sent to jail for selling heroin.

During his years with me he had had no trouble with the police. His wife, having engineered his departure from my care, now started to say that all their troubles had been caused by my discharging him.

I tend to be too trusting, even when I have already suffered as a result. In spite of changes at the Home Office, I had remained friendly with Bing Spear and I knew he liked to be kept informed about interesting cases. During one of the periods between bouts of illness when he was in the office, I sent him the correspondence with Mrs Khalid's solicitors. I knew it would interest him.

So it did. But it also got into the hands of someone who had an interest in damaging me. Information in the letters was passed to the GMC, who, as I already knew, were looking for material to use against me in a further trial.

This was the beginning of my second trial before the GMC. Khalid provided what they had been looking for.

Shortly after Khalid left my care, in December 1985, I received my next official visit from the Home Office. This time the interviewer was Donald McIntosh, the new Senior Inspector of Drugs for London and the Southeast. Again John Gerrard was the scribe, but whereas earlier interviews had been presented in the form of notes, the official record of this one was presented as a 'transcript', even though it had been taken down in the same slow longhand. It covered twelve pages, in contrast to Lawson's three and a half.

McIntosh was much younger than either Spear or Lawson, and unlike them he conducted his interview somewhat like a police interrogation. He seemed to accept without question the standard police and DDU view of drug addiction. The fact that patients were referred to me by general practitioners did not interest him. Nor did the fact that many areas of Britain and even of London had no facilities for treating drug addicts. He told me things about one of my patients that seemed so unlikely that I later instituted enquiries. I discovered that he had received in good faith false information from a policeman who had an extreme dislike of addicts, and who had been suspended for corrupt practices.

McIntosh believed that addicts refused to go to clinics 'because doctors are prepared to prescribe on a long-term basis so patients are not prepared to come off or attend clinics'. This was reminiscent of Dr Bewley's letters. He also held the standard DDU view that all addicts should reduce their drugs quickly, as laid down by the Guidelines. In discussing individual patients, he disregarded such matters as how well they were doing or how stable their lives were. The only thing he seemed to care about was whether their doses could be reduced.

Home Office inspectors were always interested in addicts' employment because they believed that, if they were not working, they must be living on the proceeds of illegal drug sales. I always tried to get the best available proof of employment before I accepted an addict patient but it was impossible to keep it up to date. Someone might be in employment one month and unemployed the next. Some officials and others seemed to think that the doctor should know exactly what every patient did every moment of the day.

One particular patient of mine was in employment; I had a letter to that effect from his employers. I also had a letter from his GP pleading with me to look after him. This did not satisfy McIntosh. He implied that referrals from GPs were invalid if requested by the patient. His information said that the patient was not working, and this was the only information he regarded as important. Indeed, throughout the interview he made it plain that his information came from policemen and that he seldom met addicts. This was very different from the approach of Bing Spear and John Lawson.

McIntosh also suggested that private practice deprived patients of the 'excellent facilities' in the NHS, which had 'greatly improved' during the previous two years. In other circumstances I would have thought he was joking. Extensive enquiries on my part did not produce any evidence of improvement; Bing told me he didn't know of any either.

When Gerrard had finished writing, I made a silly comment about the cost of running our house in Devonshire Place, saying that we had overheads of £75,000 and needed to earn enough from the practice to meet them. This statement appeared in the transcript, completely out of context. I don't think this was intentional, but it later caused me a lot of trouble.

At the end of the interview, however, McIntosh did say: 'We are in no doubt that you are genuinely motivated in treating addicts.'

After this visit I felt uneasy. A policy of prosecuting independent doctors using the Guidelines as weaponry was getting into swing. In February 1986 I decided to offer to transfer my addict patients to the NHS. I gave each of them a letter to this effect, asking them, if they refused, to give their reasons.

Not one patient took up the offer. In explaining their reasons, some described graphically their past experiences at clinics. I made copies of the replies and sent them to McIntosh. He did not acknowledge them.

Also in February, Bing Spear came to see me by himself. He looked solemn. 'As a result of McIntosh's report on you, the Home Office lawyers think there is prima-facie evidence that you have acted irresponsibly. The evidence is weak, but in the present climate of opinion . . . '

'You mean that in the present climate, they think they might be able to cook up a case!'

Bing just smiled. 'There are moves to take you before a tribunal. I can stop them if you make further radical changes in your practice and close down your addict practice as fast as possible.'

'That seems the best thing to do,' I said.

'Yes,' Bing said sadly. 'You've done your stint.'

This was true. I felt I had done enough, and had had enough stress. My chief problem now was how to get out of the field without ruining my patients' lives. I knew I would not be able to live with myself if I just dropped them.

Together Bing and I worked out a way in which this might be done humanely over the next year or so. I agreed to stop seeing new addict patients and to try to make other arrangements as quickly as possible for those I was treating. This suited me too for personal reasons: my husband was in the process of retiring, and I didn't want to work so hard.

I kept to the plan as far as I could. The only new patient I accepted after that was a pop star whom I took on at the direct request of Bing Spear. But I was unable to make arrangements for all my patients in such a short time. Because the clinics were so bad and other doctors either frightened of helping addicts or hostile to them, there was nowhere for them to go. Many livelihoods and families depended on my continued help. For instance, to mention only a few of many, there was a long distance lorry driver with four children. Another father of four had alternated between clinic attendance and prison for ten years before coming to me and was now a foreman in a factory while his eldest daughter was working for A levels. He was an able, intelligent and moral man. This was his first 'honest job' for fifteen years; he was delighted with it and so was his wife. Another addict now owned a factory, which he would have to shut down if he had to return to the black market. A mother of three children had a responsible position controlling computers in a bank, and two young women addicts, one a mother, ran a market garden and cared for the family together. There were two post office engineers and a postman, several managing directors of companies and a builder of artificial ceilings. There were other skilled workers such as carpenters, plumbers and mechanics as well as members of various professions. Most of these would be unable to combine black-market life with responsible work, as would a career civil servant who was about to be promoted and, probably, the two journalists. I also wondered what would happen to the social worker and to the two computer programmers, one of whom was HIV-positive. There was even an addict patient who drove a van for a drug company, delivering drugs to chemists – I thought he would probably disappear with the van. If I stopped helping them, all these people were likely to lose their jobs and descend into criminal life, and their families with them. It was unlikely that I would be able to find doctors for more than a few of them. The Home Office inspectors were clearly trying to get as many doctors as possible out of the field of addiction. The inspectors had managed to persuade several doctors who might have taken on these patients to close down, and there had been a further clampdown on long-term addicts in some clinics. As a result I had received a new flood of requests from addicts who had been 'secure' for many years and were now criminalised.

There were several written from prison by addicts who had been respectable for years but had suddenly been discharged from their clinics or whose doctors had been scared by the Home Office inspectors and no longer dared to treat them. They had soon got into trouble. There were others who feared a similar fate, for example a young chemistry graduate hoping for a satisfying career; I thought he might turn to making secret illegal drugs. A pleasant young couple whom I had said I could not help came to see me to plead with me to save them. They had both been addicted for over twenty years but were among the few addicts still under a 'maintenance' regime at their clinic. As a result they had good office jobs, children, a house and a mortgage. Now their DDU consultant intended to cut off their supply of drugs within six weeks. He had left it to the nurse to tell them and had even refused to see them when they asked for an interview. This couple knew they could not give up drugs so quickly. They were desperate, fearful for themselves and their children. They were typical of many. There was now nothing I could do for them, though they could have been helped and so easily have remained the useful citizens they had become. I felt angry with the system and angry with the 'mafia' in my own profession. Why were we destroying these able, responsible people who had had the misfortune to become addicted? Why did we drive them to crime and into prison and wreck their families instead of enabling them to lead useful lives while raising their children? Why did both the government and the medical profession encourage the belief that heroin kills and that drug 'abuse' is the cause? It was the *drug policies* that killed, not the drugs themselves. During earlier centuries, when society was more tolerant of drug users, there had been many addicts who led useful lives. Clive of India, Samuel Taylor Coleridge, Bishop William Wilberforce and Elizabeth Barrett Browning were just a few of them. Even Gladstone used to take opium before making a speech in the House of Commons. So why were we persecuting all these people now?

The following week Bing telephoned to say that our scheme was not acceptable to the Home Office and that I must shut down totally within three months.

'We hold a pistol to your head,' he said. After further discussion with him I wrote a letter proposing 'to tell [my addict patients] that they must make other arrangements within three months'. I asked whether this would be acceptable.

He replied formally, on Home Office letterhead, saying: 'The arrangements you propose are quite acceptable to us.'

It was obvious that I would not be able to make arrangements for many of my long-term addict patients. Some doctors in my predicament had simply discharged them to the black market. I didn't blame them but I felt unable to do this myself. The whole point of being a doctor, my whole professional life, was negated if I treated patients in this way.

Meanwhile the Department of Health and Social Security published results of research they had commissioned which showed that doctors had become more hostile towards addicts and more determined than ever not to help them. This accorded with my own experience.

By now I had three albums full of photographs of my addict patients and their families, at work and at play, at home and on holiday. They were photographs of normal people enjoying themselves. I felt proud that I had made this possible for them. If I dropped them, many would revert to being street junkies.

McIntosh had still not answered my letters. Eventually I wrote him a letter confirming the points we had discussed and saying that my efforts to make other arrangements for my addict patients were not yet complete. 'I shall be sending you a report as requested,' I concluded.

When McIntosh failed yet again to reply, and when I failed repeatedly to reach him on the telephone, I sent him a long letter setting out the problems in some detail.

Bing Spear replied briefly asking for a list of addicts and the drugs and doses that they were on. McIntosh did not reply. In fact I never received a letter from him.

By now I had heard unofficially that my letter caused 'quite a stir' in the Home Office. I also heard that a copy of it was sent to the DHSS for their comment.

At about this time a kidney became available for Bing. He went into hospital for his transplant, which proved successful. Before he left he told me that I was now safe as far as the Home Office was concerned.

I was by no means the only doctor under threat. Dr C., a friend of mine, received the same warning from the Home Office: he would appear before a Home Office tribunal unless he shut down his addict practice within three months. The wife of one of his patients, fearful that her husband would lose his job, appealed to the Home Office and asked what he should do. She received the following reply from McIntosh.

Dear Mrs Y.,

Thank you for your letter to Mr Spear of 9 June about your husband's treatment for drug addiction. I am afraid that I can be of no assistance to you since it is a matter for the professional judgment of the doctor as to whether he will prescribe drugs as part of treatment for addiction. The proper course would be for your husband to seek the assistance of your family doctor and if he is unable to help he should ask to be referred to a drug dependency unit.

Chapter 11

More Accusations

The second of September 1986 was an ordinary day until lunchtime. I saw patients all morning and was looking forward to lunch with my daughter Emma and her eight-week-old daughter Rebecca, my first grandchild. As Emma walked in through the back door, the postman arrived at the front with a recorded delivery letter. My secretary Anne Lingham sighed when she saw the envelope.

The letter was from the General Medical Council and accused me once again of serious professional misconduct.

There were two separate charges. One was that I had abused my position as a medical practitioner 'by issuing, in return for fees, numerous prescriptions for methadone hydrochloride and other drugs in an irresponsible manner'. The other was abuse of my position by issuing to Khalid A., 'in return for fees, numerous prescriptions for controlled drugs in an irresponsible manner'. In particular, I was supposed to have failed to conduct a 'conscientious and sufficient physical examination' at the initial consultation; to have monitored his progress inadequately; and to have discharged him from my care 'without making any arrangements for him to receive on-going care and treatment from another medical practitioner'.

This was the last thing I expected just then. My latest correspondence with the Home Office had been based on the papers that the GMC were now using as the basis of a charge. I had only recently been assured by the Chief Inspector of Drugs that there was nothing against me.

I felt sick. I also had a busy day ahead. I decided not to do anything about it that day but simply to get through my work and then try to collect my thoughts. When I did get a moment to think, I realised that the wording of the letter implied that, as before, there had been no official complaint from the Home Office or from anywhere else.

Ironically, this was the day on which I was due to go to the Temple to attend a legal conference on behalf of Dr Taylor, the Ghanaian doctor for whom I was acting as an expert witness. When I reached the chambers I was told by the clerk that no conference had been arranged. At that moment a man from the Medical Defence Union arrived and was told the same thing. It turned out that we were right: a conference had indeed been arranged, but no one had told counsel and he had gone home. We would have to come again next week. The man from the MDU showed his annoyance and shouted, '*This is very expensive!*'

I had even less confidence than before in a bunch of lawyers who couldn't arrange a simple meeting. It didn't matter who had made the muddle – they were all retained by the MDU. This confirmed my determination not to have them for my case. I would have my own lawyers even if it meant selling my house to pay for them. I wanted my old friend John Calderan; at that moment I felt he was the only lawyer I could trust.

After a turbulent night, I telephoned him. I told him what had happened and said that, come what may, I wanted to retain him.

'Of course I'd be delighted to represent you, Ann, but do you realise how expensive it would be? I'm not in a position to do much to lower the firm's fees. Wouldn't you prefer to be represented by someone who works outside the City and is not so expensive?'

I said that I would not. I was asking him to act for me at my own expense. It was a formal, binding request. He seemed pleased.

'I'll start off by setting up a meeting with counsel,' he said. 'I can think immediately of two who would be particularly good on this. One is Christopher Sumner, whom I know to be a man of principle. He has a rare sense of justice and he's also a part-time judge.'

I said that I didn't suppose there was any more hope of the MDU paying for John than there was last time, but added that I wished to keep in touch with them all the same. He agreed.

Kate Allsopp, my friend at the MDU, was away. Her secretary arranged for me to see Dr John Wall.

John Wall was a large, genial man whose manner gave me confidence immediately. He told me that he had dealt with my case about twenty years ago when an article I had written for the *Sunday Telegraph* magazine was sold behind my back to a girlie magazine. We laughed about it and this made me feel more relaxed.

I told him what had happened and showed him the letter from the GMC. I had also taken with me Khalid's notes and other papers. Then he said: 'Of course we must send you to Hempsons.'

'No, I'm sorry. After what I went through before, I simply wouldn't have any confidence in the MDU lawyers.' I said I wanted John Calderan. John Wall asked about him and made a few remarks about the importance of protecting clients and how some doctors want to use solicitors who are personal friends but who only do conveyancing, etc. I was beginning to switch off, thinking, 'Here we go – the old paternalism.' Then I realised that he was agreeing. Subject to his committee's agreement, the MDU would pay for me to be represented by John.

I showed my delight.

'It isn't a blank cheque, you know,' he went on. 'The MDU will wish to be represented at all the meetings with lawyers.'

'Of course, I understand.'

John was delighted. It took much of the strain out of the situation for me and the embarrassment for him. He said, 'I want you to write a "skeleton", five or six pages, about the background of the case for counsel. I want it by the end of the week.'

The next day I spoke to Bing Spear, who was still convalescing. He knew nothing about what had happened or about the part that his own department had played in the case.

'I'm astounded, I'm amazed,' he kept saying.

He told me that the Home Office had agreed with the GMC that the Council would not pursue doctors for irresponsible prescribing; this would be dealt with by the Home Office at tribunals, unless there were also ethical considerations.

'It seems to me,' I said, 'that the GMC has only to say that there are "ethical considerations" to get the information they seek.'

'If I'm not there, it might amount to that.' He said he would make enquiries to find out how it had happened.

Bing called back a few days later to say that the Home Office had not made a formal complaint against me. They had simply sent the details of my prescriptions to the GMC when requested. Bing had refused to do that last time, even when asked.

I realised that this might be important. Bing was confirming in a roundabout way that no complaint about me had gone from the Home Office. One of his underlings, acting on his own initiative and behind Bing's back, had sent information to the GMC.

A few days later I attended the delayed legal conference on behalf of Dr Taylor, which the lawyers had managed to organise properly this time. Of course I could not tell them, and did not wish to, that I myself was about to be in the dock.

Counsel started by asking me directly: 'Dr Dally, we should very much like your advice as to how, *without tackling the medical establishment head-on,* we can best defend Dr Taylor.'

I was glad not to be using lawyers who were so terrified of offending the medical establishment.

Next day was the conference with Christopher Sumner, whom I came to like and admire. Also present were John Calderan, Dr John Wall and several other lawyers. I felt how absurd it was that all these busy people should have to spend so much time on vendettas in the medical profession.

At first they were concerned mostly with small details such as why hadn't I written to Khalid's GP. The lawyers seemed to think everything would be gone through in a routine fashion. But gradually the emphasis changed. The lawyers said the charges were remarkable for their 'vagueness, innuendoes and malevolence', and started talking about challenging them. Since we knew that the Preliminary Proceedings Committee, before which the case would go first, was simply a rubber-stamping operation, the lawyers considered (but ultimately rejected) the idea of refusing to explain anything at this point and letting it go straight through to the full hearing. That way the GMC would have no idea what we were going to do.

Finally it was decided to write to the GMC saying that we could not help them unless they were more specific, and to ask them to confirm that the Home Office had made no formal complaint but had acted at the request of the GMC itself. It was also decided that the lawyers would visit Khalid in jail.

Afterwards John Calderan drove me home. He seemed to be in good spirits. I felt pleased, too, and as we arrived outside my house I thanked him.

'Ann, you can thank me when I've successfully prosecuted every member of the GMC for conspiracy!'

A few days later I went as an 'expert witness' to Dr Taylor's Home Office tribunal. It was held in the large room in Church House, Westminster, in which the House of Lords sat during the Second World War. The tribunal consisted of five men in late middle age whose names were displayed on notices in front of them, obscured by papers and glasses of water.

I was questioned for nearly two hours. Both defence and prosecuting counsel asked many questions about the Guidelines and the committee that prepared them. I could see that they were fascinated. The chairman also asked a lot about the Guidelines. I was able to describe some of the skulduggery that had gone on. A member of the committee said: 'I can understand the effect on an idealistic doctor of a first experience with a scientific committee.'

There was also much questioning about the expertise of the Committee that had produced the Guidelines. I insisted that many of its members knew little about treating addicts. Prosecuting counsel tried to show that this was false. I stuck to my guns. I mentioned some members who I did not think knew much about treating addicts, and counsel seemed shocked. He said: 'But those people sit on the Advisory Council on the Misuse of Drugs!'

'Yes,' I answered, 'but that means only that they probably know something about *addiction*. They don't necessarily know much about treating addicts.'

When I told Bing what we had decided at my legal conference, he said: 'If you throw googlies at the GMC like that, they'll take weeks to answer.'

He was wrong: they answered by return of post. The package also contained Khalid's statement which, to my surprise, was hostile to me. But I could see that the statement had been constructed from answers to leading questions which put the way I treated him in the worst possible light. For example, it said that I didn't do any blood tests. Khalid would never have thought of that himself.

Later, in the witness box, he refused to confirm much of the statement, admitting that it was full of lies and motivated by anger. Since I had never quarrelled with Khalid I could not understand how he had been cajoled into signing the document.

There was a further hostile statement from his wife, and also one from another former patient, Cathy, an unpleasant and dishonest young addict whom I had regretted taking on.

I wondered what had made Khalid turn nasty. Perhaps someone had told him they could alter the charges against him if he testified against me. I knew this would make him say anything.

John Calderan rang the following morning. He wanted me to

telephone everyone I could think of who might be willing to appear as an expert witness on my behalf. I felt reluctant to do this. Many people hold definite views but are unwilling to state them in public, especially if they are minority views. But next morning I started making phone calls.

My first was to Dr James Willis, Regional Director for Drug Dependency Services for Merseyside and someone who saw the problem in much the same way as I did. He had written to the *British Medical Journal* to defend the 'liberal' point of view at the time of my first case. Sadly, Dr Willis had been injured in a train crash the previous week and was likely to be in hospital for some time. He would not be returning to his job.

After this bad start, everything went amazingly well. I got on to a network of well-informed people who were appalled at the establishment stranglehold in drug dependency and seemed pleased to have the opportunity to say so to the GMC.

Dr John Marks in particular was extremely helpful. He had replaced Dr Willis in a powerful position on Merseyside and was a known advocate of more liberal prescribing and humane attitudes. He gave me introductions to a number of consultants in Edinburgh who were angry at how the drug dependency establishment, despite the warnings of local doctors, refused to prescribe for addicts or allow them syringes. This had resulted in a growing epidemic of Aids.

Aids was becoming a problem. Many people, including many doctors, still believed it to be a disease of homosexual men and something that could be ignored. But it was now spreading among heterosexuals through drug users who used other addicts' syringes, caught the HIV virus from these, and then passed it on either by the same route or sexually. A far-sighted doctor had recognised what was happening in Edinburgh, while the official policy, implemented chiefly by doctors and police, was to prevent addicts from obtaining clean syringes. This doctor warned that unless the policies changed there and then, there would be a terrible epidemic of Aids in Edinburgh which would gradually spread over the country. The authorities took no notice. The police and the doctors continued as before. The epidemic was now in evidence, just as the doctor had predicted, and threatening the whole country.

As a result of all this, I noted a good deal of hostility among more enlightened doctors towards the drug dependency 'mafia'. I found experienced and eminent doctors who were willing to come as witnesses to defend me. Some saw it as an opportunity to explain the situation to the GMC and perhaps other doctors and the press. I was encouraged that so many were on my side.

The only exception was a psychiatrist who started by sounding eager, but who, as we talked, seemed to express anxiety that I might be asking him to step out of line. In the end he suggested the names of several doctors prominent in the drug dependency establishment! But he did make one good point. 'It's unfortunate, but doctors have a tendency to hound a colleague who is in trouble.'

Meanwhile I had heard more about Khalid through Doug, his brother-in-law, who was also a patient of mine. He had discovered that Khalid had made his vituperative statement because he had been charged with selling heroin and was due to be tried at the Crown Court. 'His solicitor told him that his only hope for leniency was to blame the doctor.'

The lawyers were clearly uncertain how to deal with the latest letter from the GMC. Christopher Sumner said: 'I've written a draft letter but I've had difficulty doing it calmly because I feel so disgusted at the venomous attitude of the GMC communication. It's no more specific than the first letter. They've simply thrown a whole lot more material at us which they should have provided in the first place.'

John Wall confirmed Sumner's feeling: 'I've never known the GMC initiate a case with such a head of steam.'

We all agreed that Christopher's draft letter was clever and witty, but we had doubts about whether it would be useful. 'Do you think it smacks of lawyers' games?' asked Christopher.

The other lawyers thought it did.

'I wrote it late at night,' admitted Christopher.

A lot of ideas were tried out, some completely contradictory. I found this fascinating. Trying to study the case in a detached way was something I practised to help me get through this nightmare.

Working on the case pushed me to the edge of exhaustion. Had I been able to concentrate on it totally it would have been easier, but I was seeing patients all day long. I compared myself with Wendy Savage, the obstetrician who had recently been on trial because her 'unorthodox' views about childbirth had attracted the hostility of powerful colleagues. Since my original dispute with the GMC she had become famous: a big case had attracted much publicity in the papers. In the end she was found not guilty and completely vindicated.

Wendy became a friend and gave me thoughtful and imaginative help with my defence. Perceptive journalists were quick to point out the similarities in our cases. We were, for instance, both women doctors who were attacked by rigid, powerful branches of the medical profession because we did not agree with the standard way of managing patients. We were both outspoken and not easily intimidated.

In one way Wendy had had an easier time than I; she was suspended from her hospital job and so was able to work full-time on her case while her opponents were trying to gather evidence of her supposed misdeeds. Exhaustion made me particularly sensitive to any hint of criticism. I worked almost unceasingly for two days to produce the list of witnesses John had asked for, but when I gave him the list he said: 'Oh, Ann, you swamp me.'

I found this deflating. John had moments of insensitivity, particularly when he was anxious, uncertain or under pressure, but he did try to repair any damage he had done. Realising he had been tactless, he said he hadn't meant it. 'I'm going to read it all at the weekend, and with great interest.'

He also said that they had decided they needed a leader, a QC. 'I'd like to have Neil Taylor and so would Christopher. Like Christopher, he has a strong sense of justice and isn't afraid to speak out.'

Neil, a leading counsel and part-time High Court judge, was a good friend of John. I had met him perhaps half a dozen times, and I was pleased at the idea of his working on the case.

Next day the papers were full of stories about a woman being prosecuted in California for taking drugs during pregnancy. Life for drug users was becoming harsher. They were increasingly being used as scapegoats by hostile people, including doctors.

On the morning of the Preliminary Proceedings Committee I slept until 3 a.m., then dozed until 6.30. I knew that the proceedings were merely a formality, but I still felt queasy. It was unnerving to think of all those committee-doctors nodding their heads and agreeing that I should go for trial.

One of my friends in the GMC told me there had been a row there about the tendency of the Preliminary Proceedings Committee to rubber-stamp everything. 'The result is that a lot of silly cases have been coming up for full trial,' he said.

That same day, two patients whom I had discharged earlier in the year in my attempts to reduce my addict practice returned in a distressed state. One was covered with abscesses from injecting black-market heroin. She hadn't injected when she was under me. I knew she was HIV-positive, and now she was working as a prostitute.

I was distressed to see them both in that state. There was nowhere they could go for help: no one seemed to care about the Aids.

On 10 October the GMC's letter arrived by recorded delivery. As expected, the Preliminary Proceedings Committee had decided that the case should go forward for full trial in the session beginning 17 November. I was due to lecture in America in the weeks before this date; 17 November was one day after my planned return.

The immediate problem was to get the case postponed so that I could go to America. I felt that this was an important part of my struggle to keep my head high. If I started crawling to the GMC, I was lost. Only later did I realise that it is a mistake to ask them for anything.

John Calderan telephoned during the weekend. He was reassuring, and said: 'I'm worried not at all about offending the GMC. The more they are provoked into silly pomposity the better for the appeal.' He seemed to assume that the GMC had already made up their minds about my case.

On 17 October, the *New Statesman* published a long article by Tim Malyon, who had come to see me a couple of weeks before to discuss the drug situation in Britain. The article attacked the government's policies about drugs, quoting Bing Spear about the part played in the present problem by the clinic consultants. This was the first time I had seen the specific activities of the drug dependency establishment described in print.

There seemed to be more common sense from the general public on the subject of drugs, and I felt that our pressure was beginning to have some effect. In the London *Standard*, a letter pointed out that doctors used to provide drugs to long-term addicts and there was no trouble, so why couldn't they do that again? The following week the *Mail on Sunday* printed a letter saying much the same.

The charges against me arrived from the GMC solicitors. The document was a photocopy, with the words 'as a result of a complaint' crossed out.

Our request to the GMC for postponement was turned down straight away. The letter contained a gratuitous sneer suggesting that nothing I might do in America could be of importance. My immediate reaction was of shock, chiefly at the letter's unpleasant tone. Even though I knew that this was the standard mode of GMC communication, it never failed to upset me.

I felt I couldn't go to America now, but John Calderan urged me to go for a shorter period. If I went for two weeks only I could fulfil my commitments. 'You need a change,' he said. 'Even if you don't enjoy it, you'll feel better afterwards. There's a lot of lawyers' work to do now which we don't need you for. We can get on with it while you're away and we can start again when you return.'

It seemed sensible and I agreed.

John also said: 'We've got to the stage when some publicity would be a good thing. The one thing those so-and-sos don't like is that. I'm willing to talk to journalists on your behalf.'

John was right. Things did look different from the other side of the Atlantic. But of course I thought about the case constantly. Nick Davies, a journalist on the *Observer*, rang on the second morning to tell me he had seen Khalid in Pentonville prison. Khalid told him that, contrary to what the prosecution had implied, he had not agreed to give evidence against me and he didn't want to. He hadn't even answered the GMC letter asking him to.

Khalid didn't know how the GMC got on to him: he was certain that no one had complained about my treatment. But the GMC wrote him a letter, and then a man called at Khalid's house saying that he came from the GMC. He was very charming and said he had heard that I had discharged Khalid without making any arrangements for his further treatment and that he was very concerned about this. He persuaded Khalid to make the statement against me, which he wrote and Khalid signed.

After that, Khalid heard nothing for many weeks. Then he received a letter saying that there would be a hearing against me and asking him to give evidence. Khalid didn't answer the letter. He didn't want to give evidence because he feared the effect it would have on the many addicts who might lose their doctor; they would take it out on him, he thought. On the other hand, his wife was threatening to leave and take the children if he didn't. She was still angry because I had discharged him.

After this call I felt light-headed: not exactly anxious, not exactly pleased, but something of both, for I realised that the situation was absurd. I also realised that the information about the way I had discharged Khalid must have come from the Home Office.

Next day my friend Arnold Trebach rang from Washington. He was upset to hear what was going on and wanted to write a column about my case for Louis Blom-Cooper at the *Guardian*, who had asked him to write on the subject of drugs. He wanted to concentrate on the fact that I was being tried for being a dissenter. I was challenging authority in the best British tradition, and as a result, in the worst British tradition, I was being persecuted for it by the establishment.

Arnold also asked me to become a member of the Organising Committee for the First World Congress of Drug Policy Reformers, to be held in London in July 1987. He said he would have asked me in any case but my lawyers might be able to use this as evidence of my international status. I accepted, though I didn't think it would impress the GMC.

In addition to giving my lectures as arranged, I wrote a long letter to my friend Ian Munro, editor of the *Lancet*, telling him what had happened. I knew I would not have much time for writing letters once I was back in England.

It was a rush from the moment I reached home. As I came through the front door, John was on the line with a lot of information, including the fact that the BBC wanted to devote a whole *Panorama* programme to the issues surrounding my case. John Ware, the producer, came round to see me the next day and I spent more than three hours with him in spite of my fatigue and jet-lag. John Calderan clearly thought that this programme was important and I was determined to do my best to cooperate. But I also had to see my patients, which was always particularly exhausting just after a holiday.

Two days after my return, John told me: 'The latest round of shots has arrived from the GMC.'

It consisted of statements from policemen, mostly saying that certain of my patients were 'known to the police'. 'So what?' asked John.

There were also notes based on Home Office interviews and an extraordinary statement by a Mrs S., the wife of a public figure and the mother of a former patient of mine. Her statement was full of hearsay; it could hardly have been anything else since she had never met me.

In her statement Mrs S. said her son had told her he had to pay me £50 every time he saw me. Alan had told this lie presumably to get money out of her. Now it would be used by the GMC in an attempt to show that that was what I charged an addict for a consultation. I found it extraordinary that she was prepared to state this as though it were a fact and that the GMC lawyers had accepted it. John said: 'It shows that they're pretty desperate to find material to use against you and that they're short of hard evidence.'

At the same time as contacting possible witnesses for the case,

I was now having to think of people who would agree to be inter-viewed for *Panorama*. One of my lawyers said it might be helpful for witnesses to appear on the programme, as they could say things they couldn't otherwise say and could then be questioned in court about them. Others disagreed.

One difficulty was that neither the lawyers nor the television people seemed sure what they wanted. Eventually the lawyers decided they wanted patients who had done well in coming off drugs, reducing dosage or making stable lives for themselves. The *Panorama* team wanted people who had been saved from crime by me. An immense amount of discussion seemed to go into the minutiae of each. Both groups were interested in the patients who had died after being refused drugs because of official policies.

One ex-patient I wrote to was Bill Nelles, who had come off drugs entirely. Although he finished his treatment in the Bethlem Hospital he attributed his 'cure' almost entirely to me. He was now the drug liaison officer of the Terence Higgins Trust (for the victims of Aids). Like all the addict patients with whom I discussed the case, he was anxious to help. Even those who were drug-free and no longer my patients – and so had nothing to gain – expressed their willingness.

On Sunday evening I telephoned Patrick Monahan, the surgeon who had been so appalled at the way he was treated by drug dependency doctors when he tried to get help for his relative that he now devoted his spare time to helping addicts. He was willing to be interviewed, and John Calderan said that he would see him personally rather than sending his articled clerk.

This was the kind of gesture that endeared me to John. He told me he was doing most of the work himself because he wanted to. Yet he had many assistants to whom he could have delegated it.

The telephone rang as soon as I put it down. It was John Ware calling from Merseyside, where they were filming for *Panorama*, con-centrating on the connection between crime and drugs. He had learned that lots of the young people who were smoking and snorting heroin were now beginning to inject it, and this was becoming a problem. I was particularly interested because so many people had told me that my 'injectors' were out of the ordinary. I always felt that a proportion of those smoking heroin ('chasing the dragon') would begin to inject as their habit increased. A heavy habit is expensive, and injecting achieves the greatest effect for the money. People also become hooked on the 'buzz' they get from injecting. This was exactly what John Ware said had happened. Yet most of the drug dependency establishment refused to consider the idea. It was contrary to the particular myths they wished to project.

Efforts by Emma, Nick Davies and others seemed to be having some success in alerting the media, or at least the serious press. Oliver Gillie of the *Independent* was showing a special interest and had arranged to come to lunch.

John Calderan seemed to be working full-time on the case: he had been seeing both patients and doctors almost continuously all week.

One patient, Steve, lived in the same area of North London as Khalid. Since becoming 'stable' under my care he had started his own wholesale fruit business and had become quite prosperous. He always brought me presents of fruit as well as paying his fees promptly. He told me that Khalid was out of jail and an in-patient in David Marjot's unit at St Bernard's, Southall. Steve asked him why he had made the statement against me. Khalid replied that the man, who said he came from the GMC, had persuaded him.

I came to understand how difficult it was to bring evidence to court. We all believed that Khalid had said what Steve described, but could we use it? It seemed unlikely.

On 19 November we had our first legal conference with Neil Taylor QC, who was to be my senior counsel. It was held in the late afternoon, after the courts had risen, at Neil's chambers.

Neil rose from his desk as we entered and greeted me as an old friend. He is a hugely tall man, about six foot six, with enormous hands. Carolyn Hay, John's articled clerk, took the notes.

Neil started by pointing out that the GMC were laying the complaint themselves and then judging it. He said: 'I question the legality of that. The information on which the case is based came from the Home Office. Yet if the case had gone before a tribunal, they could have stopped Ann from prescribing. So why did it not go before a tribunal? I question the motives of those in the Home Office who drew the case to their attention. It's obvious that this is a political trial.'

When the question of the *Panorama* programme arose, Neil expressed doubts about it. He thought it could damage me, and suggested that we ask them not to broadcast until the case was finished. I became rather nervous at this because the programme had been approved by the lawyers (including Neil) in my absence and so I had encouraged it. But Neil was adamant.

Christopher Sumner said: 'There's so much at stake anyway. The GMC clearly intends to strike Ann off the register if it can, so a case could be made for playing for high stakes.'

Then Neil leaned towards me and asked: 'How would you feel if you were struck off the register because of *Panorama*?'

I was feeling gloomy but I spoke out. 'If the situation is so bad and I am to be struck off the Medical Register, I would feel terrible if I had also been party to muzzling *Panorama*. Now there's a chance of presenting the true picture. I would never forgive myself if I spoiled it. If I was struck off it would be painful but it wouldn't be the end of my world. I could rebuild my life.'

John Wall backed me up. 'It's not like a quiet GP from a country town who's in trouble with the GMC and takes part in a programme before the hearing. Ann is used to the media. She knows what she's doing and what she should not do.'

In the end they agreed I should play as small a part as possible and certainly not allow the BBC to film me treating patients, which I knew was what they hoped to do. 'Be very careful,' Neil said.

Finally Neil dropped a bombshell. He asked me to prepare short case histories of all patients mentioned in the lists of prescription details, nearly two hundred of them. This was a huge task. I could have cried at the thought of so much detailed work. I felt I was nearing breaking point. All the same, I knew it was a good idea. If we could show what had happened to the addicts, we would probably be able to show that most of them did well. Neil also implied that he thought I was going to be struck off the register. He said he was very unhappy about the three cases specifically worked on by the GMC.

At the end of it all I was bearing up surprisingly well: adrenalin seemed to counteract fatigue.

That evening I missed a meeting of the Drug Discussion Group, a collection of professional people, doctors, lawyers and journalists, who met at my home. David Marjot was among those who came, and he told the group an extraordinary story. A private detective had telephoned him at his clinic and said he was working for the GMC. He wanted the names of all David's clinic patients so that he could check whether any of my patients were 'double-scripting', getting double supplies of drugs. Presumably he was going round all the clinics. Unfortunately Marjot was so enraged that he told him to go to hell and didn't keep his telephone number.

John Calderan had decided that the lawyers needed a doctor to sit with them and comment on the scientific evidence. He suggested John Harman, a friend who had taught me clinical medicine at St Thomas's. He had played a vital part in defending Dr Bodkin Adams on a murder charge, and had one of the best brains I knew for exposing medical guff. I thought it would be a good idea, if the overture was successful, to get him then to comment on the Guidelines and on the various establishment papers which the prosecuting solicitors had sent. He seemed pleased to be asked.

One weekend we stayed in London to go to John Calderan's party celebrating his recent marriage. During the party John said, 'We aren't going to talk shop,' and then proceeded to do so. He was interested in the story about the private detective telephoning Marjot's clinic. It seemed to tie up with the mysterious man who called on Khalid at his home claiming to be from the GMC. 'If it could be *proved* that the GMC pays private detectives to look for scandal on doctors they are persecuting, *that* would be a scandal!' he said. 'But of course the difficulty is turning rumour into fact. All the same, in the witness box Marjot will be able to describe what happened.

John also told me how much Carolyn, his articled clerk, was enjoying the case. I could understand that, and said so. John seemed pleased. 'That shows you have the right attitude. Having fun over a case is an important part in winning it, and if the defendant can experience this too, it's a very good sign. In your profession you have anaesthetics. We don't. You can enjoy it only if you can bear the pain.'

The most upsetting thing that happened that week didn't concern me directly. A patient, Gillian, telephoned in distress. She was among my nicest addict patients, one of my witnesses and due to appear on *Panorama*. She had a daughter, Tanya, just fourteen, who had written a powerful piece for me on what it was like to be the daughter of a drug addict.

The previous day, Tanya hadn't arrived home from school. Gillian was frantic. Later in the evening there was a knock on the door from two social workers and two policemen. They informed her that, because Gillian was an addict, they thought Tanya was in 'moral danger' and that they had moved her to a 'house of safety'. One social worker demanded Tanya's clothes and started to walk up the stairs. Gillian refused to let her pass, saying that her husband would bring any clothes they wanted. I knew this was typical of the way officialdom treated many drug addicts.

*

I was becoming disoriented. For instance, one morning I woke up and dressed, thinking it was 7.20. I must have identified the hands of the clock incorrectly: it was actually 3.30.

John Calderan told me he had seen Bing Spear and got a lot of information out of him. Bing didn't want to give evidence because of his divided loyalties, but he was keen to help with statistics and other information. I knew that his real strength lay in those.

Bing suggested that John contact Dr Cindy Fazey, a sociologist and criminologist from Liverpool. Her name was on the list of possible witnesses that I had made two months before. By coincidence, John Ware had just told me of a recent piece of research by Cindy which showed that a methadone maintenance clinic had saved a hundred million pounds from the black market and that the Liverpool police were delighted. Cindy agreed to give evidence.

On 29 November the *Lancet* carried an article suggesting that heroin should be legalised. It was reported on the morning radio news. I felt that the tide was beginning to turn at last.

On 4 December the House of Lords upheld the Reading magistrates in the case of an addict's baby who was taken into care on the grounds that drug abuse in pregnancy equals child abuse and child abuse is a reason for removing a child from the care of its parents. This seemed to me a rationalisation of prejudice which would allow social workers to grab children if they felt so inclined. Already ugly stories were circulating about social workers who took children from their parents if they could find any excuse. I felt that the decision would encourage pregnant addicts to conceal their addiction from their doctors.

My own patients were becoming anxious about my situation and their concern compounded mine. I wondered what would happen to them and their children if things went badly for me.

Arnold Trebach's article had appeared in the *Guardian* on 5 December, opening with the forthright statement: 'They're after Dr Ann Dally again.' Ever since, people had been writing and telephoning to commiserate. Some were friends and some unknown to me. A lot of people were aware of the deceit put out by the drug dependency establishment.

Less gratifying was a telephone call from John Calderan. The GMC had heard about the *Panorama* programme and were seeking an injunction to stop it being broadcast. John said: 'There's to be a screening for the benefit of certain members of the GMC. This will be followed by a case in the High Court in which they are seeking the injunction. I've been invited to attend but have declined on the grounds that it has nothing to do with us and we are indifferent to the outcome. This is the equivalent of "No comment". If I went along, I would be bound to make an enemy on one side or the other.' I agreed. He laughed and added: 'The GMC are trying to pretend that they are *real* judges!'

My solicitors wrote to all the people who had given references about my character last time. They sent each a copy of their previous testimonial and asked them either to initial the copy to indicate that it still stood or to write another letter. As a result, even more people rang me to commiserate. George Mikes said: 'The only change I've made in my letter was to change "I have known her for twenty-six years" to "I have known her for twenty-nine years".'

The GMC backed down in their efforts to obtain a High Court injunction against *Panorama*. After seeing the programme their lawyers apparently told them their case was slender. John said the programme might be important in the case because even if the GMC had closed minds, their wives might see it and say, 'Why the hell are you prosecuting that woman?'

John told me that my lawyers were going to insist on getting answers to two particular questions. First, what were the charges? So far we had not been able to find out. The GMC had sent huge schedules of prescriptions without saying what they thought was wrong with them. It was as though they had given us the telephone book and said that the information required is in there. The second question was, 'Who is complaining?' This went to the heart of the witch hunt.

John said that the case for the prosecution was likely to last all day Tuesday.

Carmel Fitzsimons of the *Observer* telephoned. She was interested in the case and couldn't think why they had not got hold of the story before. I pointed out that many journalists still believed the official line on drugs and indeed had vested interests in so doing. I happened to know that some members of the editorial staff of the *Observer* were hardliners and particularly closed to new ideas. They knew about the story but had chosen to ignore it.

Later that evening a young barrister I knew told me that almost all the young barristers, who spent much of their time defending addicts on drug charges, were in favour of me. This was reassuring.

I felt good and a little strange. I was aware of my predicament and had had extraordinarily little sleep during the past weeks, no more than three or four hours a night. Yet I didn't feel tired; indeed, I had more energy than normal. I found myself running up the stairs two at a time, which normally I seldom do.

Anne Lingham, my secretary, seemed to show more anxiety than I did. She was waking 'abominably early', thinking about the case. So, on his own admission, was John Calderan. Everyone was tensing up, but my family were wonderful in their attempts to free me of as much responsibility as possible so that I could concentrate on the case.

The weekend before the case was due to begin, I slept for one and a half hours on Saturday afternoon. At 9.30 p.m. I was overcome with fatigue and slept for six hours, one of the longest sleeps I had had since the ordeal began. When I woke on the Sunday, I did not feel anxious but was conscious of the kind of tension that an athlete or performer must feel. I was in good heart and mind for the struggle.

That day I learned several interesting things. First, Dr Connell, the drug dependency consultant and powerful committee man, had refused permission for *Panorama* to use any part of the interview it had recorded with him. I also learned that the 'private detective' everyone had been searching for was a retired Drugs Squad 'chemist sergeant'. His job had been to go round chemists' shops checking prescriptions. He now did private work, and was sometimes hired by Waterhouse, the GMC solicitors. This certainly fitted both the story about the telephone call to Marjot's clinic and the one about the man who called on Khalid saying he was from the GMC. I telephoned John to pass on the information. He didn't seem to mind being rung on a Sunday. 'These things are all pieces of a jigsaw puzzle.' He also said that Connell would have no legal right over the film of the interview he made. 'It would be like saying: "I withdraw my statement." '

On the day of the hearing I woke at 2.30 a.m. and felt a *frisson* of apprehension, but no more than that. Then I returned to my current mood of concern and concentration, as before an important examination. I slept again until 6 a.m. unusually late for me, and was soon drinking coffee and writing my diary before the day began.

I went out at 7 a.m. to buy newspapers. The *Independent* contained its first article on my case. I found it simplistic and disappointing, without hint of wider issues. It referred to the need for addicts to lead a 'clean and sober life'. To me this suggested undertones of the puritanism that had done so much to bring about the present deplorable state of affairs. The article also indicated that I had said that the case brought against me was at least half due to the desire of the establishment to 'get' me. I was rather appalled by this. Although it was what I believed, I hadn't said as much to the media. Later I discovered who had. However, the article could have been far worse, and at least it wasn't an attack.

I had patients until about 11.30. In a way it was a burden to have to keep seeing them, but it also gave me something to do during the anxious waiting hours. One of the addict patients, Kevin, brought his small daughter Louise and a present of a box of wine glasses. 'These are for the celebration after it's all over,' he said.

My work was made difficult by almost constant interruptions from journalists. Some knew nothing about the case or about drug problems. They had simply been told to ring up and get the story. It was frustrating to try to explain the situation in two minutes to someone who didn't know what heroin was and had never heard of the GMC.

The lawyers were to come to my house at 12.30 for a conference before the start of the case. At twelve John Calderan rang to say that the case had been postponed until ten the next morning. Nevertheless, he said, we would hold our conference just the same. The delay might be a good thing because it gave us more time to prepare. As usual John was trying to take advantage of setbacks. He seemed nervous about the remark in the *Independent* that the establishment was out to get me, but he was quite cheerful about this too. 'After all, that is our defence!' He advised me not to speak to the press, at least until we knew what counsel thought.

The lawyers and their team arrived punctually, bringing huge suitcases and bags full of documents. We all sat down in the living room, which was comfortable but lacked tables for papers. This didn't seem to worry them. We worked steadily until 4.45 p.m., apart from a break of about forty minutes for lunch.

It emerged that only now were the GMC saying which of my prescriptions they were questioning. The lawyers had been pressing for the information for three months.

The work consisted largely of going through the prosecution statements and my answering detailed questions. I didn't do well with some of them, and Neil was stern with me. I was shaken to discover how easily my words could be twisted but I learned a lesson from it. At the end of the afternoon Neil became softer and said: 'You mustn't be depressed, because we have been dealing only with the worst bits. There was no need to discuss the good bits with you.'

One other thing Neil said to me during our discussion I shall always remember. 'Leave the indignation to me.'

Shortly before 6 p.m. John Ware of *Panorama* telephoned. I had been wondering why he had not been in touch for so long and feared that it might be because of changes he had been induced to make in the forthcoming programme. I decided I was probably right. It was clear to me that, far from the GMC 'backing down', as Ware had said, it was really the other way round. The BBC had made a deal with the GMC and had agreed to do as they wished. I found this worse than the cuts themselves. Apparently at Connell's request, they had omitted the interview with him and weren't even going to mention that they had been gagged. I was disappointed and appalled. Realising this, Ware said: 'All the same, I think you'll be pleased with the programme. It says some very important things that will help your case.'

I had planned to have dinner with my family and with Carmel Fitzsimons, who had written a piece in the *Observer* the previous Sunday. Wendy Savage joined us. At 9.30 p.m. we all watched *Panorama*. It was a pathetic watering-down of the grand programme that had been conceived, discussed, and made. Not only was Connell absent but so was all mention or sight of addicts who lead normal lives, including the film of my patients which John Ware had been so pleased with. They had been cut as part of the deal with the GMC. The programme also omitted most of the interview with me, though I was relieved about that. Apart from splendid appearances by Cindy Fazey and John Marks, both of whom were coming to give evidence for me, the programme was the usual dreary footage of housing estates and crime on Merseyside and the methadone bus in Amsterdam, all of which I had seen several times. We all agreed that if we had not had a personal interest in the programme, we would have switched off early. For me the worst part was the concealment of the pressures under which the programme had been altered.

As she left, Wendy told me that her solicitor had advised her before her hearing, 'Think before you speak.' I made a resolution to remember this when I gave my evidence.

Chapter 12

The Second Hearing

The next day I got up at 5 a.m. John Calderan arrived at about eight-fifteen and worked on papers while I saw a patient. Soon after nine Carolyn Hay arrived and then my daughter Jane, who had caught the 6 a.m. train from Leeds.

John, Carolyn and I took Jane's taxi for our short journey to the GMC. Photographers were waiting for me at the door. 'Smile!' said John.

The room set aside for the defence seemed slightly better than the bare cell I remembered. It even had a carpet and prints on the walls. In the bay window stood an ugly vase of artificial flowers, mauve and dirty green. But we didn't spend much time there. John and I waited alone for a few minutes before being called into the hearing room.

The chairman of the committee, Professor Duthie, looked more human than I had come to expect. Someone had described him as 'a straight up and down surgeon'. He showed some sense of humour and his manner suggested that he was trying to be fair.

The public galleries were packed. The commissionaires had to open up the second gallery, though, like last time, not until the first was overflowing.

Timothy Preston QC, the same prosecuting counsel as before, delivered the opening speech for the prosecution. Predictably, he summarised his review of my prescribing by using cumulative statistics – what I had come to call 'shock-horror' figures. During a certain period I had apparently prescribed 99,000 ampoules of methadone, 403 litres of linctus, 21,000 tablets of methadone. It sounded horrendous until one worked out the length of time and the number of patients, when it wasn't very much. But reporters rushed out to file stories, doubtless having done the arithmetic to show the street value of what I had prescribed. This, presumably, was the intention of the GMC.

Preston went on to say that he hoped the case would be confined to the charges and would not become 'political', though judging by the recent flurry of activity in the media, he feared that this was unlikely.

The first part of the charge was irresponsible treatment, which Preston defined as: taking on so many cases that I could not treat them properly; prescribing privately for fees to some patients who could not be expected to pay without selling some of the drugs; prescribing successively large amounts on single prescriptions; accepting addicts who lived far away and from areas where there were adequate NHS facilities; and failing to reduce the doses, thus not following the Guidelines. It was to be the centrepiece of his argument that I had not conformed to that document.

In addition Preston mentioned the case of 'Mr A.' This was the name by which Khalid was to be known. Mr A. alleged that I had given him no examination and no adequate monitoring, and that I had discharged him without making proper arrangements for his future.

John Gerrard was the first witness. A small, bearded Home Office Drugs Inspector, he had taken notes at both relevant Home Office interviews with me. He read out his notes of the interview by Lawson in April 1984.

In questioning Gerrard's notes, Neil began to show his strength. Standing on one leg and holding the other ankle, he looked with his immense height rather like a huge stork. He questioned on and on in a mild, bumbling manner. Warned against naming patients, he asked someone to kick him if he did so, which shortly afterwards he did. As a result of this it was decided that all parts of the proceedings concerned with patients would be held in camera, to protect the patients.

With great skill Neil proceeded to use Gerrard to make lots of points that had nothing to do with him. He got him to confirm that the interview had been conducted 'in a friendly manner'; that I was on extremely friendly terms with Spear, the Chief Inspector of Drugs at the Home Office; that the Home Office had no complaint about me; that I disapproved of the type of contract I was accused of not making with patients; that my actions had enabled many patients who had not been helped by the clinics to lead normal lives with their families.

Next came McIntosh, the inspector whom I suspected of starting the trouble. He was very much against me, but Neil managed to get him to smile over one of his favourite tricks, the use of cumulative shock-horror statistics. He agreed that one had to reduce them to 'reality', which was that they represented a modest dose for each of a number of patients. There were further smiles when Neil talked about Procrustes, the robber who made everybody fit his bed, and compared this with current clinic policies. And once again he got the prosecution's witness to make numerous statements favourable to the defence. McIntosh admitted that only about 40 per cent of long-term treatment was carried out in clinics and that clinic patients also sometimes sold their drugs. He knew nothing of the feelings of the parents of addicts. He admitted that his office had always accepted that 'Dr Dally was genuinely motivated in taking on addict patients'. He tried to qualify this but was not very successful.

At the end of the afternoon we learned that the committee could not sit on Friday or, after that, for a further seven weeks – 26 January. So after the next day's hearing, the case would have to be deferred until then. I found this amazing: we had previously asked the GMC to have it deferred until January, but they had refused on the grounds that the case was so urgent. Arnold Trebach, one of my witnesses, was already in the air from Washington. Had we had this information even one day earlier, we could have prevented him from setting out. I was again struck by the way in which the GMC seemed to like inconveniencing those who had to deal with them. The lawyers took it in good part, saying that you could not expect consideration from a body like that.

Next morning the press reports of the case were disappointing, even in the *Independent*. One report, in *Today*, said that psychiatrist Ann Dally sold £30 prescriptions for heroin substitutes . . . without ever using the word 'alleged'. There wasn't a single reasoned or informative account.

Neil Taylor was upset by these reports. 'The fact that you have had to endure them,' he told me, 'makes me all the more determined to win the case and show how things really are.'

The next morning, Thursday, Arnold Trebach arrived at our house straight from the airport. Christopher and John followed soon afterwards. I gave them Peter's consulting room and saw a few patients myself in my own room until it was time to go to the GMC.

The proceedings started again at 9.30 a.m. with a discussion between Neil and Preston. The name of Trebach was mentioned. Since he had now arrived from America the lawyers were thinking of interposing his evidence on Thursday afternoon, so that he would not have to come over again in January. Preston referred to him, sarcastically, as 'the prominent *Guardian* writer'.

Preston began by completing his opening statement, which had been delayed because there was still doubt about whether Khalid was coming. Then Khalid himself appeared, haggard and scruffy. He gave his evidence in public but Neil asked that the cross-examination be in camera because of the intimate details that would come out, and because of the danger of Khalid's real name being mentioned.

While the committee were considering the question we were all banished. Carolyn Hay and I agreed that we hated Preston's hectoring, bullying manner. I said I dreaded being cross-examined by him. Neil leaned over and said reassuringly: 'You aren't afraid of *him*, are you?'

One prominent point in Preston's argument was that Khalid had claimed that he never spent more than five to ten minutes with me. In fact Khalid said it averaged 'ten minutes give or take five minutes', which Preston instantly repeated as 'five to ten minutes'.

Khalid's evidence was mostly in my favour and contradicted much that was in his statement. He agreed that his first interview with me had lasted for about half an hour; that he had been living on the black market for two years before; that he had brought me presents; and that he had got into trouble with the police almost as soon as I discharged him. He admitted selling drugs but insisted that he had only sold to drug addicts, and that he knew they would inject what he sold.

After this evidence the chairman said that it hadn't been necessary to go into camera. The committee had already been hostile towards Neil: now they were more hostile than ever.

Khalid's wife gave evidence next. On a number of occasions she contradicted both herself and Khalid, but she seemed to say what the committee wanted to hear.

After her came Mrs S., the mother of my former patient Alan. My lawyers had warned me that the committee were likely to find her sympathetic 'because she'll remind them of their wives'. To me she appeared a battered-looking woman, an angry mother with a sour face, a disastrous son and great bitterness which she had clearly fixed on me. Nearly all her evidence was hearsay, to which Neil objected with some success.

Mrs S.'s evidence was muddled, and much of it differed from her statement. She said that, at a particular time, her son had been at death's door due to my treatment – but on the very date mentioned, she had written to me saying that she couldn't come to London to talk about him. She also maintained that Alan was the only one of her children involved in drugs, and that he had become so only in his adult life. But we had a newspaper cutting in which Alan had appeared in court with his sister, both charged with drug offences; and I had a record that he had told me of being expelled from school for using drugs. Neil suggested that she was motivated by vindictiveness. She replied in a loud, ringing voice: 'I do not feel vindictive. I just want justice to be done!'

The hatred in the face of that wreck of a woman was frightening, but I also felt sad for her. The memory of her twisted face haunted me during the coming weeks.

No one mentioned either then or later that her son had not been told that she was giving evidence against his former doctor. This was not difficult to guess, but it was only some time later that I confirmed the fact because he came to see me. He had talked to his mother the previous week but she had not mentioned the case. The GMC had clearly made no effort to get in touch with Alan.

When Neil started to cross-examine Mrs S. he naturally referred to my case notes about Alan. As he did so, one member of the committee objected that the patient's records could not be used without his permission. This really was Kafka-esque. The GMC had not contacted the patient and were accusing me on the hearsay of his mother. Yet they were refusing to allow me to defend myself by using his records on the grounds that he had not given permission.

Neil said he couldn't examine the witness without the records – how could I defend myself without them? The committee went into camera to discuss the use of case notes, and when they returned the chairman again announced that the notes could not be used without the permission of the patient. Neil said that if his client couldn't use the notes he would sit down. 'I call no further evidence or cross-examine anyone else. I shall take the remedy elsewhere. . . . If Dr Dally can't use her case notes, then injustice has been done.' Mrs S.'s evidence should be ruled out if it could not be cross-examined, he added.

The legal assessor said that Neil should wait for his final speech. Neil replied that the evidence should be ruled out now. The legal assessor said that it was not usually the committee's practice to rule out evidence in the middle of a case.

The committee were in camera again during the tea-break, which meant tea for the GMC. We, the defence, had to sit and stand in the tiny room for about an hour, with no refreshments. This was typical of the unfriendly atmosphere of the GMC.

After the break we all trooped back and Duthie announced that it had been decided to abide by the GMC guidelines and to refuse to allow a patient's notes to be used unless that patient had given consent. As Neil had pointed out, this ruling meant that I could not defend myself and he could not cross-examine adequately. At that particular moment it meant that he could not continue to cross-examine Mrs S., who had said so much against me that was directly contradicted in her son's case notes. Neil had only just begun the cross-examination and he never had the opportunity to continue it. At that moment the chairman announced that the session was at an end.

That evening I relaxed at home with my family. This was the first occasion for a long time that all my children had been together. John Calderan came round and so did Christopher Sumner, who was parking his car in our garage during the hearing. Philip went out with him and saw Tim Preston sitting in it. We all found it rather funny that this high and mighty prosecutor should end the day sitting in our garage. Christopher had told me that he wasn't really an unpleasant man, it was just his prosecuting manner.

When I arrived on the third day I felt more distressed than at any other time in the proceedings. Waiting in the defendants' room and in the council chamber, I felt as though I was disintegrating. Once the hearing started I felt better, even though this was to be the most unpleasant day so far.

We learned from the lawyers that the chairman had made a mess of his ruling about confidentiality in the use of case notes and had been told so by his solicitors. He wanted to reverse it, but Neil now wanted it to continue. Neil said he was only prepared to concede if they would quash the charges.

At the opening the chairman reaffirmed his ruling about confidentiality but changed it to include reasonable attempts to find the person. He asked Preston to continue, but Neil interrupted and made a speech rather like that of Mark Antony over the body of Caesar. He pointed out that the effect of the ruling was that I could not give evidence. I had a primary duty of confidentiality to my patients, and none of them, including those whose cases were being used against me, had given permission for their case notes to be used. 'In short, because of the confidence rule she is precluded from giving any evidence unless . . . she is able in fact to get [a patient's] consent – and may well not be able to, and if she does not that is the end of it, she cannot answer the charge. . . . '

Throughout Neil's long and rather magnificent speech, Dr Ashworth and the Reverend Smith, the lay member of the committee, were smirking and smiling.

Preston defended the chairman's decision, saying that Khalid had given permission. But everyone knew they were in a muddle. Neil asked for an adjournment so that application could be made for judicial review to consider the problem. He pointed out that if the case went on, the same situation would arise as had arisen on the previous day.

There followed long legal arguments. Unsurprisingly Preston resisted the idea of dropping the charges or adjourning the case for judicial review. Neil stood up and said that he reserved the right to object as from this stage.

At this point there was an adjournment while the committee withdrew in camera to discuss an important legal point, about whether the GMC is a court. While he was waiting for the gallery to reopen, a lawyer specialising in medical law told my son-in-law Dick that this was a very important point and that the committee 'should go away and think about it for a very long time'.

They didn't. In fifteen minutes they came back and the chairman announced that they would not agree to dropping the charges. They accepted that they were not a court; they did not see the need for an adjournment. So on we went.

The next witness was Miss B., known to me as Cathy, my ex-patient. Her evidence consisted largely of lies, distortions and innuendo.

Cathy said that I had seen her without an appointment and without a referral from her general practitioner. This was untrue and we could prove it but by this time I believed that the GMC would take no notice. She tried to make out that I had ruined her financially, though she had scarcely ever paid a fee. I had taken special trouble over her and had given her several appointments for an hour each to discuss her personal problems. Cathy said she could not remember these. She said that she was now drug-free and implied that this was in spite of my treatment, when she had been through a course of detoxification which had ended only a few weeks before. We had evidence that she returned to drugs almost immediately and was again selling heroin on the streets of her home town. Cross-examination revealed some of these lies, but none of the committee showed any interest in the fact that she was shown to be a liar. Neither did the press, which reported largely her dramatic and exaggerated lies, in quotation marks.

Throughout the proceedings my lawyers and I – and friends and family in the gallery – had been increasingly appalled by the behaviour of some members of the committee. Most conspicuous was Dr Ashworth, a retired GP from Manchester. His conduct nearly became the subject of our appeal: at the suggestion of the lawyers, several people observed him closely and took notes. When Neil asked questions he sighed and yawned, raised his eyes towards the ceiling, threw out his hands in gestures of despair. He and Dr Scott, sitting on the other side of the table, affected mutual despair. Both had sat on the last committee that condemned me. Sometimes Ashworth went through the same gestures with the Reverend Smith. When Preston made a point against me, they smiled and nodded in agreement. When there was a point in my favour, they showed their disapproval.

'It's surprising that such behaviour is permitted,' remarked one of the lawyers who had been studying Ashworth. 'Though I suppose nothing is surprising in this set-up.'

'It's a real kangaroo court,' said another.

Later some of the observers tried to organise a petition protesting at the behaviour of certain members of the committee, especially Dr Ashworth.

But he wasn't the only one who behaved as though he had decided I was guilty before he had heard the evidence. While travelling to work, a clerk from my solicitors' office had overheard a man boasting: 'I'm sitting on this committee trying this doctor who's been prescribing to all and sundry!'

When John Calderan heard about this he brought the clerk to the GMC during the hearing. She looked at the committee, identified the man and signed a statement about it. We all thought it would be Ashworth but it turned out to be the legal assessor.

'It just shows', said John, 'that you shouldn't talk about your cases in the train.'

Towards the end of Cathy's testimony Dr Ashworth asked a question that indicated his line of thought. Leaning forward in his chair, he said to her in a sanctimonious voice: 'Madam, for years you have been a member of that dark, dreary, unhappy culture, the drug scene. Do I gather that Dr Dally's name is well known in your culture?'

Cathy was enjoying the attention. She enunciated the answer, loud and clear. 'It is *renowned*.' (My emphasis as she spoke it.)

'Do I understand or gather that it is renowned because she maintains you all and makes no effort to reduce or to refer you to any detoxification centres?'

'Yes.'

This was too much for Professor Duthie. 'Dr Ashworth, that is too much of a leading question. You are telling her what to say. I am sorry, I must object to that.'

But Dr Ashworth had already made his point. Looking pleased with himself, he leaned back and continued: 'Then tell me, how was your health during this time that you were under Dr Dally? Was it deteriorating with this regular drug maintenance?' He pronounced the words 'regular drug maintenance' as if they referred to something so sleazy as to be almost unmentionable.

Cathy agreed eagerly, although she had continually emphasised to me how much better she felt now that she did not have to use the black market.

Dr Ashworth continued: 'You know that there were other ways of treating drug addiction – do I understand then that your main criticism of Dr Dally is that she did not reduce you and she did not refer you to any other detoxification centre?'

I remembered the many times I had tried unsuccessfully to persuade Cathy to go to an official clinic. She had always refused, saying that from long experience she knew it would not help her. She had been as hostile to the clinics as she now was towards me. I had done my best to help her with her drug problems, her unsatisfactory relationship with her boyfriend and her difficulties in her job as a hospital telephonist. Now her voice rang out loudly, complaining that I had prevented her from going to a clinic, almost as though I had forced her to come and see me. She could, of course, have gone to a clinic any time she liked without any help from me.

She was also questioned by the Reverend Smith:

'Miss B., we rejoice in the liberation which you appear to have found and we hope this continues. That is sincerely intended by us all. Can you tell me . . . when you first visited Dr Dally you indicated that you wished help to come off drugs.'

'Yes.'

'Did Dr Dally discuss how she proposed to do this?'

'No.'

'Did Dr Dally ask you specifically about your job and the income you derived from it?'

'Yes.'

'From what you told her do you think it was evident that your income . . . could meet the fees?'

'Yes. We lied.'

'You lied in the amounts you were earning?'

'Yes.'

No one suggested that because her evidence rested on lies she had told me that she might now be lying to the GMC.

I thought it significant that the only two patients produced by the prosecution both claimed to have been drug-free for only a few weeks. The Reverend Smith displayed his ignorance of drug addiction by congratulating Cathy on having achieved the drug-free state after so short a time.

At lunchtime there was gloom. Neil tried to cheer me up, saying: 'It will get better from now.'

The afternoon was given over to the evidence of two doctors, both heads of apparently ideal clinics and clearly pleased to be asked to help the GMC. But Neil made them too look like witnesses for the defence, eliciting testimony about the lack of facilities and the failure to treat long-term addicts. He also got a lot of material suggesting that their thinking was illogical. For instance, one doctor didn't think there was a need for long-term use of drugs, yet later admitted that he had patients who had been injecting for twenty years or more and whom he supplied with injectables.

The more experienced of the two doctors said one thing that amazed me. Asked why most addicts didn't go to clinics, he replied: 'Some clinics are not user-friendly.'

I couldn't have described them better myself.

When these doctors had finished, the hearing was adjourned until 26 January, more than six weeks ahead. I felt exhausted. All the family were at home to cheer me up.

I knew I had to work out a strategy to keep going through the coming weeks. I began to think about the virtue of fortitude, 'the greatest of all virtues', according to Dr Johnson, 'because unless a man has that virtue, he has no security for preserving any other.' I felt I would survive.

I was beginning to receive offers of help and support from many people. Some came from my remote past. Some were doctors, addicts and others both known and unknown to me. One letter came from a solicitor whose addict client had been my patient.

On the other side I heard that the judge in a case for which I had written a report had said in open court that he was paying scant attention to my report because he had read about me in *The Times*.

At around this time, my secretary Anne Lingham telephoned the BBC to change the date of my next phone-in programme, which coincided with the adjourned case. She was told there was a letter in the post. I took that to mean that the BBC was not renewing my contract, and I was right. After nearly ten years, this was done without thanks or appreciation for all the work I had put into the programme. Since those I worked with had always been sympathetic, I assumed that they had received a directive from above and wanted to keep their noses clean.

They weren't the only people who behaved like this. One bureaucrat who had supported me suddenly found that he had mysteriously 'lost interest' in the drugs question. His interest did not return until the case was over.

This behaviour made me appreciate even more the support of others. With one exception, my real friends did everything they could to help.

Wendy Savage advised me to compare my figures with those of the clinics and show where possible that mine were better or at least not worse. She had done this during her own case with her perinatal mortality figures and had shown that her figures were rather better than those of her colleagues who were alleging that she practised dangerously. My problem was that one of the things wrong with the clinics was that they neither monitored what they did nor published adequate figures, and the figures they did publish were usually unsatisfactory. On the other hand, some figures analysing my practice might be useful. I decided to try to prepare something.

Two days before Christmas I received a friendly letter from Cindy Fazey, the criminologist who was willing to give evidence on my behalf. I thought she might be able to help in studying my figures. Wendy Savage telephoned again, reiterating how important it was to produce figures. I was learning that Wendy had an uncanny ability to spot the dishonest and devious elements even in the best of people. I thought I was good at doing that until I met her.

On Christmas Eve I had a letter from John Calderan enclosing a copy of an 'astonishing' letter from Waterhouse, the GMC solicitors. The GMC were now trying to reverse their ruling that confidential medical material might be used only with the written permission of the patient. No one could understand these changes, least of all myself. The GMC cited the case of Dr Rahman, whom they had suspended during the week *after* my case. It did seem extraordinary but I had long realised that the GMC would throw in anything, no matter how irrelevant, in order to get what they wanted. I looked forward to seeing how my lawyers would reply.

A few days after Christmas I saw Doug, Khalid's brother-in-law. Khalid had told him again that he regretted what he had said, and Doug thought he might be willing to retract it. But I felt that the GMC would believe Khalid only when he said what they wanted him to say, and that anything else would be branded as lies.

On New Year's Eve we went to a party given by our friends Jimmy and Margaret Hudson. It started badly for me. When Margaret greeted me she turned to the man standing beside her, a medical professor, and said: 'Ann is up before the GMC!' A sickly smile spread over his face and he turned away. I wanted to go home, but it's difficult to go home early from a New Year's Eve party. So I decided to stick it out, and later it improved. The room was full of distinguished doctors, not one of whom had a good word to say for the GMC. Some of them were vociferous in their contempt for it.

Towards the end of the meal I found myself sitting near the former member of parliament Dr Shirley Summerskill, a cousin of Jimmy's. I had met her on many occasions during the previous twenty-five years and thought she knew who I was. I was taken aback when she suddenly asked: 'Have you been reading about Ann Dally?'

At first I thought this must be just an odd way of introducing the subject of my case, but I realised rather late that she didn't know who I was. 'You must know her. She must have been at Somerville about your time.'

I wondered whether to explain, but found that the moment had passed. She talked on, and I realised that she seemed to have read the newspaper reports uncritically, which I found surprising in a former MP. I didn't disillusion her but later wished I had.

Professor Duthie, the chairman of the GMC committee, was knighted in the New Year Honours list.

A few days into the New Year John Calderan told me that Neil Taylor had decided not to go to the High Court over the suggestion that the ruling about patients' confidentiality might be reversed when the committee hearing resumed. He also told me that Neil was working from a hospital bed. He had had an accident with a motor scythe while cutting grass and was in plaster.

Meanwhile the press was swinging increasingly in my favour. Some journalists had begun to realise that official policies for treating

drug addicts were nonsensical and that the war on drugs could not
be won. Articles were published suggesting that I was not a monster
but an idealistic doctor who was being persecuted by a high-handed
establishment. But it would be another year or more before this view
became commonplace in the press, and even then no politician dared
condone it. At the beginning of 1987, newspaper editors were still
reluctant even to mention the subject.

One article in *Time Out* made me a little nervous. The author made
it look as though I had discussed the case with her, when in fact she
was using material I had given her two years previously for another
article. I was worried about this because I had been scrupulous in not
discussing the case with the press.

My husband Philip had been seeking out and visiting old patients
who had become drug-free. The lawyers wanted some of them as witnesses, since they felt that the GMC was unimpressed by the idea of
stable addicts who could lead honest lives with a regular prescription.
Most of my patients were of that sort. Philip found several who were
now free of drugs, who were willing to come to testify in my favour.
The protest against the behaviour of Ashworth and other members of
the committee had been written; the question now was, what to do
with it. In fact nothing was done because events moved in a different
direction.

On 8 January we learned that Neil Taylor was still in hospital
and would be unable to work until 16 February. The GMC took
the view that the case must go on without him, but John Calderan
insisted that his absence would prejudice my defence. He asked for an
adjournment. 'Any normal court would certainly grant that, but this is
far from being a normal court. I should think they'll be delighted to
get rid of Neil.'

This put a new strain on my equilibrium just when things had seemed
to be going more my way. Now I had the chance to find out how well I
had cultivated the virtue of fortitude. Someone pointed out that there
might be advantages in the change because Neil sometimes rubbed the
GMC up the wrong way. It was clear that he lacked all sympathy with
the committee and the way it did its business. I supposed it might help
to look at it in that way. The main thing was to think positively.

We talked about the possibility of Christopher Sumner carrying on
alone. He was an excellent advocate but could not do the paperwork
as well, and he had mastered that in a way that no one else could at this
stage. John pointed out that it might be difficult to get another leader at
this stage in the case, but said he would ask around the Temple. 'If the

GMC take the application for postponement seriously, they'll want to know what efforts we have made to find a replacement.'

Later that day a patient called Susan told me that Alan, contrary to what his mother Mrs S. had said, was not off drugs. Alan had visited Susan the previous September looking for a regular supply of heroin. Susan gave me his London address and telephone number, which I passed on to John.

I felt bad that day. I seemed to be caught in a network of other people's lies. This was the nearest I got to being seriously depressed.

On the same day something else happened to increase my gloom. Another addict patient told me of a telephone call from a policeman who used to be deputy head of a regional Drug Squad. Now seconded to chemists' shops, he had been working for the GMC in collecting material against me. He told a patient of mine that he had recently spent time with two psychiatrists discussing how best to produce evidence against me. The only effect of his telephone call was to upset the addict by telling him that he was going to lose his doctor.

Next day John sent me a copy of a letter from the GMC refusing to postpone the case. He also enclosed a copy of the transcript of the first three days of the hearing. Reading it upset me, particularly the lies the witnesses had told. John said that he was going to instruct someone called William Gage as my new leader.

My anxiety level had risen again. I slept well, but only until 3.45 a.m. It was a measure of my state of mind that I regarded this as a good night's sleep.

That evening I rang Neil Taylor and talked with him for at least an hour. He told me about his accident. He was alone when it had happened and, with extensive lacerations and a compound fracture in his foot, had driven himself to hospital. That told me quite a lot about him.

Neil expressed anger about some of the things that had happened in the case. 'I've appeared before many tribunals and committees but never one like that! The reason they behave like that is that there is no case.'

Many of my patients had turned detective in my cause. One morning within an hour I received information that all three of the patients concerned in the case were not only back on drugs but dealing on the black market. Alan S. had never been off drugs at all, which I already

half-knew. On the previous Sunday he had called at the flat of two of
my patients asking them to buy heroin for him. They refused. One of
them asked about his drug status and he said that he had never been
drug-free. They told him about my case and the part played in it by
his mother. It was the first he knew of it.

John was delighted with this information. But we had no hard
evidence on Khalid or Cathy.

The next morning Alan telephoned. 'I hear my mother has been
saying things about you.'

'Rather more than saying things,' I said. 'She has been giving
evidence against me.'

'I've been abroad for a few weeks. I only heard about the case
three days ago. I think it's dreadful what my mother's been doing,'
he said. 'She often does this kind of thing. She likes making trouble.
I've had to live with it all my life.'

Before we could go any further he began to sound agitated.
'There are people here. I can't talk. Can I come and see you – today,
please?'

I said he could come at three-fifteen, then rang John to tell him
what had happened. I hoped that he would also be able to see him
that afternoon. 'I'll cancel one of my appointments and be available
to see Alan after he has seen you,' John said, and asked me to write
him a letter recording in detail my meeting with Alan. 'Contemporary
documents can be useful in a court of law.'

I was busy in the practice until the time of the appointment and
there were many distractions. London was in the midst of a cold spell.
We had a frozen pipe, and one of our secretaries had not turned up
because of the weather. When the other one went out to the bank, I
was overworked and did not have the time that I would have liked to
think about the coming interview.

Alan arrived just after three, with his girlfriend. He looked a little
scruffy but was reasonably tidy. His manner was a mixture of friendly,
apprehensive, inquisitive and manipulative.

While talking to him I made notes. I knew that his visit and the
way I handled it might be important for the case. Occasions such
as this made me realise how upset I was about the whole wretched
business. But I wanted to get the best out of the interview and not
do anything that might damage my case or annoy my lawyers.

He began by saying that he was sorry that his mother was trying
to make trouble for me. He hadn't known about it. He had been in
Morocco, where he went in late November, returning only two weeks

ago. He hadn't been home since his return. He had seen his mother on one occasion, in London shortly after he had got back. She had not mentioned me or the case.

I said, 'It must be painful for you to hear about this.'

He agreed that it was, but again said it was something he had to learn to live with.

I asked him about his present drug status.

'Just the same,' he said. 'I've never been off drugs, but I have to buy now on the black market and I don't like doing that. I was hoping you would give me a script.'

'At the moment I'm in no position to take on patients,' I said. I was anxious not to get into a bargaining situation and careful not to give him the impression that if he cooperated I would give him drugs. We talked for a while about how all the doctors who helped addicts were being closed down and harassed, and how difficult it was becoming for addicts to survive.

I then went through the notes that I had made about his mother's evidence. Point by point, he denied nearly everything she had said. His mother had said that while he was my patient he looked ill, and he replied: 'The only time I felt really well was when I *was* your patient.' She couldn't have known about his 'erratic behaviour' because he almost never saw her. He had been addicted throughout the time she told the GMC he was drug-free. He had not broken up with his girlfriend, as she claimed. And he was still living on the black market.

He explained, 'My mother has fantasies. She is often vindictive. She enjoys attacking people in this way. She's always doing this sort of thing.' He then said, 'I'd like to help you. What can I do?'

I replied that it might be helpful if he would talk to my solicitor. He agreed to go there that afternoon, and I gave him the address.

I was disappointed though only mildly surprised to hear that he did not arrive at the solicitor's. Alan was as shifty and exploitative as I remembered him. I believe that if I had agreed to give him a prescription, he would have cooperated. But I felt sure that most of what he said that day was true. All these things accorded with my former knowledge of him.

Soon after I saw Alan, an addict I did not know telephoned and offered to come to the GMC on my behalf. He told me that Khalid was trying to buy drugs from him.

We now had evidence that of the three patients used by the GMC, two were back on drugs or had never been drug-free, and we had circumstantial evidence that the third had also relapsed. But addicts, however presentable and intelligent, rarely impress lawyers as potential witnesses.

Jeremy Laurance of *New Society* rang to say they were publishing an article on my case. He made an appointment to come and see me that afternoon and stayed for over two hours. I told him I would talk about the issues but not about the case, difficult though it was to avoid that subject.

That day I also received a letter from a clinic consultant informing me that he was taking over one of my patients. His letter was typically offensive. It is unethical to take another doctor's patient without having the courtesy to ask that doctor first. Moreover, the Guidelines said specifically that in drug dependency a doctor should ask for reports from a patient's former medical advisers before treating him. This had been the ostensible reason that Bewley reported me to the GMC in 1984. This doctor's letter asked for no report. It was typical of drug clinic doctors to regard private colleagues as undeserving of normal courtesy, but I was too occupied with my troubles to think about that for very long.

The legal conference with William Gage was scheduled for the following Thursday. This seemed a long time away, nearly a week, and the case was due to reopen the following Monday. I was worried. John was also arranging a meeting of all the expert witnesses on Friday morning. I found that even harder to bear, not so much because I was excluded as because they would all get to know Gage before I had even met him. I knew that lawyers aren't interested in this kind of feeling so I kept it to myself.

When I next spoke to John he had been talking to Neil Taylor again. Neil much approved of William Gage. He told John that he had recently done a case with Gage at the Assizes with many defendants. The only ones who got off were their clients.

John thought my account of the meeting with Alan S. was very good. 'We can use it as evidence. I've already sent it on to counsel.'

He also said that one of my nicest former addict patients, now drug-free, had made an excellent statement emphasising how much I had helped him, and he was willing to come and testify.

That morning I received a series of distressing telephone calls. One was from an addict named Edward, a reliable, hard-working, inoffensive man. He was in tears. The day before, as he was leaving

Portman's Pharmacy in Baker Street with his prescription, he was arrested. A pharmacist at Portman's confirmed the story. He was upset at the way the police were behaving towards my patients and convinced they were running some campaign against me. Apparently Edward was one of many to have his legal drugs confiscated.

Edward later told me the details. He had walked out of the chemist's with his prescription, talking to no one, when two plainclothes police officers stopped him. They asked what he had.

'I've got my prescription.'

'You're nicked.'

At the police station, when my name was mentioned, the station officer said: 'She must be worth a bloody fortune.' Edward was kept in the cells all day and made to sign a form saying that the police could destroy his drugs.

The other call came from the distressed wife of a patient. She did not use drugs. She was calling from the court where she said she was up on a charge for the first time in her life.

She had gone with her husband to collect his drugs from Portman's Pharmacy. He had no pockets so she put the drugs in her handbag. As they walked down Baker Street, two policemen stopped them and took them to the station. They were kept in the cells until 7 p.m. She was charged with illegal possession and he with supplying her.

The GMC had said that if a patient is caught 'supplying' drugs prescribed by a doctor, that would count as evidence of serious professional misconduct on the part of the doctor. Was this what they were trying to fix?

Both these cases went to the Crown Court. At great expense to the taxpayer, and much suffering to these innocent people, all the defendants were found not guilty. This was a story I knew well: it had happened to many of my patients.

Later that day Carolyn Hay rang to say that the legal conference, which I had been anxiously awaiting, had been postponed until Friday at 4 p.m. To me it was almost unbearable that William Gage, my new leader, was leaving it so late on the last working day before the case. I felt anxious and vulnerable, and I said so.

Next day John telephoned in the late afternoon. He had read my account of the police harassment of my patients and wanted to collect all possible details and then write to the Police Commissioner. Anne Lingham and I put our heads together to remember as many as we could of the patients who had been treated in this way.

John had heard from Carolyn that I was upset about the postponement of the legal conference and tried to reassure me. 'Gage is there
to get you off, not to make you feel good. If he had asked to see you
as soon as he came into the case and had then said, "I don't understand
what all this is about and I want you to tell me," you wouldn't have
liked it at all.'

He was right and I knew it.

The press continued to take a serious interest in the issues involved in
my case. Later that day Carmel Fitzsimons of the *Observer* telephoned
to say that she wanted to do an interview with me to be published in
the paper that Sunday. I knew I would have to be careful not to talk
about the case. This could be difficult if the interviewer was sympathetic. Edward Vulliamy was going to do an article in the *Guardian*
on Monday and was coming to interview me on Sunday morning.
Andrew Veitch, the medical correspondent, was doing one that day
based on my paper 'Analysis of my Practice'.

Jeremy Laurance's *New Society* article was disappointing. He
had gone for the sensational, such as my relationship with Margaret
Thatcher, and had invented a bit about my treating an addict member of
the royal family. He put in a number of rather hostile comments and not
only repeated the distortion about the £75,000, but also compounded
it. I thought the article was even-handed; Philip found it hostile and
offensive. But later Jeremy Laurance was to be converted to my way
of thinking. Along with David Lipsey, his editor, he became a useful
supporter.

Next day, 24 January, I saw patients all morning. It occurred to
me that this might be the last full day I ever worked with patients.
The committee had the power to strike me off the Medical Register
or suspend me without notice.

I was conscious all the time of the meeting of expert witnesses
that was going on at the lawyers' office. John had decided to hold the
meeting without me so that they would all be free to talk about what I
did and to criticise me if they wished. 'People are inherently courteous
and will tend not to be so outspoken about you if you are there,' he said.

The expert witnesses included Drs John Marks, David Marjot,
James Willis and Dale Beckett, all psychiatrists with special experience
in treating drug dependency; Dr Cindy Fazey, the criminologist who
had been doing research on Merseyside; and Patrick Monahan, the
surgeon. John Wall of the MDU was also coming.

Another encouraging piece of news was that Jane Goodsir, the director of Release, an organisation that helped addicts with their legal problems, had apparently said she would like to give evidence. At Release they heard a lot about the doctors who treat addicts, and I was said to be the only one who really cared about them. I heard this from a patient who had been talking to her social worker.

Even more gratifying was a telephone call from the mother of a difficult patient of mine who had eventually become drug-free. She had read the newspaper reports about what Mrs S. had said and was so outraged that she wanted to come and give evidence to say how I had saved her son. She said that he would like to come and give evidence, too. I had received several telephone calls and a number of letters on these lines but this one was particularly moving.

This call came just before I left for the legal conference. On my way there I realised I had forgotten to make a note of William Gage's address. While finding it in a public telephone box, I left behind the large envelope containing the newspaper cuttings and other papers I had been bringing to John Calderan. The lost envelope contained, among other things, the Thatcher correspondence. I never got it back.

I liked William Gage immediately. He could be comforting and abrasive at the same time, an interesting combination.

He asked me to produce the practice's bank statements on Monday. Although there was nothing in them to be afraid of, this was the sort of probing that I disliked, particularly as I had heard that there had been malicious gossip at the GMC about our accounts during the last case. It was an invasion of privacy, a kind of violation.

There was some concern about the finances of the practice. The lawyers couldn't understand our accounting or our accountant. Neither could we. This wasn't surprising since, unknown to us all, the accountant was an alcoholic and working up to a nervous breakdown. A few months later he departed from the professional scene leaving chaotic papers behind him.

The case would resume at 9.45 a.m. on the Monday. Bill (as we now called William Gage) would be there at nine-fifteen. It was getting near. I seemed to have lived through a lifetime since the adjournment.

When I left, John came downstairs with me. He gave me a peck on the cheek and told me to telephone him over the weekend if I wished. As I waited at the top of Middle Temple Lane, a taxi drew up and out stepped a young man with blond hair and a charming manner. 'Hello, Dr Dally, see you on Monday!' I realised that he was Jeremy

Stuart-Smith, Preston's junior, who I thought the only person on the other side who looked pleasant. When I mentioned that to Bill Gage he said one should not judge a lawyer by his smile.

On Sunday morning Ed Vulliamy of the *Guardian* came to interview me. When I told him about the *Panorama* programme and the way the GMC had managed to muzzle it, he became excited and rang John Calderan to check about using the information in his article.

When I telephoned John later myself he brought up the subject of the newspaper evidence that Alan S. had been charged with illegal possession along with his sister. The mother had stated in court that Alan was the only one of her children who had ever been involved in drugs. Mrs S. had not been properly cross-examined because of the fuss about the confidentiality of the medical records. 'Her lies have not been fully exposed when they should have been. I intend to follow it up.'

When I woke up on Monday the twenty-sixth, the day of the resumed hearing, I didn't feel as anxious as I had before the first part of the hearing in December. I was beginning to weary of the whole thing. I was still obsessed with the case, but only hoped that when it was over I would soon be able to think about something else.

I knew I was likely to go into the witness stand that day and I was afraid. I would like to have had time to get to know Bill Gage better and more practice in the technique of giving evidence. Not only was it the opposite of what I had been trained to do, but it was also different from the way in which I normally gave evidence in court, which was as an expert witness with the judge and lawyers being polite and grateful. At the GMC I would be battered by an experienced Old Bailey prosecutor.

John had given me brief but useful advice. The main points were to sit up, speak up and shut up. 'Don't say things like "You are twisting my words." Don't lose your temper: every time a witness does this, it's a point for the other side. Remember that almost every question can be answered with Yes, Yes and . . . Yes but . . . or No, No and . . . , No but. . . .'

I read Ed Vulliamy's article in the *Guardian*. It was good – neutral, factual, no shock-horror. I knew that neither side would like reading about the muzzling of *Panorama* by the GMC. A few years ago people would not have believed that it could happen. I didn't thing there would be much disbelief now. Later George Mikes heard from someone in the

GMC that until the article was published the Council had been crowing over their success in getting the programme watered down. Since the BBC too had kept quiet, the GMC thought they had concealed their activities.

The committee had shrunk. Two of the original ten were ill and two had not been re-elected to the GMC at the end of the year. That left only six.

The proceedings started with the complicated reversal of the decision about patients' notes. We had been stopped from using them in cross-examination, though the GMC had used them in preparing the prosecution. Then the chairman had modified his ruling and said they could be used if there had been attempts to get the permission of the patients to disclose the records. During the adjournment John had written to every one of the two hundred or so patients. Now, after some discussion, the chairman announced that the decision was again reversed and that, contrary to what had been said before, it was now 'in the public interest' to use confidential medical records.

I felt the whole force of the GMC behind the chairman. Move the goalposts whenever this will get you more goals.

At this point, to the astonishment it seemed of everyone in the room, Dr Michael O'Donnell spoke.

Could I just say, sir, that the statement you have just made is so much at odds with my understanding of the position and purpose of this Council, and having said, when we last discussed it, that I would not want to be a member of a committee that operated under the ruling you just issued, I think the only honourable thing I can do is to withdraw.

Then O'Donnell, the one person on the GMC who knew what was happening in drug dependency, stood up and walked out.

I was aghast. I didn't understand why he had acted in this way. Peter said later that he thought O'Donnell had done it to help me and that this would emerge in the morning papers. It didn't. Michael explained later that the GMC had framed the charges in such a way that they could try the case only by breaking their own rules, and he was protesting against that. He thought it would help me. My lawyers thought otherwise. I still don't fully understand why he did it. In the view of many, he would have been far more effective had he made a formal protest but remained on the committee.

The atmosphere at the hearing had changed markedly. Tension and hostility had largely disappeared. Gage and Preston chummily agreed to make deals over matters such as police evidence in order to shorten the proceedings, and I was confident that all this worked in my favour. The case then whizzed along so fast that for a time I forgot Michael O'Donnell and his conscience. The morning was taken up with police witnesses. An inspector came from Scotland Yard to give details about the convictions of certain patients. Bill Gage whispered to me that with few exceptions they showed that my patients had fewer convictions when they were under my care than they had before.

At lunch at Devonshire Place that day, John Wall of the MDU came in rather excited and took John Calderan into the sitting room. Later I heard what he had told him. Over the weekend a member of the GMC, Professor Philip Rhodes, with whom I had once been friendly, had told a lecture audience that in drug cases the GMC warns the doctors the first time and strikes them off the register the second time. He had added that a case was in progress at the moment in which the doctor would be struck off. Since there was only one case in progress, there was no doubt to whom he was referring. A doctor who had been present made a signed statement about it.

After lunch the case for the defence opened. Bill outlined what seemed to be the criticisms of me. I was said to have treated too many patients and to have used inadequate techniques, urine sampling and so on; to have prescribed 'for a fee to persons who in common sense could not pay without resort to crime'; and to have prescribed 'excessively large amounts on single prescriptions' in excess of the doses laid down by the 1984 Guidelines. There was also criticism of my writing weekly instead of daily prescriptions, and of treating patients who lived too far away. The 'crux of the case' was that I had allegedly made 'no attempt' to reduce the dosage of controlled drugs. The charges concerning Khalid A. were reflections of the general charges.

Eventually the summons came. 'I propose now to call Dr Dally.' I walked across the chamber to the witness table.

Chapter 13

Cross-examination and Defence

Being questioned in court by a first-class advocate is a curious experience. Once one settles into the rhythm it is comparable to playing a duet, or perhaps tennis. Examination by one's own counsel – 'examination in chief' as I learned to call it – produces this effect most markedly. It can happen more harshly in cross-examination.

My nerves settled down during Bill's initial questioning about my qualifications, degrees and so on. Soon I was following him easily as he led me carefully and clearly through the history of my involvement with treating addicts and then through my whole philosophy of treatment.

After dealing with the preliminaries, Bill asked whether I had written about the subject of addiction and then handed Dr Duthie a bundle of my publications, mostly from the *Lancet* and *British Medical Journal*. He read aloud a passage dealing with the problems in present clinic practice. It concluded that treating addicts outside clinics

enables many addicts to become physically healthy, to lead normal lives, earning normal money without the necessity to steal, and with time left for families and hobbies. If an addict cannot find a doctor to help him on the NHS then private treatment means about a tenth of the cost and only a minute proportion of the time needed to maintain a drug habit on the black market. Thus money and time are saved, lives are improved, real work is done, and marriages are mended. Burglaries are avoided and prostitutes come off the streets and get proper jobs. This, surely, is what the British system was all about until we lost sight of it in the social upheavals of the last quarter century and in the strangely rigid system we imposed on the changing pattern of addiction.

I remembered that in my early discussions with the lawyers, Christopher Sumner had said after reading some of these articles: 'I can see why the establishment feel threatened by you.'

Bill questioned me at length about my working practices and about existing services in the NHS, whose inadequacies I was thus able to point out. I explained my scepticism about routine urine samples, and my decision to start doing them in 1984 because of the imminent Guidelines. The question of routine physical examinations, on which the clinics and I differed markedly, also arose.

Then we came to an area in which I differed even more strongly from my colleagues in the clinics. Under their regime, addicts were not permitted to go away from home because few doctors allowed them even an extra day's supply of drugs. Going on holiday or abroad was unheard of. Patients were often told peremptorily that travel was forbidden. Yet a Home Office procedure existed under which the doctor wrote a letter giving the dates of absence and the quantities needed. The Home Office then issued a permit for the export of that quantity of drugs, which the addict could take to the consulate of the country he intended to visit and get it stamped. The consulates always obliged. This arrangement seemed to me a humane system for addicts one could trust, but some people disagreed.

Next came the allegation that I did not attempt to reduce the dosage. 'As a matter of generality,' asked Bill, 'is that right or wrong?'

'It is totally untrue.' I always tried to reduce them, I said, but for long-term addicts this could usually only be done slowly. The six months envisaged in the Guidelines was not possible for them. I reduced the dose as quickly as I thought possible while still keeping the patient stable; if it was done too quickly he would go back to the black market. I emphasised the importance of giving the addicts time to sort out domestic matters as well as the addiction problem. 'I think one has to deal with each patient differently,' I said. 'It is a very individual matter.'

I was able to talk about the bureaucratic indifference with which individual needs were so often submerged in rigid routines. I even got across points which were probably too subtle for some members of the committee. One of these concerned patients who attended me for a long time on gradually reducing doses but finally came off drugs elsewhere.

Q. Do you think the benefits of your treatment are necessarily reaped by you, the person who is treating the patient, or somebody else who is subsequently treating the patient?

A. No. Very often the final stages take place elsewhere, perhaps in an in-patient unit or a drug clinic.

Q. Why is that?

A. Because I get them either to the stage where they are capable of coping with that regime of being an in-patient or they can tolerate the out-patient reducing regime on linctus. So you may say they take the credit.

This point was important because some clinic doctors gleefully cited cases in which my long-term patients went to a clinic and immediately succeeded in becoming drug-free. One doctor had even come up to me at a meeting and sneered about it. The same suggestions had been made by Mrs S. and by Cathy during the first part of the trial. The truth was that those patients could never have tolerated the clinic regime had I not put in years of hard work with them beforehand.

Bill also enabled me to make the point that patients who transferred elsewhere for a 'cure' didn't necessarily remain friendly to me. 'Some of them remain very friendly. But some of the extreme in-patient treatments tend to make them, as part of their treatment, hostile to anything related to their former life with drugs, so that they may become very unpleasant and hostile. It is rare but it does happen.' It had happened, I felt sure, with Cathy, and perhaps also with Khalid.

When the questioning came to Khalid, I had to describe in detail every aspect of my treatment. I was relieved that I had done exactly what was my custom at the time. I was able to point out that I had seen him for longer than the 'five to ten minutes' that Preston alleged, and that I had discussed his personal problems with him. The prosecution apparently believed that all I did was write prescriptions and collect money.

I also shed light on Khalid's testimony that he sometimes got a prescription from my secretary. This was one of the ways the GMC was trying to trip me up – taking its cue, I felt sure, from the drug dependency doctors. When I went on holiday I used to give patients prescriptions for the whole period to be dispensed at stated intervals by the pharmacists. But some of them persuaded the pharmacist to let them have it all at once, or to let their friends have it, sometimes with disastrous results. For this reason I had developed the practice of leaving some scripts with my secretary while I was away. She knew the patients and would not give scripts to the wrong people or before they were due. We charged a small fee for the service and it had worked well. But people were trying to make out that I didn't bother to see patients myself but 'sold scripts' handed out by my secretary. Criminal doctors sometimes did just that, and there were many attempts during my trial to link me with them.

Another picture they wanted to get across was of hordes of addicts waiting to see me, just as they did with the criminal doctors. Khalid had testified that he sometimes saw twenty patients in our waiting room. Even Christopher had had this impression at one time. I pointed out that Khalid used to come on a Monday morning, which was always the worst time. On Mondays all the doctors who had consulting rooms in the house were at work, and all their patients used the waiting room. Patients who did not have appointments, having run out of drugs over the weekend, sometimes used to walk in. But there were never as many as twenty at a time. Khalid had exaggerated, and I said as much.

Bill said that Khalid had given evidence that he had to sell ampoules to make money. 'Had you any idea he had done anything like that?' No, I said. I always told patients that if they were caught selling, I would discharge them. If they were picked up or even seen by me or my secretary in an area where drugs were sold, such as the West End, I would discharge them. 'I tell everybody that during the first interview and I make a record. . . . That ensures I have told him so he cannot come back and say, "You never told me." '

Bill then turned to Khalid's wife and the difficulties she had caused. We went through the specific charges she had made point by point and I refuted them. The only point I could not refute concerned my failure to write to Khalid's GP. I explained that I had thought Khalid would shortly come back and resume treatment. 'I put the file on one side anticipating that, and it did not happen.' I did not think I was leaving him in the lurch. I was sorry about discharging him but I could not see what else I could do, especially as the MDU had strongly advised me to do so immediately.

The prosecution made much of this point. I never understood how it was made to appear so important. Had I thought Khalid was permanently discharged, I would (unlike many doctors and clinics) have written to his general practitioner. As it was, I told Khalid to see him. He went, then refused to take the doctor's advice.

Finally Bill took me through the 'S.' case. There was a small sensation when I related how Alan had visited me on his own initiative. I felt disappointed that Bill did not make more of it but knew that he had his reasons. He went on to ask about some of the Home Office material, then the court adjourned for the day.

I didn't feel too exhausted but I knew I still had to give most of my evidence and to face cross-examination. So I kept my feelings under control and remained calm.

While giving evidence, one is not allowed to talk to one's lawyers even during breaks or in the evenings. My lawyers shunned me ostentatiously during breaks and turned away when I appeared; they didn't come to my house as they usually did. I knew it had to be that way but I felt lonely and isolated. If ever I needed support, it was now.

At least I had my family with me that evening. They thought my evidence was coming out well and did their best to encourage me but, as Christopher said later, 'They wear spectacles.' That night I didn't sleep too badly and felt strong, knowing that I had to face Preston's cross-examination next day.

On Tuesday I was on the witness stand nearly all day. The first hour was taken up with the last part of Bill's examination, still largely on the Home Office material. Then Preston rose to his feet and cross-examination began.

Again and again Preston tried to twist my words or put the worst interpretation on them. I knew that this was the adversarial method. Regardless of whether I thought such tactics appropriate for a 'fact-finding' process, I had to deal with it as best I could. Preston was retained by the GMC to ask questions which contained innuendoes, and he did it skilfully. But I felt able to stand up to him because few of the things he was trying to show about me were true.

Predictably, Preston started off by emphasising my lack of formal psychiatric qualifications. This went on for some time. Then he attacked my whole approach to long-term drug addicts, often trying to tie me up in knots to achieve his aim. For instance, contemptuously he picked up a reference of mine to the 'handicaps' of being a drug addict.

Q Do you really believe that those handicaps – your word – add up to living a normal life?

A They can do, yes. They can lead very normal lives. I do not think there is a gross handicap.

Q Do you not agree that such a life is a very poor second best to being able to give up drugs altogether?

A Yes, but it may be very much better for some people than giving up and not being able to.

Q But do you agree that it is a very poor second best?

A No, I do not, put like that, I do not agree.

Q You agreed a moment ago.

A I qualified it. I only agreed with the qualification.

Q There is no doubt at all, is there, that very much the best solution, if it can be achieved, is that the addict should become free of his addiction.

A With that qualification, yes.

Q What qualification?

A If it can be achieved.

Q I made that qualification . . . If it cannot be achieved and you say that it is the case for the totality of your patients, do you not?

A No.

Q The vast majority?

A No.

Q Management has to be undertaken.

A No, I would not put it like that.

I was surprised at the hostility with which the prosecutor used the word 'management'. In ordinary medicine 'management' refers to the total care of the patient, of which 'treatment' is only part. In medical school we were taught that one must always plan the management of a case and never think only of the treatment. But here at the GMC it meant something different and this reflected what the whole argument was about. It amused me, in so far as one can be amused under those circumstances, that Preston had either been deceived or had decided to play it that way, making out that 'management' was somehow reprehensible.

He began to attack from another angle, trying to show that I had been negligent in not giving my patients a full physical examination. I don't think I ever managed to get across the point that general practitioners who refer patients to psychiatrists are normally still in charge of the patients' general health, and that most want it to remain that way.

Preston went on to ask about urine samples. To me this was an old story. The drug dependency establishment was fanatically keen on urine testing even though patients often cheated, for example by bringing someone else's urine or quietly dropping a drug into their own. The clinic procedures for collecting samples were regarded as a joke among addicts, as were the assertions of clinic doctors about their importance. Even when there was no cheating, the tests used in most laboratories were unreliable and often misleading. But the Guidelines emphasised the importance of routine testing. Although I knew that some of my expert witnesses agreed with my views and would say so, I could see I was in trouble. Preston hammered away at his point, apparently trying to show that the patients were so deceitful that I should not have been seeing them.

Q You have of course been deceived yourself, have you not?
A Yes.
Q Often?
A Not often.
Q Mr A. deceived you, did he not?
A I am not sure how much he deceived me and how much he deceived the court.

Endlessly, it seemed, Preston was trying to equate my patients with other, quite different, ones. Dr Farrington, a prosecution witness, had said that he prescribed no injectables. Preston took this to mean that he was more successful than I was, whereas it meant only that addicts who were injecting did not go to Dr Farrington or, if they did, obtained their injectables on the black market. Preston was, after all, hired to put the point of view of the drug dependency consultants.

When Preston came to Miss B. – Cathy – I simply denied all the lies she had told about me. She had criticised me for not trying to reduce her dose or send her to hospital. In fact she had been totally resistant to reducing and the question of going to hospital had not arisen.

The prosecution had done sums on my patients over a period of eight months. Among 149 patients there were only 40 who had not reduced their doses during that time. Considering the histories of the patients I thought that was pretty good, but Preston thought otherwise. I remembered John Lawson's warning: 'You will be judged by the standards of the clinics and if found wanting . . . ' The clinics reduced their patients' doses compulsorily according to a prearranged plan and without consideration of the patients' needs or feelings so that, on paper, everyone was 'drug-free' pretty quickly. I didn't work that way and so I couldn't compete.

In examining me about the details of my prescriptions, Preston repeatedly made comments such as 'You and your advisers have had those prescriptions for months, so presumably you could have found that out.' But the truth was that my lawyers, despite repeated requests, had never been told what I was believed to have done wrong. Thus we could not know what we were supposed to be looking for in the documents.

Preston also laboured the question of addict patients selling their drugs to finance their treatment. Khalid and Cathy had both said they did so.

This was an old chestnut. The black market in prescribed drugs was about 0.1 per cent of the total yet the drug dependency establishment used it to justify attacks on doctors who tried to help addicts. It could also be conveniently forgotten that, whereas private treatment might cost a long-term addict £30 per week, failure to treat him meant that he would have to find £600 per week, £80–£100 per day or more to pay for his drugs on the black market.

I answered: 'Well, they both said they did. I do not know whether they did.'

Q You think they were giving perjured evidence; is that what you mean?

A Well, if they knew that they were actually not speaking the truth, yes, but I do not know whether they knew or not. . . .

Q If you are neutral as to whether it might be true or not, it follows that you accept that it might be true. If it is true it is a horrifying state of affairs, do you not agree?

A Well, *if* it is. Again I would qualify that because I do not know of any evidence that ampoules are sold other than to addicts who would otherwise buy even more horrifying black-market heroin.

Q Is that your answer, that it is better that your patients should sell on to third parties than go to the black market?

A No, I am not saying that. I am saying that it is better for a black-market addict who has not got a doctor to use clean drugs and clean syringes than dirty drugs and dirty syringes, that is all I am saying from the point of view of the third party, but I am not advocating it. I would do everything I could do to stop that happening, but that is the bit that you seem to have omitted from your questioning.

My lawyers had told me firmly to keep my temper and not answer back. I was doing my best but feeling the strain.

Preston toyed with the McIntosh interview, then turned to the Guidelines. Bing Spear had predicted that they would be turned into 'tablets of stone' with which to attack doctors whom the drug dependency establishment disliked. Here it came. Preston suggested that my treatment 'breached, or at any rate ignored, a large number of the recommendations in the DHSS Guidelines'. I insisted repeatedly that I did not agree. My treatment conformed to the Guidelines 'as far as I could even though it was difficult to do this because long-term addicts, as most of my patients were, had deliberately been omitted from the Guidelines'. This was the centre of the whole argument. If I could convince the committee of this, I had won. Or so I thought.

We then went through the Guidelines at some length. I tried to be as polite about them as I could. When he finally asked why I let the Guidelines go out under my name 'with what I understand you to say is a serious omission', I explained again what had gone on behind the scenes.

Preston was, I am sure, genuinely in the dark about that dishonesty. I think he and the committee believed that the Guidelines were the honest product of the best minds in the so-called specialty.

I wondered whether the GMC committee would sit up and take notice of this, or whether they were so used to the rigging of committees that they would not think it noteworthy. No one seemed in the least surprised or interested.

Preston went on to the question of Khalid's wife and her attempts to stop her husband's treatment. When I suggested that she might 'manipulate the truth in order to bring about some situation in her relationship with her husband', Preston acted surprised. 'She would manipulate the truth like a drug addict? Her husband was the addict, not the wife.'

'I do not think manipulation of the truth is confined to drug addicts,' I replied.

Preston tried to trip me up over Khalid's work, maintaining that he had not done any. His wife had said that he had not worked in 1983 and scarcely at all in 1984, but we were going to produce evidence that this was untrue.

Since Khalid and his wife had both now been shown to be liars, I thought their evidence would be discounted. It wasn't. Meanwhile Preston went on to the circumstances under which I had discharged Khalid. Although I thought the exchange that followed was merely nitpicking, John seemed to think it was what tripped me up. It was the only bit that the defence did not cover. It had been discussed with Neil Taylor before Christmas but was so trivial that everyone had forgotten to discuss it with Bill when he took over. After all,

I had followed the MDU advice in the matter. Thus it was omitted
from the examination of the expert witnesses. It was to be a serious
omission, but I was sure that if I hadn't been tripped up by that, my
opponents would have found something else.

Preston also tried to make out that the fact that Khalid owed me
money when I discharged him should have suggested that 'his means
were straitened'. I agreed, but pointed out that I didn't push him to pay
for that very reason – and because I expected him to return eventually.
I had told him 'to go back to his GP, who was the right person to decide
his next treatment anyway'.

Preston then quoted Khalid's testimony that I had said to him, 'If
your wife were to apologise to me I might forget about it.' I pointed
out that that was totally untrue. Then he suggested that I had 'resented
the intervention' of Khalid's wife, whom he depicted as 'a loyal and
loving wife'. I tried to explain that telephoning behind Khalid's back
and then refusing permission to talk about it to him was manipulative
and put me in a difficult position: 'trying to get into a relationship with
the doctor behind the patient's back is always difficult for the doctor.
It is not very nice, but it often happens, especially with relatives who
are a bit disturbed.' I denied that her behaviour was as innocent and
blameless as he made it out to be. 'I could not help her directly as
long as he did not know because he, after all, was my patient.'

Preston seemed determined to emphasise the quantities of drugs
rather than the quality of treatment and tried repeatedly to make
it look as though I had led some sort of criminal life. For instance
Cathy had told the court that I periodically went 'on a binge and you
would hear all about it on the street that it was coming. The police
are coming so she is going to start hassling again and you are going
to be cut down and everyone would be cut down together. You would
know it was going to happen.'

Q Is there any truth in that?
A None at all, no.
Q It is true, is it not, that you imposed a blanket reduction
     on every addict following Mr McIntosh's visit in December?
A That was after she had [left my care]. I had never done
     it before and I have never done it since.

There had always been a conflict between doing the best for my
patients and trying to avoid the threat of disciplinary proceedings.
tried to explain but, as is the nature of cross-examination, each point
was turned against me. Bill had produced Khalid's business letterhead

with his name on it, but the impression seemed to persist that he had been unemployed and impoverished.

When the cross-examination was over the chairman questioned me about various aspects of treating addiction. His questions were sensible enough. Then Dr Ashworth took over. His tone was clearly hostile. I thought it evident that he had already formed an opinion on me and my practice. After questioning me about my use of social support services, he said:

Q We have heard in this chamber over the years the stories of drug addicts and how they all gradually go downhill. This is not your experience?

A Most of mine go uphill.

Q [Disbelieving] Do they?

A Yes.

Q What stimulus is there for these patients to come off drugs if you are prepared to prescribe for them according to their own demands?

A As I do not prescribe according to their demands I cannot answer the question.

Q [Sarcastically] There is a difference, is there, between your type of prescribing and prescribing on demand?

A Yes, a very great difference.

Q [With disbelief] What difference?

A I prescribe what in my opinion is the minimum dose that can keep the patient stable and leading a normal legal life. . . . That is totally different from prescribing on demand. There is no connection between the two.

Q If they come back in a month's time and tell you they cannot manage on that dosage, up goes the dosage?

A No, quite often if they do that my response is to say: 'I am sorry, you are one of the many addicts I am unable to help because I cannot provide it.' I often say that.

Dr Ashworth went on to ask about the pharmacies my patients used.

Q You said there were reasons why addicts went to particular chemists in your vicinity which you could give. We did not hear those reasons. What are those reasons?

A They treat them like human beings. That is one of the problems about a lot of pharmacists. They treat them very badly, and they [addicts] do not like it and so they prefer to go

to the pharmacists round here. I think it is unfortunate because
I think too many of them go to too few pharmacies, but that is
basically the reason.

In other words, many pharmacists reflected the prejudices of the
medical profession and of society. They used them for an exercise in
licensed nastiness, sometimes making addicts wait for hours, sending
them repeatedly to the back of the queue and even announcing to
other customers that they were 'just dirty junkies'. Concerned at
such behaviour, I had compiled a list of chemists who treated addicts
humanely.

Another doctor asked questions about physical examinations and
tests, which I answered. In my reply I told the story of a patient who
feared he was infertile. He and his wife, who was not addicted, wanted
a child very much. I told him to see his GP about referral for specialist
investigation and treatment. When he did visit his GP, he was told he
was a dirty junkie and could not have children.

None of the committee showed surprise or concern.

At this point the Reverend Smith, the lay member of the committee,
began to question me. His approach seemed to be much the same as
Dr Ashworth's.

Then Ashworth himself returned to the fray. He said that Neil
Taylor had referred to 'a considerable body of expert opinion' that
supported my philosophy. 'I have no idea who is coming as witnesses
but so far in the papers I have not read any evidence of those people.
Can you tell me what body there is that supports your philosophy?' He
sounded disbelieving and sarcastic. This man who sat in judgement on
me was not even aware that there was another point of view. I recited
him a list of people and added, 'There are quite a lot. I don't know if
that satisfies you.'

During tea – tea for the GMC, that is – we sat in our dreary
little room. Suddenly I realised that my ordeal by cross-examination
was over.

After tea came the expert witnesses, most of whom I had never
even met. Testifying for me was particularly brave of those who
worked in drug dependency: they risked reprisals, as indeed later
occurred.

The first was Dr David Marjot, one of the few critics of the drug
dependency establishment who themselves ran a clinic, and probably
the only such critic in the London area. David had suffered dearly the
only time he had previously spoken out against the establishment. A

former Surgeon-Commander of the Royal Navy, he had an imposing presence and a bumbly, teddy-bear appearance. He answered the few questions directly. Sometimes he introduced a rare magic into his turn of phrase. He described the term 'to savage', derived from the case of Wendy Savage, as meaning to trawl through a doctor's records looking for material to use in disciplinary proceedings. Marjot refused to be bullied by Preston and dealt with him by becoming even more bumbly. Observers in the gallery said he clearly annoyed the lawyers.

David Marjot supported my way of dealing with patients. He emphasised the difficulties of urine testing, and mentioned 'the defensive use of diagnostic aids'. Since the Guidelines were published, he said, 'I think the impression amongst my colleagues, and myself probably, is that they are becoming a code of practice rather than guidelines and that there is some criticism if you don't go by the book. . . . I'd hate to have it used as a stick with which to beat me. . . . ' He emphasised that doctors get the patients who feel they can help them: so doctors who insist that all addicts can be got off drugs in a few weeks or months will only get those patients for whom this is possible. 'They will offer them what they have on offer,' he said, and if patients don't conform with a particular practice, 'they either don't come or they stay away.'

When Bill quoted the clinic doctors who had testified as saying that all addicts could be reduced and finally stopped altogether within four to six months, Marjot replied: 'That is obviously their experience. It wouldn't be mine.' He talked about the years it may take for an addict to become drug-free. 'I don't know what Dr Dally's mortality is, but I would expect a number of her patients should have died if they were not cared for.'

David was the last witness of the day. Next morning's press accounts of the case were much better, apart from *The Times*, which saw fit to publish nothing except the fact that I had a pop star among my patients! There was also the usual obsession with royalty. The day before they had even got hold of the idea that I was psychiatrist to Princess Margaret.

The next day's proceedings began with Dr Dale Beckett. He was one of my favourite doctors, wise, shrewd and caring. His testimony echoed that of David Marjot. When asked about the policy of making all addicts drug-free within six months, he said: 'I do not think it is going to succeed. It would be interesting to know what the motive is behind it. . . . ' This remark referred, of course, to the tactics of the drug dependency doctors who tried to impose their rigid regime on all addicts.

About urine samples Beckett said: 'If one goes about them intelligently then I think they are quite helpful, and by "intelligently" I mean recognising that the addict is also intelligent. . . . ' He did not think them necessary as a routine first examination test.

After Beckett came two of my patients. When the first, referred to as 'H.', took the stand, I began to feel emotional. I knew I had saved this able young man from degradation and probably from death. His grateful mother had wanted to give evidence about this. He described how awful his life had been on the black market, how unhelpful clinic doctors had been, how good his life was now, and how it would deteriorate if I could no longer prescribe. For the first time since the hearing started, I felt tears in my eyes. I could take all this stress for myself, but found it hard to take it for my patients.They had more to lose than I.

After H. came M., a gentle man who was struggling to cope with his addiction and raise four children. He had a rough time in cross-examination, and got in a slight muddle about his former purchases on the black market. He said first that he had not used the black market since seeing me, meaning that he had not had to rely on it. Later, when he described how on one occasion he had resorted to it, Dr Ashworth angrily interposed. 'You have told lies to Dr Dally about your purchasing drugs on the black market, you previously told us this afternoon lies about your purchase of drugs on the black market and now you have confessed to purchasing drugs on the black market. Why should I believe anything you say?' I thought it interesting that Dr Ashworth leapt on this inconsistency after ignoring all the lies told by prosecution witnesses.

Later, members of the committee and others from the prosecution were seen in the chamber trawling through my case notes, 'savaging' them, to use Marjot's word. Apparently they had unpredictable views on the confidentiality of case notes.

We had invited a few witnesses to lunch, both before and after their evidence. This invitation included addicts. Two of my patients came, one with his wife, and at lunch they had an earnest discussion about their teenage daughters, particularly about what they would do if the girls 'lived in sin' before they were married and how they would feel if they brought home boyfriends who used drugs. I wondered how many people knew that drug addicts were concerned with such problems.

Cindy Fazey, the Liverpool criminologist whom I hadn't met, came down to give evidence that afternoon. She had analysed my figures and found them very much to my advantage. I prescribed less than what was prescribed in the Drug Dependency Unit in Liverpool. But Preston objected that she had been 'put forward as an expert witness not as a statistician', and on those grounds she was not allowed to present many of her findings. She was then prevented from commenting on matters that might be regarded as medical. I felt unhappy about her. She had taken a lot of trouble to come and had been humiliated.

'I'm used to being treated like that by doctors,' she told me later. 'The medical establishment often behaves like that.' She was going to do more work on my behalf overnight and was only sorry that she hadn't been allowed to give all her evidence. So was I.

Arnold Trebach arrived that evening from Washington. He spent the evening with us and seemed to be in good form. When my son-in-law Dick told Arnold that he was drinking a 'GMC martini' to dull his anger at the proceedings, Arnold said: 'A GMC martini – that must be made with two parts gin and one part bile.'

All that week my problems had been making headlines. I was thankful that these were chiefly in the quality newspapers and magazines: the arguments had apparently become too complicated for the tabloids. 'RACKETEER OR RESCUER?' asked *New Society*. 'DRUG DOCTOR'S DILEMMA', announced *Time Out*. The *Observer* headline was 'DOCTOR BATTLES TO CONTINUE HELP', while the *Guardian* said 'NOWHERE TO GO FOR DRUG ADDICTS'.

The next day was spectacular. John described it as 'pure theatre' and whispered to me during Bill's performance: 'This is advocacy at its best!'

Arnold Trebach testified first and made some good points. Bill seemed pleased. Then came Dr John Marks, Regional Director for Drug Dependency Services on Merseyside.

Dr Marks, whom I had not met, believed strongly in what I was doing in drug dependency. Not only did he agree with virtually all aspects of my practice but he expressed himself with rare clarity. He eloquently attacked the current orthodoxy and the way it ignored long-term addicts. 'London has no services for chronic addicts,' he said. Someone later heard journalists filing reports beginning: 'Liverpool doctor slams London drug clinics'. His evidence turned into a fascinating lecture on the history of drug dependency. Everyone listened intently, and the chairman asked Marks to talk to him further during lunch. I thought that was a good sign, but realised that in his mind Duthie might separate the witness from my case.

In a way, the most remarkable thing about Marks's testimony was his tone of voice. It suggested bemusement at the whole proceedings. For instance, every time Preston asked a question about doses, reducing or injectables, Marks answered as though he was surprised to be asked, as though it was so obvious as to be scarcely worth mentioning: of course you have to maintain some long-term addicts; of course many of them need injectables; of course you cannot reduce their doses rapidly as laid down in the Guidelines. He contradicted the official line on almost everything and emphasised the absurdity of the 'Misguidelines' as he called them. He also denied that he was unorthodox, pointing out that what he said was backed up by important research.

My lawyers praised Marks's performance warmly. Bill said that he was one of the best witnesses he had ever seen.

When Marks had finished, the prosecution seemed to rethink their line about my not sticking to the Guidelines. They scarcely mentioned this again. I felt that at last this absurd document had been exposed and discredited in a way that would make it difficult for anyone to take it seriously again.

Marks said only one thing that could be held against me. When asked to rate my performance as a doctor, having praised me a good deal in his previous evidence, he said that it was 'fair'. I was surprised and disappointed at this, and learned only later that 'fair' in the North of England means 'good', and that was what he had meant.

However, it was too late. When he got home he realised what he had said. He sent a telegram to the GMC explaining what had happened. It did not arrive, or at least was not produced in court. In his closing speech Preston made much of the fact that Marks rated my practice as 'only fair'. It was one of the unlucky happenings of the hearing.

After lunch came a journalist addict, Sandy. He bravely resisted attempts to shake him. Then came Patrick Monahan, the surgeon from Swindon.

Patrick was giving evidence with some risk to himself. His testimony concerned a close relative who had been a heroin addict. He didn't wish her to be identified, and said so, but when the press found out who it was they published the information. Meanwhile Patrick told a harrowing tale of being on the receiving end of the drug dependency services. He described what happened when, in an emergency, he sought treatment for his relative.

We tried to get her seen at City Roads [a special unit for emergencies in drug dependency], St Mary's and Charing Cross, all without success. They did not have the time to see her, and nor was the doctor able to see her. We tried to get her into the Maudsley Hospital to be seen as an out-patient. [My wife] was seen by a nurse and she was told that there was no possibility of my relative being seen for two weeks as an out-patient, and she went on to say that if she required in-patient treatment there was no chance of her getting [it] for one month.

Q Did this come as a surprise to you?

A I was appalled. I work in a unit which is open twenty-four hours a day, caring for the needs of people in crisis and I could not believe that my relative would not be offered reasonable guidance and treatment within the National Health Service during that crisis.

By this time the relative was injecting heroin four times a day. Patrick and his wife were 'desperate'. After another futile attempt to arrange care through a local psychiatrist Patrick managed to get his relative admitted for in-patient treatment in Birmingham. After leaving hospital she immediately started injecting heroin again, and by this time she had fairly severe hepatitis. Finally they got help from their local GP. He got her admitted to a local cottage hospital – far from the specialists – and they gradually reduced her on methadone. 'It was not only the use of methadone,' said Patrick, 'but the fact that for the first time my relative had the chance to be able to talk with a friendly doctor and friendly nurses, something that had been denied to her for quite a long time.'

About eighteen months had passed since Patrick's discovery that his relative was an addict. He was absolutely appalled at the delay, he said, and described how he had tried to 'make certain enquiries and investigations into drug treatment'.

I wrote to four national newspapers and said: 'Here am I, a privileged person within the National Health Service, and I, as a privileged person, cannot get reasonable treatment for a close relative of mine, and if there were other people who had had similar problems would they contact me to see if we could do anything about it.' Within twenty-four hours our phone was inundated with calls and the calls went on for several days. We got numerous letters. . . .

Asked about an article by Dr Philip Connell saying that available National Health resources catered for all the addict population, Patrick was definite in his views. 'That is false, with respect.'

He then went on to say how he knew me, and to say that he considered me 'a kind, compassionate lady with a very thorough knowledge of the problems that beset both addicts, parents and friends. I have been most impressed by . . . the vigour with which she is prepared to question the system of treatment in the UK, which I and many others feel is far short of that which it should be.' He said that he saw a place for the treatment of addicts by private practitioner, and that he would not have hesitated to send his relative to me had he known about me at the time. And he mildly but firmly attacked the views of the clinic doctors who had given evidence against me.

> I think the problem with the present system, governed very much by the drug dependence units, is that they have formulated a rigid, totally inflexible form of treatment for drug addicts, and, with respect, most illnesses in medicine require half a dozen variations in order to make treatment suitable both for the patient and the end result.

He found it difficult to understand how the current orthodoxy could apply 'one single remedy to every single case. . . . Yet this seems to be the philosophy adopted within the drug abuse field.'

In cross-examination, Preston tried to suggest that Patrick's gruelling ordeal had been exceptional. He read a glowing description by Dr Connell of drug dependency services in London, and asked how that 'squared' with Patrick's account of his difficulties in getting his relative seen at the Maudsley, Connell's own hospital. 'All I can say is that my wife, who is also an ex-nurse, went there [with the relative] and was told this by a responsible member of the staff of the clinic.' Patrick would not be shaken on this point. Nor would he agree that the situation had steadily improved in recent years. He spoke from personal experience of the Wessex Regional Health Authority, of which he was a member.

To my surprise, my daughter Emma was next called as the last witness of the day. After all the middle-aged witnesses she looked fresh and young, almost a girl. At least two members of the committee sat up in a way they had not before.

Emma and her husband had employed Khalid to do pointing and painting at her house in 1983, the year that his wife said he did only one or two odd jobs, and again in 1984, the year his wife said he was too ill to work at all. Emma even managed a little joke with the committee about doing first the front of the house and then the back, explaining that they 'couldn't afford to do both at once'. When asked whether Khalid had worked full-time or part-time, she replied: 'Like builders do.' Everyone laughed.

There was also one dramatic moment in her testimony. Under examination by Bill she had said she was certain that Khalid had worked for them in May 1984. Preston, referring to the testimony of Khalid's wife, asked how she could be so certain.

'I know the date precisely because I had a miscarriage in May 1984 and Khalid commiserated with me.'

Even Preston didn't try to argue with that.

It looked as though the case would finish next day. All the evidence had been called, though some had been curtailed.

I didn't sleep much. I got up at 5.15 a.m., trying to come to terms with the fact that this might be my last day working as a doctor. The previous day four people had told me, separately, that they thought I would be struck off the register, which would mean I could no longer practise as a doctor. John Harman said that he couldn't think what else they could do, given that they had admonished me last time. Also Roger Toulmin, a civil servant friend, described from vast experience how bureaucratic people manage to retain their beliefs while listening to evidence that contradicts them. Gloomily, I could see that he was right.

I found all this hard to take. I still had a feeling of confidence which came from my clear conscience and a belief, albeit shaken, in other people's sense of justice. But I had had the same feeling during the first hearing, yet they had found me guilty. My son-in-law Dick said something that made me feel better: 'You are privileged to have the opportunity to stand up for your principles. This doesn't happen to many people.'

On Friday, the last day of the hearing, there were the final speeches for the prosecution and the defence. Preston's speech of submission for the prosecution did not mention the Guidelines, though his opening speech had emphasised them consistently and most of his cross-examination had been based on them. This was a kind of victory in itself.

Bill's speech was thorough and succinct. I felt a little disappointed that it lacked passion and emotive appeal, though I could see that this would have been inappropriate. I knew that the idea of a speech like Dr Manson's in *The Citadel* was absurd yet I still had it tucked away in my mind.

We had to wait for gruelling hours while the committee withdrew for discussions. The waiting time was improved by lively conversation with the lawyers. One told a story about two psychiatrists on opposite sides in court. Unable to agree on the case, they were put into a room together to thrash it out. Eventually they returned and said: 'Well, we can't agree about the patient but we do agree that there is something funny about the judge.'

When the committee finally returned, they found me not guilty on the main charge concerning my prescribing system and general treatment.

They found the second charge proven. This was the one about Khalid. They didn't say what I had done wrong but they found that it constituted serious professional misconduct. I found this extraordinary considering that nothing I did was different from what my colleagues as expert witnesses had said they themselves did. But I learned that the GMC were not legally obliged to give reasons for their decisions.

Having announced their verdict, the committee then retired to consider punishment, which meant more suspense for us. I think everyone assumed that I would be struck off.

When the committee returned, the chairman announced that they had decided to suspend my right to prescribe or possess controlled drugs for fourteen months. The ban was to start in 28 days' time, or, if we appealed, up to the time of the result of the appeal. The chairman said something about getting doctors to send reports to them about me.

Despite my shock and anger I was curiously exultant. With the major charge unproven, they had done what seemed to be about the minimum, given the strength of the forces that were out to get me. I heard later that many members of the medical 'mafia' were disappointed. After all that, the GMC had been unable to condemn my method of treatment. They had, of course done their best to ensure that no one would be tempted to follow it. But the moral victory was mine.

Chapter 14

The Appeal

On the evening the hearing ended my family gathered. It was a joy to sit with my baby granddaughter at the end of that tough and nasty day.

I felt calm and determined to fight on. I did not even know what the committee had actually condemned me for. 'Serious professional misconduct' was a damaging label when all I had done was provide humane treatment for a neglected group of people who needed it badly. More important, I felt I must fight for the sake of long-term addicts.

The evening news bulletins reported the result of the case and the fact that it had already 'created alarm' among those involved in the treatment of drug addicts. Dave Turner, director of the Standing Conference on Drug Abuse (SCODA), an official, government-funded body, was interviewed on television. I was pleasantly surprised at his remarks. He said that my addict patients would now have nowhere to turn and the result was likely to be 'a disaster'. If 'no real services are offered' (and of course everyone knew they would not be) 'the GMC itself should be had up for serious professional misconduct'. He said that London lacked facilities for treating chronic addicts and also pointed out that what the GMC had done to me would deter other doctors from helping addicts, who would be forced to commit crimes and become 'antisocial'.

A number of journalists telephoned or came to the house. The case was generating enormous interest, they said. I learned that much of this interest would not be visible immediately: some editors did not like to risk the wrath of their masters by printing 'controversial' material. Henceforth I myself would be regarded as controversial. But many now understood what was going on in drug dependency; publicity on the subject would never be the same again.

The telephone rang all evening. Friends, strangers, journalists, well-wishers, informants. People on the inside, particularly those who knew the GMC gossip, thought the result was better than expected. Most had expected me to be suspended from medical practice for a period or struck off the register permanently.

Next morning the press reports were very different from those published at the beginning of the case. I was beginning to understand what people meant when they said that the moral victory was mine and that I had changed public opinion. Many people, including members of the GMC committee, had learned that there were valid points of view other than the official line, and that using the Guidelines as an excuse for a witch hunt was absurd. The stranglehold of a clique of doctors, if not broken, would get less public sympathy. They would now probably feel obliged to show at least a semblance of change.

All this brought some satisfaction after all the horrors. When Wendy Savage telephoned next morning to commiserate, I found myself talking cheerfully and optimistically. Bing Spear rang and said that the case 'has really brought things out into the open. It will be in everybody's minds.'

After a weekend in the country I felt revived. When I arrived back in London there was a message from John Calderan asking me to ring him. He wanted to talk about the appeal. It was to the Privy Council, that is the House of Lords, whose Judicial Committee hears appeals from professions and from remaining outposts of the British Empire. John had already talked to John Wall, who was in favour of our appealing and would be putting it to the MDU committee shortly. They agreed to pay, and the appeal process was set in motion. 'It seems that they have found you guilty of serious professional misconduct because you didn't write to the doctor when Khalid left,' said John incredulously. 'It's absurd.'

I found it hard to see patients and to explain the position to each. Many rumours were circulating. Some people thought I could not prescribe, and when the addicts heard this they were naturally upset. How people love to spread bad rumours! The truth was that I could prescribe as normal until the appeal was decided.

I also heard that some of the drug dependency consultants had been gleeful about the case while it was in progress, telling their addict patients: 'Within a month or two, all the private doctors will be driven out!' One told his patients, 'We've got her!' Another said that they had better not think of finding private doctors because they would all now be stopped from prescribing.

Hysteria was increasing in some quarters. One patient told me that his wife had lost her job with British Telecom. Someone knew that her husband used drugs, and when this man told his colleagues they voted by 40 to 2 not to work with her. Apparently they thought she would give them Aids.

I heard another example of petty nastiness. Either the Home Office inspectors or members of Scotland Yard's Drugs Squad had told pharmacists that if a patient was late in collecting his drugs, they were to dispense less than the amount prescribed. This was inhumane. An addict who was prevented from getting to the pharmacy on time would be likely to develop withdrawal symptoms. If he went next morning, he would already be sick and in need. He would need yesterday's drugs in order to restore his equilibrium. To deprive him of this made it more difficult for him to remain stable.

A journalist telephoned from a paper called *General Practitioner*. He asked what would happen to my patients if the ban on prescribing came into force. I told him how hostile GPs were, and suggested that he report that in his journal and ask for volunteers to take over my addict patients. He did. As I expected, not one replied.

A few days later one of my patients happened to meet Khalid for the first time. Khalid knew he was an addict (but not that he was a patient of mine) and tried to buy drugs from him, 'enough to sell and have a fix myself'.

On 7 February 1987 the *Lancet* contained an excellent article on my case, easily the best yet, by their legal correspondent Diana Brahams.

At 3 p.m. that day we had our legal conference in Bill Gage's chambers. Bill explained something of the review procedure. It seemed there were many grounds for appeal, but he did not think the chances of any were good. 'One part of the establishment doesn't like to attack another part of the establishment, and in particular, they don't like to attack the medical establishment. They like to believe that doctors are the best judges of their own affairs.'

We did not know then that no comparable case had ever succeeded.

Bill put the chances of success at 20–25 per cent. Later John Calderan said counsel always tend to pitch the odds on success low, just as doctors tend to give a worse prognosis than they really believe, so that it will look good for them if it comes out better.

In describing some of the possible grounds for appeal, Bill repeated that the Judicial Committee of the House of Lords is always loath to go against the GMC. He also raised the possibility that my lawyers had actually made my position worse by succeeding in knocking out the first charge. 'Well, at least it saved her from being struck off the register,' said John Wall. 'There's a lot to be said for reaching the end of one's medical career without actually being struck off.'

Later that day George Mikes telephoned. His friend who was a member of the GMC had told him that, even before the defence had been heard, it was widely intended throughout the GMC to find me guilty and strike me off the register. This confirmed what I already knew. The friend had asked George not to tell me until after the case. 'They are totally unscrupulous,' said George. 'They don't give a damn about the evidence. The profession doesn't realise what is going on in the GMC, but when they do, they won't stand for it.'

I asked why this situation had arisen.

'The GMC has fallen into the hands of a bunch of megalomaniacs. Much of it is a question of personal vendettas, which now cost the profession more than patients' complaints.'

I could understand that what he said was true. I had come across many personal vendettas in the profession, and could think of at least six cases going on at the time.

Most of my patients were understandably worried about what would happen to them. One of them said: 'I'd be safer on the black market than at a clinic – but the trouble is that it increases one's habit so much.'

Without a steady supply of drugs, the addict tends to take more than he needs to guard against the time when he hasn't got any. This increases his tolerance and thus his habit. It is one of the results of criminalising addicts.

John Forsyth, of the radio programme *File on Four*, telephoned to tell me that they were doing a programme based on the case, and were recording John Marks next day; they had already done an interview with Connell. Because of my impending appeal to the Privy Council they thought it advisable that I should not take part.

Jonathan Dimbleby also telephoned. He wanted to make a programme for *This Week*, and said: 'I find your case weird!'

That evening John Marks telephoned and told me something of the political manoeuvres and whispering campaigns that had been going on in the drug dependency world. He also said that the Royal College of Psychiatrists were to hold a meeting in Llandudno to discuss the motion 'That maintenance has no place in the treatment of drug abuse'. He was to be the principal speaker opposing the motion.

I had already heard that Khalid had been sent to Coventry and beaten up by angry addicts. In the area where he lived there were slogans on the walls saying rude things about him. Several people had told me that he was badly hooked on drugs again and looked dreadful. His brother-in-law Doug said that the case had caused a rift in the family, and that Khalid's wife was divorcing him.

That week Michael O'Donnell's column in the *British Medical Journal*, 'One Man's Burden', was devoted to his resignation from the committee.

One day in mid-February some of my family gathered to hear the Radio 4 *File on Four* programme about my case. All agreed that it was excellent. In it David Marjot admitted that although he was one of the few doctors who held a heroin licence he was 'shit-scared' of using it because of the medical establishment. He also said that doctors 'do not put their heads above the parapet' because 'if they do, they get their heads shot off'. Dr Philip Connell made a short contribution, justifying his prohibitionist views by saying that they arose from his thirty years' experience. He said that although you can make out a theoretical case for prescribing methadone on a long-term basis, in practice this is always wrong. I was struck again by the way the drug dependency doctors either disregarded or failed to appreciate the importance of clinical judgement.

Perhaps the most interesting part of the programme was the contribution from Sir John Walton, president of the GMC. As he had in the *British Medical Journal* after my first GMC hearing in 1983, he now clearly felt a need to justify himself: 'The question of differences of opinion on management of addicts are not our concern. When I talk about bona-fide prescribing, I mean responsible prescribing; I mean that doctors should see the patients regularly.'

This reminded me of addicts' frequent complaints that at clinics they almost never saw the doctor, sometimes not for years on end.

Sir John gave all the arguments of the drug dependency establishment without dealing with the arguments against them. The interviewer then asked him: 'Some doctors we've talked to do feel very vulnerable because of the approach of the GMC to this issue: they feel that if they are in favour of methadone prescription, there is a likelihood that the GMC will, at the very least, take a long, hard look at what they are doing. Are they right to feel that?'

Sir John answered: 'Only if the issue of serious professional misconduct arises and if there is evidence to suggest that they have not undertaken the regular assessment, the suggestions that I've made about the frequent seeing of patients and the prescribing of small doses: if they are acting in what a responsible body of medical opinion would accept as being a responsible way, they have nothing to fear.'

The interviewer commented: 'The judgment against Dr Dally appears to hold doctors responsible for the conduct of patients outside the consulting room, and despite Sir John's assurances, supporters of methadone maintenance still feel exposed. They fear that the "responsible body of doctors" of whom Sir John talks are the same small group who began to dominate policy ten years ago. . . . '

Candida Tonbridge of Granada Television telephoned me. Granada wanted me to go to Liverpool on the weekend of my birthday to take part in a television programme of the type known as a 'Hypothetical' which would be conducted through an enquiry by a barrister. I would have found it amusing, but to give up the whole weekend, particularly a family weekend, was another matter. I hesitated but in the end agreed.

Bill Nelles, my ex-addict patient who now held an important position in the Terrence Higgins Trust, was taking part in the programme and tried to persuade me to come too. 'Your case has forced people to take sides in the dispute. You have a particular talent for highlighting the lunacies that go on.'

Bill also told me that the DHSS had sent a directive to all London DDUs asking them to adopt more flexible attitudes towards treatment. Some of the staunchest of the old guard had at last dropped their opposition to providing clean syringes for addicts. He also said that the rigid system of catchment areas was likely to be reviewed soon.

Ironically, however, the revelations of my case and increasing anxiety about the part played by injecting addicts in spreading Aids led to a tightening of attitudes and regulations. The area around Harley Street was full of addicts trying to find doctors or to buy drugs from those who had doctors. The few doctors who might have been willing to help were scared by threats from the Home Office and by the recent behaviour of the GMC. Meanwhile those who should have been looking after them, the clinic consultants, were still ignoring long-term addicts. And the police were harassing addicts, arresting them and confiscating their (often legal) drugs.

John Calderan told me that he had written a 'defamatory article' for a legal journal, saying that the GMC was the worst and most unjust organisation he had ever seen. The article was never published because John was persuaded to wait for the MDU's forthcoming criticism of the GMC. This did not amount to much in the end but the article was lost.

That week both the *Lancet* and the *British Medical Journal* printed letters about my case. Each journal carried one 'establishment' letter; the rest were sympathetic to me. The letters in the *BMJ* were inspired by Michael O'Donnell's article, and included a long and to me incomprehensible letter from David Bolt, a prominent member of the GMC. John Marks, who contributed a letter of his own, told me that Ian Munro, the editor, had commented on the number of letters arising out of the case. If I had been judged by these, he said, I would certainly have been found 'not guilty'.

That day I was told by a patient whose sister attended the DDU at Charing Cross that a worker there told patients: 'Dr Dally forces patients to use injectables.' I had ceased to be amazed by the lies that were spread about me.

Next day the post contained an invitation for me to attend the meeting of the Royal College of Psychiatrists in Llandudno which John Marks had told me about. It was the same weekend as the Liverpool television programme and I decided that I should combine the two.

I had another long talk with George Mikes, who had been pursuing his investigations. He talked about the Spearing Bill, going through Parliament at that moment, which ostensibly gave the GMC greater powers and enabled them to convict on 'professional misconduct' instead of, as at present, 'serious professional misconduct'. George had discovered that, despite the apparent increase of power the Bill would give them, the GMC were against it. 'The Bill opens up the whole way the GMC operates to greater inspection and they certainly don't want that. At present the conduct side is buried in paper, and it suits them if it stays that way.'

On 7 March *New Society* contained an article by Jeremy Laurance about recent changes in policy regarding the treatment of long-term drug addicts, now encouraging a 'more flexible approach'. It said that the DDU consultants had been told they should mend their ways. I was amazed at the change of tone. But I suspected that he was wrong about the change of policy at the DHSS.

My suspicions were confirmed when I telephoned Dr Dorothy Black, who worked in the Drugs Department of the DHSS. She said that Jeremy Laurance had got it 'out of context'. There was no change of policy. The DHSS wanted to attract more addicts, and were thinking of harm-reduction – that is, accepting that some addicts will continue to use drugs and helping them do as little harm to themselves and others as possible. Harm-reduction was never mentioned in the days when I was in contact with the DHSS over the Guidelines. Clearly things were changing.

'A consensus says that we must widen our boundaries,' said Dr Black. 'But there are no plans for new Guidelines. Being less rigid is part of the consultation process. There is now an urgent need to get in touch with more addicts, though Aids is top priority. Maintenance is a matter for the individual clinician faced with an individual patient.' She added, 'London is beginning to emerge as flexible.'

This was indeed a new tack. 'Maintenance' had been a dirty word for many years. But I doubted that things were changing in London, and I soon realised that 'flexibility' too was a word which, under pressure for change, was adopted by Drugspeak to cover the same old attitudes and practices.

On Friday 27 March, I travelled to Liverpool to film the Granada programme. Granada Television had invited spouses and partners too, so Philip came with me. The first person I saw on St Pancras platform was Sir Henry Yellowlees, a former Chief Medical Officer of Health to the DHSS and one of my judges at the GMC. He was one of our party, and although he looked inoffensive, just seeing him gave me an unpleasant feeling. He and his lady boarded the train behind us. I didn't want to sit in the same carriage as them so we moved to the next one. The only empty seats were next to several members of the drug dependency establishment. The rest of the compartment was full of people who worked in the drug field and lawyers who were interested in it, including Bing Spear and Bernie Simons, a well-known progressive solicitor.

It turned out to be an instructive journey. One of the drug dependency doctors, Dr P., tried unsuccessfully to impress the solicitors with his knowledge of the drug scene. Later he turned to me rather aggressively and asked what I hoped to see in Liverpool.

'The cathedral,' I replied.

'Which one?' I could sense that he was trying to throw me and expected me to say something like, 'Oh, is there more than one?'

'Both,' I replied.

He was visibly annoyed.

Later he asked me how many grandchildren I had, then boasted that he had more. 'They say I'm a soft touch for them – but not for anyone else.' He seemed to be proud of this fact.

Dr P. drank a whole bottle of wine, followed by a small bottle of whisky. During one of his frequent absences I remarked on this to someone, who laughed and said: 'Oh, he's just topping up.'

We arrived in Liverpool shortly before 10.30 p.m. A coach was waiting to take us to the Atlantic Towers Hotel, where we ate our belated banquet and then went to bed.

Next morning Philip and I woke early and had a quick breakfast before leaving for Llandudno, a journey of about one and a quarter hours. Granada provided us with a car and driver. We arrived at the Aberconwy Centre on the Promenade in time for the session, which began at 9 a.m. In the chair was Dr Thomas Bewley, with whom I had clashed two and a half years before. Bewley was now in his last few months as president of the Royal College of Psychiatrists. He was bustling round the hall wearing his presidential medallion of office. At first I couldn't think what he was doing but then realised he was concerned with ashtrays. A fanatical anti-smoker, he had told some of the younger delegates to remove all the ashtrays. I thought this an amusing authoritarian alternative to simply asking people not to smoke.

One of the first people I saw was Dr Philip Fleming, who had given evidence for the prosecution in my case. He greeted me cheerfully.

'Hello, Dr Dally, we met in other circumstances!'

I couldn't resist saying, 'We didn't meet, actually.'

John Lawson also greeted us warmly. He was now based in Bristol as Chief Home Office Inspector of Drugs for the West of England and Wales. Another who greeted me was Dr Brian Wells, Senior Registrar in Drug Dependency at the Maudsley. A self-confessed ex-addict, he strongly favoured abstention as a condition of treatment for all addicts. It had worked for him.

Soon after we sat down, John Calderan and his wife Barbara arrived and joined us. I thought how lucky I was to have a solicitor who cared so much about the case that he spent a weekend, at his own expense, studying the opposition. He and Barbara had attended the sessions on the previous day.

I had not met my opponents *en masse* before and the experience shocked me. Even more shocking was the standard of debate. Indeed, there was no debate. Each speaker went in turn to the rostrum, spoke his bit and returned to his seat. Bewley, comfortable in the chair with his chain of office round his neck, did not comment or try to influence the proceedings. There was no machinery for questioning. As a result, numerous absurd statements went unchallenged.

Andy Fox, a social worker, announced that clinics giving out drugs and needles in the 1960s had created 'drug-related illness'. I knew of no evidence for that and he did not provide any.

A well-known hardliner deplored the fact that John Marks's scheme in Liverpool gave out needles 'on a non-exchange basis'. Marks explained that the scheme brought in more needles than it gave out, but the doctor seemed unimpressed.

A weird psychiatrist whom I had never seen before announced in a slow, sonorous voice: 'It – shouldn't – be – easy – to – inject – drugs.'

Another psychiatrist gave us his message for addicts: 'Personalise your syringe!'

A delegate who said he was concerned with 'ethical and moral issues' informed us: 'It is bad to participate in what is bad in order that good may come of it.'

Fleming's summing up of the first motion, that needles be made available to injecting addicts, seemed eminently sensible. 'To get people into treatment,' he said, 'we may need to look at our prescribing policies. If we supply clean needles, why do we not supply clean, injectable drugs as well? Aids makes us all look again. We now need carefully controlled exchange schemes.'

Sound stuff, but the motion was not passed. The vote was 27 in favour (people who were positively against providing clean needles to those who injected) and 27 against. By coincidence there were also 27 abstentions. No one would now believe that the drug dependency psychiatrists were keen to stop the spread of Aids. Bewley as chairman gave a summing up which I could not understand. Neither could Philip or the Calderans. As we trooped downstairs for coffee, John said that he was amazed at the rigidity of thought displayed at the meeting.

The next debate, if one could call it that, was on the motion that 'maintenance has no place in the management of drug addiction and related conditions'. I thought that only a bigot, a lunatic or someone with a financial interest in prohibition could say that maintenance had *no* place. However, I soon found that many psychiatrists believed that it had not.

John Marks proposed the motion, speaking of 'controlled availability of drugs' as 'amelioration of a condition'. He pointed out that there were many people who were simply not interested in coming off drugs or who could not possibly do so.

> During this period in an addict's life, it doesn't matter what you do to him. It will make little or no difference. He will continue to take drugs. Doctors don't want to be innkeepers in the supply of clean drugs, yet they took on this responsibility. Having taken it on, they now refuse either to carry out the function or to relinquish it. They insist on keeping the power without helping the addicts. They go along with prohibition and so illegal drug-peddling has become virtually an epidemic.

A disturbing number of psychiatrists, most of them in charge of drug dependency services for a particular region, wanted to ignore the problem. Typical was one who clearly liked to think that there were no addicts in his area. 'If no one prescribes, no one requests,' he said. 'Let's not spoil our beautiful virgin territory.' Later I heard that this doctor had been in trouble with the Home Office for failing to notify the addicts in his area. Clearly he preferred to think that they did not exist.

Dr Brian Wells, the ex-addict psychiatrist, used an extraordinary argument to emphasise the importance of being drug-free. He told of a patient at the Maudsley clinic who was prescribed 72 ampoules per day (my average prescription was 4) and 'sits like a zombie all day except for his visit to the chemist'. Wells seemed to see this enormous dosage as an argument against all prescribing. This was typical of what passed for argument during the meeting.

Another doctor said complacently that we couldn't cope with all addicts so we should concentrate only on those who want to come off drugs. This was in fact the official line but was not usually described so openly.

A psychiatrist speaking in favour of the motion said that alcohol is 'mildly dangerous' and opiates are 'very dangerous and kill many'. He offered no evidence for this statement, which didn't surprise me since there wasn't any.

I wasn't surprised that the vote went against the motion. Two-thirds were against *any* form of maintenance. Another eleven abstained.

Clearly the drug dependency establishment, or a great number of them, were not prepared to alter their attitudes to help long-term addicts, even if doing so would prevent the spread of Aids.

John Calderan said: 'I was tempted to get up with my best Italian accent and say "I am a member of the Mafia. For my sake, please do not introduce maintenance." '

The next day, back in Liverpool, we went by coach to the Albert Dock, where Granada had restored the handsome old Cargo Exchange building as a studio. The floor was largely filled with a huge horseshoe table and armchairs, with two rows of chairs round the periphery for the audience. Above was another floor with a super-modern news studio.

Coming downstairs, I was confronted by Sir Henry Yellowlees. We acknowledged each other politely.

The programme went according to the usual formula of 'Hypotheticals'. Representatives of every profession concerned with drug dependency took part, with all participants closely questioned by Jane Belson, an impressive young barrister.

One of the most dramatic occurrences during the programme was a clash between Bill Nelles and Dr Connell. Without waiting for the barrister to lead him, Bill called across the table at Connell that his policies were responsible for a lot of suffering and death, and for the spread of Aids. Connell looked unhappy. The attack was echoed by Carlin Wilkowski, another patient of mine, and Jennifer McVeigh (billed as 'wife of an addict'), who was standing in for her husband Kevin.

Yellowlees, clearly impressed, began to talk about the importance of looking again at the Guidelines. Connell agreed that it was time for a 'new look', even at the question of maintenance. He emphasised the lack of evidence for maintenance, which was not true, but his statement was remarkable from someone well known for insisting that nothing was wrong in the treatment of addicts and that everyone was well provided for. The questioning had been such that it would have been difficult for him to say anything else.

My feelings about the programme were mixed, but the producers found it 'sensational'. Connell and Yellowlees had been seen to shift their stance during the programme. Most people seemed to think that the apparent change of heart of some of the participants was the indirect result of my case at the GMC.

We got back to London at about 7 p.m. We were about to drink a bottle of champagne to celebrate my birthday when a young barrister we knew arrived. He was obviously excited, and told us that a brief given to his room-mate concerned an addict charged with offences related to heroin. In the addict's statement to his solicitor, who apparently knew nothing about me or my case, he said that most of his police interview consisted of the officer asking whether he or any of his friends had evidence against me. 'I have friends interested in people giving evidence against Dr Dally at a tribunal. If you yourself can give evidence or you know people who can, there will be a financial reward. We know Dr Dally charges £60 for a prescription and that people are selling prescriptions for profit.' The policeman also said that if the addict cooperated, he would help him find a hospital for detoxification and this in turn would help him with the charges against him in court.

John Calderan was indeed interested but somewhat sceptical about being able to turn this into hard evidence. He would send someone to the court to cover the case and maybe use the information later. In fact it was never used. The lawyers decided to omit all evidence of bias or corruption from the appeal on the grounds that it would annoy the Privy Council.

Meanwhile I was pleased to watch my addict patients banding together into a self-help group. I had long thought that this was the only way they could get their plight taken seriously. Now the urgency of the situation seemed to strike them and I encouraged them to try to organise a pressure group to make the true situation known.

They called their new organisation the Drug Dependency Improvement Group (DDIG). Their first meeting lasted more than four hours. Andrew Veitch, then medical correspondent of the *Guardian*, was there. I wrote a document for them with suggestions for running a campaign, though I was not going to get involved in it myself.

On Friday 1 May I went to Bill Gage's chambers to discuss with the lawyers the document that would form the basis of the appeal, which had to be at 6 Downing Street by 4 p.m. on the following Tuesday. John Calderan was on holiday so a colleague, John Kelleher, was there in his place.

Bill Gage said that the evidence of prejudice in the GMC committee wasn't good enough. It was one of those many situations when we all knew what had been going on but probably could not prove it in a court of law. This was disappointing though not surprising. The thrust of the appeal was to be that the main charges were dismissed and that I didn't treat Khalid any differently from the rest of my patients. Bill also dwelt on the loss of half the committee during the hearing and seemed to think that he might make something of that. Someone pointed out that those who left the committee might have said things which influenced those who stayed. To me this did not seem compelling.

The next day Bill Nelles told me that a member of the GMC Professional Conduct Committee had told him he now felt unhappy about what had happened in my case at the GMC. I was grateful for this information but it had the effect of making me even more unhappy. I felt sure that even if this distinguished doctor had had a change of heart, he would not do anything about it, and I was right.

That week the *Lancet* published a powerful editorial entitled 'Management of Drug Addicts: Hostility, Humanity and Pragmatism'. It pointed out that while Aids had made the DHSS and Home Office admit that the present system was failing, all the arguments for a review would hold even if Aids had never existed.

I soon learned that, in spite of increasing anxiety about Aids, and the fact that drug users were spreading it through the heterosexual community faster than any other group, the government working group on Aids contained not one drugs expert. I was not overly surprised, having realised that the government wanted as little fuss about Aids as possible.

The government's actions were predictably cosmetic. A committee set up to look into the problem made mild recommendations for change, such as improved facilities for long-term addicts. Publication of the report was delayed, then the government announced that it was doing nothing about it. The treatment of addicts continued much as before.

I also heard of concern that John Marks, after his performance on my behalf at the GMC and after repeating his views many times in public, would be attacked by the drug dependency establishment. He was not aware of the danger he was in, and one informed well-wisher hinted that I should warn him. 'He should make sure that he rallies his supporters and so cannot be set aside as a lone maverick.'

I did try to help him, without success.

George Mikes had been pursuing his researches. He said that the close relationship between the Privy Council and the GMC made the appeal unlikely to succeed. 'They're always in and out of each other's offices and handing out honours to each other.' He also said that anxiety in the GMC after my case had caused the Council to set up a working party to look into the procedures of the Professional Conduct Committee.

When John Calderan returned from holiday I told him I was

disappointed that we weren't going to use any evidence about the prejudice and dirty tricks of the GMC. He too was disappointed but said that the law, like politics, is the art of the possible. When I told him what I had heard about the relationship between the GMC and the Privy Council, he replied: 'The Law Lords feel that they need to keep in with their doctors.' But he seemed optimistic.

I suggested to some of the addicts who were setting up the self-help group that, since my appeal was coming up soon, they should try to find out how they stood in relation to the drug clinics. With change in the air, I felt that some clinics might be persuaded to accept long-term addicts on terms that were acceptable to them. I drafted a letter for them to send to all clinics in London and the Southeast. The letter explained their predicament and asked whether, and in what conditions, the consultant might be willing to take them on.

Then they waited for the replies, very few of which came.

On 21 May I myself wrote to the consultants in an attempt to make arrangements for my patients.

That afternoon, just as Philip and I were preparing to leave for the bank holiday weekend, John Calderan rang to say that there was some uncertainty about when the appeal would be heard. Originally scheduled for October, it had been moved forward to the end of May. But now there was talk of October again. He would know definitely on Tuesday.

It was a strain not knowing what was happening all that weekend. Then I spent Tuesday in suspense waiting for John to telephone. Eventually I told Anne Lingham to put John through to me even if I had a patient – a thing I very seldom do. He rang finally to say that the appeal would now begin on Monday 27 July.

In the meantime, it seemed that the expected attack on John Marks had begun. An official complaint had been made to the local health authority about his needle exchange scheme. One of his supporters pointed out that because of him, Liverpool was the only major city that did not have an Aids problem. When I told John Calderan this, he said: 'And that's enough to annoy the establishment.'

In May, a letter from Bing Spear was published in the *Lancet*. He said that the Guidelines ignored long-term addicts, and proposed the term 'stabilisation' rather than 'maintenance' for their long-term treatment. I was delighted that after years in the Home Office, unable to speak out, he had at last 'gone public'. But I knew that his letter would annoy the drug dependency doctors.

I was frequently surprised at the interest shown by people working in quite different fields. For instance, I wrote to the *Sunday Times* for a knitting pattern they had offered to readers. When they sent the pattern, a note was enclosed saying: 'We in the office do wish you the very best of luck in your forthcoming appeal. We hope that the authorities will come to their senses!'

A month after I had written to the DDU consultants in London and the Southeast asking whether they would be willing to see my patients, fewer than half had replied. Some of these said they would not see any long-term addicts. None offered to take over their treatment. Those who were willing to see them at all insisted on a period in which the addict would have to live on the black market while being 'assessed'.

These letters were in line with what I knew of clinics. It was no more than I had expected, even in the middle of an epidemic of Aids spread by black-market drug users.

Shortly after that, the addicts in the self-help group DDIG went to the Home Office Drugs Branch and were delighted by the friendly reception they received. But their enthusiastic accounts gave me a 'Trojan horse' feeling. I no longer trusted the Home Office. Probably they wanted to be in touch with the addicts so as to have some control if I lost the appeal. Since few clinics were willing to cooperate, eighty addicts suddenly dropped on to the black market might cause bad publicity. After all, the Home Office had been threatening to summon me before a tribunal only a year before. They had shown no concern then for what would happen to my patients. When I asked what would happen to them, I was told, 'That isn't our concern', or 'They can go to clinics.'

So what was different now? Why were my patients suddenly so special? I felt that part of the answer must lie in the media's change of attitude. Only recently, *Time Out* had published a splendidly frank article by Andrew Tyler which included a lot of things that were not usually mentioned, such as the power struggles and the 'brotherhood of psychiatrists who took the subject over'. This threatened both the Home Office and the drug dependency establishment, particularly with all the publicity about Aids. The last thing the Home Office would want was publicity about dozens of addicts being turned out on to the black market.

Doctors and civil servants were increasingly talking about 'flexibility'. But Dr David Marjot, who attended their meetings, was convinced that few consultants would change with the times. I too felt that offers or promises were likely to evaporate. In sixteen months of trying, I had

not managed to transfer anyone who still needed a high dose or who
was on injectables.

As the day of the appeal approached I could feel my anxiety rising. I
tended to retreat into myself and wake in the early hours. Sometimes
the problem seemed to be how to continue to endure it all.

But it was more difficult to cope with my patients' anxiety. They
responded to the uncertainty in different ways. One said he had lit a
candle for me in his local Catholic church. Another told me that one
of his duties as a local authority worker was to visit old people. His
'regulars' had become fond of him and trusted him so much that they
often showed him their hoards of cash and jewellery. He had never
been tempted to abuse their trust, but now, facing the uncertainty
of what would happen if I lost my appeal, he had become extremely
anxious. 'I'll be faced with the problem of raising £80 a day for the
black market, and I'm sure to lose my job for poor time-keeping. I
doubt whether I shall have the strength not to go where I know cash
and jewellery are hidden.'

Another confided: 'Since I became your patient I've managed
to save a few thousand pounds for the first time in my life. If
you are banned from prescribing, I shall go to Pakistan and buy a
large quantity of heroin to bring back and sell. It's the only way I
shall be able to survive. Of course, sooner or later I'm bound to go
to jail.'

I mentioned this to the next patient I saw. He said: 'Funny you
should say that. I've decided to do precisely the same thing. It's the
only way.'

I decided not to mention it to any more patients.

A few days before the appeal I had a vivid, anxious dream. I
was trying to find my way around the countryside, in relation to the
case. Marked on the map was a huge beacon, placed at the junction
between the land belonging to my grandfather and that owned by his
brother. In reality that land is now built over by the M24 motorway,
which runs precisely between the two properties. In the dream this
beacon was derelict and only a huge, broken slab remained. I was
with Bill Gage in the driving cab of a large truck. The only guiding
light was fixed on the *back* of the truck, like those for shooting rabbits
at night.

This dream seemed to express how much I had had to change
my views and my 'guiding-lights' during this case. I could no longer

rely on the old beacons, developed in childhood. In dreams they were derelict and in real life they were covered with concrete. I had only what I carried behind me as I drove, and this showed the way back, not forward. The past was becoming illuminated but the future was still uncertain. I woke with a strong feeling of anxiety.

At the next legal conference, Bill Gage said that the whole appeal was likely to hinge on whether he could persuade the Lords to go through the evidence. 'In the House of Lords they tend to become far removed from evidence and to spend their time debating minor legalistic points. I'm going to try to get them to see that in order to judge this case fairly they must go through the evidence with me. If we can't get them to see that, we shan't get anywhere.'

I was disappointed that so little of the true situation could be revealed, but I kept my spirits up by thinking about Bill's repeated statement that, whatever happened, I had already won a victory and had changed public opinion. I tried to concentrate on this as a means of defending myself against the indignities I might suffer the following week. During this time many people telephoned to wish me luck. This too was gratifying, but also tiring.

When the day finally dawned, I got up and wrote my diary and felt calm. After all, I didn't have to perform. I would sit back and watch and learn what I could.

The Privy Council building is in Downing Street. The Law Lords come there from the House of Lords down the road. I knew that they were due to hear another case that day, the *Spycatcher* case, in which John Calderan was also involved.

Philip, Jane and I arrived an hour before the hearing was due to begin, so we sat in the sun in the Embankment Gardens. Time passed slowly. Tourists at the end of Downing Street were peering in and photographing their children with the policemen. When the time came for us to go in, we were allowed in without hindrance or search.

John was already there with his team. He greeted me cheerfully with good news. Due to the 'packing' of the House of Lords in the *Spycatcher* case, my panel of judges had been changed. As well as Lord Goff, who was on the original panel, we now had Lord Mackay, shortly to become Lord Chancellor. 'He's a very nice man. We also have Lord Keith. Overall it's a great improvement.'

Christopher Sumner, resplendent in wig and gown, seemed pleased too. 'It won't make any difference to the outcome but it does affect the style.'

Bill Gage, looking even more splendid in a gown with embroidery on the sleeves, seemed to share their view.

'You look terrific,' I said, trying to lower the tension. 'I'm sure the judges will be impressed.'

Bill laughed. 'I wish it was as easy as that!'

The court room of the Privy Council was high, with windows on both sides. The back looked out on the garden beside 10 Downing Street, a view dominated by the thick foliage of a London plane tree under blue sky. The court had a more pleasant and dignified atmosphere than the GMC.

While we waited a reporter from *The Times* asked if he might photograph me for the paper. John said it was all right, and we went downstairs because he wanted to take a picture of me standing under the doorway that said 'Judicial Committee'.

Preston was on the other side of the waiting area. His junior, Jeremy Stuart-Smith, was also there, as were the bearded GMC official who had sat with the committee during my case and one of the GMC solicitors. Later my daughter Jane told me that during the hearing he kept staring at her in a hostile way. Debbie, John's assistant, said he did this to her too.

The court started punctually at 11 a.m. We had to wait outside while one of the judges read out a judgment in another case. Then he called out: 'The appeal is dismissed!'

I tried not to take this as a bad omen.

The barristers wore wigs and gowns but the judges did not. The judges sat in a row nearly in the middle of the room, with a white-haired man, the Registrar of the Privy Council, behind them. There were three Lords, all pleasant-looking gentlemen in late middle age. The lawyers were crammed into a small corral in front of them.

I sat behind my lawyers. There was a row of chairs against the wall on three sides of the room for press and public.

Bill told the judges that he proposed to deal with my case under the headings laid down by the other side rather than ours, and he went through them briefly. He said that the two findings were inconsistent and that to show this he must look at the relationship between the two charges. He had told me it would be difficult to get the judges to see that they must go through the whole evidence, and he asked them, oh so politely, to consider it. He emphasised repeatedly how important this was and led them gradually towards it.

The judges seemed to be interested, and I thought this was a triumph. Bill discussed in detail the fact that the committee gave no reasons for their findings, which in this case was necessary. He reiterated that Khalid had been treated no differently from any other of my patients and managed to read out some of the nastier bits in the letters written by the GMC solicitors. Later he told me that he wanted them to see just how nasty those letters had been.

I was impressed at the way the judges assiduously wrote down references and main points and looked them up in the GMC transcript, or in the law books that were provided. There was much legal discussion with references.

To my surprise, Bill managed to bring in the point that the case was really about a dispute within the medical profession. He quoted Ashworth's sarcastic doubt about my evidence that many respectable doctors agreed with me.

Bill then discussed the Guidelines. At this point he mentioned neither the fact that I sat on the committee that produced the Guidelines nor the hypocrisy that went on there. When he brought this in later, I saw the judges sit up in surprise and take notes. This was much more effective than if he had said it at the start.

Bill spoke until about one o'clock and then suggested stopping for lunch. As we withdrew, the lawyers seemed to be quietly optimistic. 'At least they are *listening*,' said Bill.

'A *good morning*,' said John. 'That is the first hurdle.'

But Christopher introduced a more realistic tone. 'The Law Lords will still be doing everything they can to uphold the findings of the GMC.'

Philip and I took the two young solicitors and all the family to lunch at the Red Lion pub in Parliament Street. Bill and Christopher came in, but I knew they would want to be on their own. Preston and his crowd were also there, but Emma assured me that they were too far away to hear what we were saying.

During the afternoon Bill continued his submission. He talked until after 4 p.m., by which time the Lords were looking weary. Bill suggested stopping for the day.

We went home by taxi. Most of the family, including baby Rebecca, now a year old, came round for the evening. The telephone rang frequently, mostly with calls from friends or journalists.

One of those who rang was Cindy Fazey, wanting to know how the day had gone. She also gave some bad news. An official committee had been sent to Liverpool to look at the drug dependency services run by John Marks. 'Its members are hoping to find dirt on him,' she said. 'They're poking their noses into everything his clinics do.'

Next morning during breakfast I heard Wendy Savage avoiding talking about my case on LBC. The interviewer tried hard to make her, but she always parried the question and steered the reply round to the subject of discrimination against women.

We were early getting to court again, and as it was raining we waited in the ante-room. The usher was extremely friendly, and to pass the time I asked if I could go to the other side of the building to look at the view from the window. 'Come into the Chamber, where you get a better view,' he replied.

He accompanied me and explained what we saw. The garden at the back of the building was cool and leafy. The side wall of Number 10 formed the left-hand boundary of the garden. Facing and on the right was the Cabinet Office. On the far lawn stood a bit of old wall which the usher told me was part of Henry VIII's Whitehall Palace. The Chancellor of the Exchequer's children often played on the lawn with their dog, he said, because Mrs Thatcher wearied of their playing under her window.

When the hearing resumed, Bill continued his submission. He said again that Khalid had been treated no differently from the rest of my patients, and went on to the subject of the reduction of dosage, about which Preston had made so much fuss. The Lords seemed to side with the GMC on this point and asked questions which presupposed that the rate of reduction of dosage was a test of the adequacy of the treatment. With superb timing Bill described the way John Marks treated his patients and pointed out that none of the doctors called by me thought the rate of reduction important. He then went on to discuss the Guidelines, the problems of long-term addicts, and the subject of monitoring.

When the question of leaving prescriptions with the receptionist came up, no one seemed to know how much I charged for this. Although it was £10, Preston told the court that it was £15. Several questions were asked which only I could have answered, but it was not for me to speak.

Then came the question of the way I discharged Khalid. I thought Bill made the GMC's accusations look absurd. Finally, at about 12.30 p.m. Bill said that he was 'pulling the threads together'. He told the Lords of their options in the case. They could decide that the findings were 'unsafe', or they could send the case back to the Professional Conduct Committee of the GMC. He then went on to discuss the severity of the sentence. Lord Keith remarked that he did not think a twelve-month ban (it was actually fourteen months) a severe sentence for serious professional misconduct.

When Bill went on to discuss what constitutes serious professional misconduct, quoting several cases, Lord Keith dismissed his argument. He also rejected the request to include the letters of submission from DDIG and from several patients. This was the only stage in the proceedings at which Lord Keith seemed to become irritated, though it was all done politely.

Bill told the judges of the changes in public policy regarding the treatment of addicts, and how there was to be a new committee under a lay person which would look into the relevance of the Guidelines. He then explained how the penalty imposed by the GMC would affect the patients.

Last, he came to the question of the quorum, and how the committee had started with ten members and ended with five. Here the Lords, especially Lord Keith, became quite huffy. 'I don't think it's your best point, Mr Gage. Five is enough if they have heard all the evidence.'

Bill put it to him in a different way. 'We are thinking of natural justice,' he said. 'Supposing it was one of us on trial by our peers, how would we feel if the five judges who started gradually became three? It might be just, but it doesn't look good.'

Bill finished his submission. Everyone agreed that his performance had been outstanding. He had persuaded the Law Lords to let him go through all the evidence in what was virtually a retrial. Not until the very end was he hurried by the judges.

John had told me that the two things most likely to win me the case were a change in public opinion and 'superb advocacy'. 'Now we have had both,' he said.

Bill laughed about the quorum episode. 'It's not a bad thing to produce a tail-end Charlie that carries no weight.'

The lawyers seemed pleased. Various reporters tried to interview me, but I couldn't cope with that.

In the afternoon Preston presented his submission. It was painful to hear it all again, especially where, as before, he put the worst possible interpretation on everything. Much of it consisted of a personal attack on me. For instance, Bill Gage had discussed the division of opinion in the medical profession about the treatment of long-term drug addicts.

John Marks had said, and Bill repeatedly emphasised, that there were addicts whose dose you cannot reduce, sometimes for years, until such time as they decide for themselves to become drug-free. Preston, talking about my treatment of Khalid, said that for months and years there had been 'no reduction, no treatment . . . ', as though this was evidence of my crime.

Suddenly Lord Goff leaned forward and asked: 'Mr Preston, what kind of treatment have you in mind that the doctor might have provided?'

This kind of question had never been asked at the GMC. Preston was taken aback. He blustered, 'Well, m'lord . . . ' and began to use words like 'reduction' and 'counselling'. Lord Mackay then pointed out that we had already heard a good deal about the difficulties of reducing the doses of long-term addicts. 'What can a doctor do under those circumstances?' he asked.

There were several such interventions. When Preston said how much Khalid had improved once he stopped coming to me, one of the judges pointed out that no sooner had he left me than he had got into trouble with the police. Lord Mackay remarked that if Khalid was drug-free at all, which he seemed to doubt, it had been for only a short time.

After Preston had finished, Bill got up again to deal briefly with points he had raised. One point had been that at the outset of the GMC hearing, Preston had expressed his hope that the hearing would not be 'political'. Bill pointed out that on the very next page of the transcript, Preston had himself made it political by accusing me of not keeping to the Guidelines, which were at the heart of the political controversy. This was a brilliant bit of quick thinking. Finally Bill spoke about costs.

The Law Lords then announced that they would withdraw. We waited in the ante-room for a while until counsel were summoned. Their Lordships intended to defer judgment until the new Law Term, due to start in October. Preston was apparently pressing for the result to be given soon, long before the full judgment had been written, but Bill was adamant. He wanted both together, all or nothing.

Bill came up to me. He was obviously pleased with himself, as he deserved to be. I asked him how he felt about it. 'The odds in your favour have increased.'

John said: 'You can no longer say that you haven't had a fair hearing, Ann.'

I agreed.

On the morning after the hearing ended, Wendy Savage was one of the first to telephone and ask how things had gone. She was just leaving home to record a programme about my case for Radio Cleveland. I had arranged to do my bit of the same programme later in the day. I told her roughly what had happened.

'It sounds good,' she said, 'but *never underestimate the establishment.*'

Chapter 15

The Sentence

On the day after the appeal ended I telephoned John Wall of the MDU. He was pleased about what had happened, and gave the impression that he thought the MDU had invested their money well in my appeal. 'Most doctors haven't a hope of winning their appeals and we refuse to pay. If they still want to appeal, they have to finance themselves. Personally I think they are throwing their money down the drain. But we agreed to finance your appeal because we felt you had a sporting chance.'

He also felt sure that the judgment, even if it had gone against me, would be accompanied by some pretty strong criticism of the GMC. He seemed to like the idea of this.

John Calderan also sounded pleased. 'I don't like to be optimistic because so many things can go wrong,' he said.

In the afternoon I was interviewed by Radio Cleveland, who tried to link my case with that of Dr Marietta Higgs, the paediatrician at the centre of the child sex-abuse furore that was going on at the time. The male interviewer seemed to think that women doctors, like women in general, should know their place and remain in the background under their male superiors.

Later I went to Capital Radio and was interviewed together with Miranda Ingram, who had written an article about Wendy Savage and myself in *Cosmopolitan*. The interviewer didn't seem interested. Like the Cleveland man, he asked silly, superficial questions based on conventional sexism. The programme was broadcast that evening but didn't include our interview. I assumed that what Miranda and I had said was not what the programme makers wanted to hear.

One of the more interesting interviews I did was with Nicholas

Woolley for BBC *Newsnight*. His questions made me think things
out, which was unusual on such occasions. For instance he said he
had difficulty in understanding why addiction seems to run its course
regardless of what anyone does. I said that most medical conditions
have a natural history and, unless there is interference or a definite
cure, they develop in their own characteristic ways. The example I
gave was untreated pneumonia. Thinking about it later I thought of
many others – childbirth, measles, micturition, menstruation, virtually
every physical (and mental) process, normal or pathological.

Nick Woolley also pointed out that many drug dependency doctors
were on different sides of the divide and yet professed much the same
views about treatment. He said he thought the difference was that one
side was basically libertarian and the other authoritarian. I had long
thought this. I felt that one of the things most deeply wrong with
the medical profession at the time, and perhaps at all times, was its
authoritarianism. The fight against it was one of the most powerful
links between myself and Wendy Savage.

One addict who came to see me had had an interview at a clinic
which made some gesture towards cooperating with my patients. But
he was disappointed. As I had expected, the doctor was prepared to
start him on the same dose as he was having with me but only on
condition that he reduce rapidly over a few weeks or months and sign
a contract agreeing to do so. The patient, who had been an addict for
many years and had a responsible job, knew that he could not keep to
this. He also knew that, unless he signed, he would not be accepted at
the clinic if my appeal failed.

Meanwhile *New Society* published an editorial about 'the persecution
of Dr Ann Dally' and how the medical establishment was using its
disciplinary procedures in order to impose its current orthodoxies.
New Society also contained a news item about my case, pointing out
how the attitude towards long-term drug users was changing.

On 4 August the *London Standard* published a full-page article about
me and my case by Jeremy Laurance. It assessed the 'fierce row' in the
medical profession about the treatment of drug addicts. Unfortunately
it gave the impression that long-term addicts got 'bombed out of their
skulls each evening', which my patients certainly did not, and suggested
that to 'hand out drugs to addicts who need them' was an alternative
to the aim of bringing patients off drugs gradually. All too often I was
misrepresented as handing out drugs to all who wanted them.

A young addict from a wealthy family asked me an odd question.
He banked at Coutts. 'Dr Dally, when I write you a cheque, please

may I leave out the "Dr"? With all this publicity, they might guess that I'm an addict!'

There was definitely a liberal trend in attitudes towards drug addicts in general, yet life seemed to be more difficult than ever for long-term addicts. The police were hounding them even more than before, confiscating syringes, finding excuses to arrest them, and so on. The DHSS was still telling doctors to keep to the Guidelines and informing enquirers that my patients were now well settled in clinics, where they were receiving long-term prescriptions and injectables. This could not have been further from the truth. But I did hear that a very senior medical officer was now 'converted to harm-reduction'. My informant told me: 'At last he has realised that if we don't stop the war on drugs, all will be lost.'

The 'war on drugs' is, of course, a war that cannot be won, at least not by current policies. It is a fantasy war, maintained by those in power to increase and maintain that power.

At the beginning of the August bank holiday weekend we left London early. I was dozing in the garden of our country cottage when John Calderan rang to say that their lordships would deliver their judgment on 14 September. He said this was probably part of the response to complaints that the judges take long holidays while the work piles up. 'At least the judgment will be given at a civilised hour, 2 p.m.' John added, laughing, that he thought it meant that the Law Lords had decided it was unfair to keep me waiting so long for their favourable verdict.

It was a nice thought, but this news came as a shock. I had thought I had five weeks in which to prepare the patients. Now it was only two. I rang John back and asked whether, if I lost the appeal, it would be possible for Bill Gage to make a submission asking that I be allowed to continue prescribing until the addicts' clinic was organised. He said he would see about it, but pointed out that if they were going against me, they were likely to take the establishment view that my patients had had plenty of time to make arrangements.

On 2 September, exactly a year after I received the second letter of charges from the GMC, George Mikes's death was announced on the BBC news. It was not unexpected but I felt sad and depleted.

I heard that more politicking had been going on in the drug dependency world in Liverpool. John Marks's position was in jeopardy. Various factions wanted to get rid of him. Some drug dependency doctors hated him and everything he was trying to do. I had observed this at the psychiatrists' meeting at Llandudno the previous spring.

That day the government launched its new anti-Aids campaign, allegedly directed specifically at intravenous drug users. The full film would be screened the following night, 'after midnight', in other words when hardly anyone, including drug users, would see it. This seemed typical of the way such subjects were tackled in Britain. Bill Nelles was on Thames TV at 6 p.m., saying roughly this. He said that it might be effective in deterring young people from injecting but that it would do nothing for the addict who was already injecting. My view was that it would be a deterrent only to those who were already deterred.

An editorial in *The Times* that week gave out the party line on drugs. The article assumed that those who were dependent on drugs were 'bent on self-destruction anyway, with or without the additional risk of Aids'. I knew that this was untrue. Most addicts were scared of Aids and would take much trouble to obtain the clean needles that were made so difficult for them to get. Their urge for self-destruction was proportional to the contempt in which they were held and, as I had shown, decreased markedly if they were encouraged to have self-respect and dignity. That was something that society seemed to have forgotten.

The *Mail on Sunday* approached the subject more realistically. A leading article said the government campaign was 'a scandalous waste of public money. . . . If the Government was genuinely serious it would have the political courage to put the money into providing free, clean needles on the NHS for addicts . . . There is probably no alternative to deal with the hideous public health crisis we are now facing.'

I decided to ask all my addict patients who injected, about eighty in all, whether, if they found themselves in a position in which the only way they could inject was to share needles, they would do so. All showed knowledge and concern about Aids. About two-thirds said, reluctantly, that if faced with that dilemma they would 'take a chance' and share the needle. Their attitude seemed rather like that of the driver at a party who thinks his blood alcohol is probably over the limit but has no way to get home other than to 'take a chance' and drive.

Many of my patients were being rejected by clinics or were being offered only the standard regime and rigid reducing programme. They had many complaints about doctors who were absent, or unconcerned, or pontificating, or sadistic. There were also tales of long waits and offensive attitudes by the staff.

One of my patients was accepted by a clinic and the doctor agreed to give him injectable drugs. He had to sign a 'contract' to say that he would be drug-free by a certain date. This rather alarmed him, but he agreed since it gave him at least a year. I knew this would not be nearly enough for him. Nevertheless, it was the first time I had known a clinic prescribe an injectable drug on a fairly long-term basis. I was beginning to think that perhaps the clinics were beginning to show a more realistic attitude until another long-term addict told me that the same clinic had offered him only the standard six-week detoxification. I felt that the clinic doctors were playing politics with my patients and that the apparent liberality was in order to display an appearance of 'flexibility'.

The addicts were, of course, becoming twitchy again as the date for the judgment approached. I still felt calm, and wondered whether this meant I had run out of emotional energy. But I was tired and sleeping badly: it was wearing to go to bed at ten and be awake again by midnight.

John Calderan and I had arranged to meet at Downing Street at 1.30 p.m. As we entered the Privy Council building, television cameras were active. I had nothing to say to the journalists who waited to question me. I simply couldn't speak. The lawyers were already there, so were my family and a number of the addict patients.

There was one case before ours; it was dismissed rapidly. Then we were on. Lord Goff was the only one of the former three judges. He now sat on the chairman's right. I gathered that the chairman was Lord Templeman (the scourge of the Spycatcher case) and on his left was an elderly judge whose name I did not know.

Lord Goff announced that the appeal was dismissed and that costs must be paid by the appellant. That was all.

We left the chamber stunned. I felt numb; the lawyers were visibly shocked. When printed judgments were handed out I was too fraught to read mine but Bill read his. 'They've gone against us on every point,' he said quietly.

He also said that the ban on prescribing controlled drugs came into force immediately. 'From now on, Ann, you must be very careful what you do.' There was no possibility of giving me time to sort out the patients.

I gave several quick press interviews. A particularly ignorant and impenetrable radio journalist irritated me with his questions. When he had finished talking to me, he asked how he could contact some addicts. I told him that until a minute before he had been surrounded by them: they had looked so normal that he had not realised they were addicts. Meanwhile, the addicts themselves had all disappeared.

Back at home, Philip and I read through the judgment. It consisted only of a list of points made by the GMC and supporting comments from the judges. They praised Bill's presentation but ignored every piece of evidence he produced, and while they mentioned differences of opinion in the medical profession, they dismissed the suggestion that the case was 'political' by saying that the GMC counsel had assured them it was not.

As predicted by so many people, one branch of the establishment had supported another.

We had just finished reading when John telephoned. He was furious. 'The judgment is amazing! I've never seen anything like it.'

He suggested going to the European Court and said he would talk to John Wall about it. John Wall thought it would be a good idea to have a conference with an eminent QC specialising in European matters.

Various patients telephoned and expressed their anxiety. During the afternoon the secretaries took the calls, but after they went home at 5.30 p.m. I had to deal with them myself. I felt miserable at being able to do so little for the addicts now. I had even been warned to make arrangements for them only through their general practitioners. Yet most GPs would do nothing and some refused even to see them.

All my children came round that evening. While Rebecca ran round eating nuts from the bowl, I did several interviews for television and radio, and the case was discussed on the BBC radio news. I didn't hear it, but gathered they had an addict talking about the tragedy of the judgment for them. In all my interviews I tried to emphasise this and to mention the lack of facilities for treating addicts in London.

The next morning was heartbreaking. When patients began to arrive I had to tell them that I could not prescribe for them. All I could offer was a few tranquillisers to take the edge off their distress until they could make other arrangements, which I knew would probably mean the black market.

The patients were terribly upset. In the waiting room grown men were in tears. One couple had run out of drugs over the weekend and already showed signs of withdrawal. Another, sweating and agitated, wanted to know on whom he could vent his anger. I gave him the GMC address and off he went. Shortly afterwards, Anne Lingham buzzed me and said that he was back from the GMC. He had spoken to a Mr Howes, who said that the ban didn't come into operation until I had actually received the letter from the Privy Council. For the present I could go on prescribing as normal.

I telephoned Mr Howes, who told me that this was true. 'You are still fully registered,' he said. The judicial committee had to report to the Privy Council, whose meetings were held at unknown times for security reasons. 'Of course they accept it automatically,' he added, complacently. 'They then write to you. From that moment on, the provisional registration operates.' He did not know how long it would take. A day, a week, perhaps even longer.

When I rang John Calderan, to keep him informed, he told me: 'Write a note to Mr Howes, confirming what has been said. And get it round there pretty quick!'

Over the next two days, I saw patients both booked and unbooked. Appointments became chaotic as the addicts poured in, hoping to get there before the ban. This was hard work, but it made things easier. I had fantasies that it would last until the end of the following week, by which time I would have seen almost all my patients and eased the heavy burden that had been imposed on them. I also wrote a standard letter of referral to give to each patient, promising to send a fuller report to any doctor who requested it. None did.

I lost count of the journalists who telephoned. One of them was Jeremy Laurance, who was writing a quick piece for that week's *New Society*. The paper had already asked me to write an article when the case was over and Jeremy said they wanted it by Monday for the issue of the following week. I knew this would be difficult but was determined to meet the deadline.

Next morning I was in the middle of a consultation with a young couple when two buzzes on the intercom alerted me to possible trouble. The secretaries had instructions never to interrupt a consultation with a patient unless it was really urgent.

It was the GMC. In an extraordinarily aggressive manner the man told me that the Privy Council had met the previous day and that the ban on my prescribing controlled drugs was in operation as from that minute. He seemed to gain much pleasure in conveying this information. His letter confirming it arrived less than an hour later, which made me realise why he had telephoned me. Anne Lingham told me later that he had been unpleasant to her and had insisted on my being interrupted.

So that was it. I remembered the dire warnings of my lawyers and didn't write any more prescriptions for controlled drugs. I had to resist the desperate appeals of several patients to 'backdate a little'. I knew that was where the slippery slope began and I was not tempted.

I had to tell the patients I saw for the rest of the day that I could not prescribe controlled drugs any more. There were still things I could do for them, though, including helping them to make other arrangements. I could also give minor tranquillisers, or so I thought, to help them until they found alternative sources. I presumed that now the ban was in operation, clinics would be willing to see my patients. But many had long waiting lists, and although I had been told they were waiving them for the occasion, I knew that in some clinics this was unlikely. Again, the authorities didn't want my intelligent, articulate addict patients disrupting the scene.

I never had controlled drugs in my possession, so I was saved the humiliation of having to hand them over. No one defined 'controlled drugs' for me but I assumed they were what practising doctors mean by 'controlled drugs', the ones that have to be kept locked up and for which prescriptions have to be written like cheques, in letters as well as numbers. In effect this covered the opiates, the barbiturates, the amphetamines and a few others. They were all clearly marked *cd* in various publications, including *MIMMS*, the monthly publication produced by the pharmaceutical industry to help doctors with their prescribing, and the more official *BNF*, the *British National Formulary*.

This assumption of mine was to have extraordinary effects.

I spent the evening writing and polishing my article for *New Society*. This forced me to collect my thoughts and put them on paper in a disciplined way, and I felt better for having written it.

The next day I talked with Jane Goodsir of Release, who was blunt in her comments. 'The judgment showed the most disgusting side of the British establishment. Although they know you've done nothing wrong, once they have started it they feel they must go through with it.'

Many of my patients had rung Release. She and her staff were finding that they could often negotiate with the clinics better than the addicts could on their own. She continued: 'You often get a clinic doctor who is intransigent with a patient and refuses all sensible help, trying only to impose his short-term regime or refusing to have anything to do with the addict. But if an *organisation* rings up and discusses it, the doctor is likely to think again. These doctors often go completely into reverse when we do that. They play power games with the patient, but will treat with Release on equal terms.'

Of the many accounts and commentaries in the press on the appeal and its consequences, only Diana Brahams in the *Lancet* made a point that particularly struck home with me. She wrote that the Lords' judgment was a 'foregone conclusion' because the Privy Council had agreed that doctors are the best people to discipline doctors.

Diana had suggested this before, and it was also the view held by my lawyers until their hopes were raised during the actual hearing of the appeal. We were all deceived then. Some people thought that the Law Lords were genuinely sympathetic but that afterwards they were 'got at' from above for political reasons, as they seemed to have been (amid much press criticism) in the *Spycatcher* case. Others agreed with the *Lancet* article that the case had been a foregone conclusion right from the start.

The government working party was sitting at last to encourage doctors to treat long-term addicts and to make the Guidelines more sensible. It had taken a long time to convene and there had been much politicking. Public opinion had definitely changed, though I suspected that any official changes were likely to be cosmetic. The question in my mind was, how far would the drug dependency establishment be able to create a semblance of change while continuing in the same old rigid and ineffective policies? The moral victory might be mine, but would this help the addicts for whose welfare I had struggled so hard?

I felt that the improved press and the educating of journalists was bound to have a beneficial effect, but this might take a long time. I knew that some articles and programmes were still stifled by editors worried about offending the establishment. But now, unlike a year before, some were being published and more courageous programmes were occasionally produced. People, many of whom I didn't know, were calling and writing all week to tell me that this was my real victory.

There was, too, some change in the clinics. While spending gruelling days trying to get my patients fixed up, I learned that the drug clinic at the Maudsley Hospital was apparently making concessions to my patients, including seeing them straight away instead of putting them on the waiting list for many months. They were prescribing for some immediately without making them spend six weeks on the black market, and were even prescribing injectables. Such things had not happened to 'new' patients attending DDU clinics for more than a decade. Even though I gathered it was strictly on a 'short-term basis', I regarded it as a triumph.

Of course there were catches in the Maudsley's 'flexibility'. Patients were made to sign the inevitable clinic 'contracts' in order to get drugs. Most knew they could never keep the contract, so they started off in a situation of deception. It didn't bode well for the future and I guessed that, once the 'emergency' was over and there was no danger of publicity about the poor quality of the services, the reducing regime would drive these addicts away from the clinic.

My prediction was correct. After a few months all the patients I knew had left the Maudsley clinic, unable – as I had predicted – to keep their 'contracts'. So much for flexibility.

A consultant at another DDU, a known hardliner, telephoned me one day. He had been totally uncooperative when I had sent my letter, and he began our conversation by telling me that he didn't believe in my philosophy.

'And I don't believe in yours,' I answered cheerfully.

But he did make what seemed to be a magnanimous gesture. 'I'm willing to give linctus to any addicts with withdrawal symptoms.'

In general most long-term addicts feel that 'linctus' – liquid oral methadone – does not help them. Yet it was the only opiate that most clinics were willing to prescribe, and then mostly on a rigid reducing regime and for a fixed time. This was one reason why the vast majority of addicts avoided the clinics and flatly refused to attend. But if they were ill and in a state of serious withdrawal from drugs, linctus did temporarily alleviate some of their unpleasant symptoms. I sensed that the doctor was proud to be able to offer help in easing the crisis.

'Thank you very much,' I said, genuinely grateful and a little surprised. 'I have a number of patients who may well need your help.'

'Well,' he said less enthusiastically, 'as long as they live in my catchment area . . . '

This gave his offer a different meaning. His catchment area was an outer suburb of London where only two of my patients lived. Both had previously attended his clinic and both had already told me that nothing would induce them to return.

Other clinic doctors didn't even go this far. At least one had refused to have anything to do with my patients, even if they lived in the catchment area. At others they were made to wait long hours. One patient was kept waiting for two hours after the time of his appointment, then the doctor went to lunch in the middle of the interview and made him wait another two hours. Altogether he was at the clinic for six hours. Like many others, he realised that attendance there would not allow him to continue his job, so he would be forced to give up one or the other.

Most patients attending the new 'flexible' clinics were obliged to pick up their drugs daily, which was also often incompatible with their jobs. And all were forced to agree to 'contracts'.

Five days after my ban came into force, Dr Johns of the Maudsley clinic telephoned me to say that the clinic would not take any more of my patients. He seemed unconcerned. It wasn't, of course, his responsibility.

The so-called 'flexibility' of the Maudsley offer disappointed the addicts who went there. Some became angry at what they regarded as a 'con'. I had a number of telephone calls from other ex-patients saying that the clinics were 'no help at all'. The current Home Office advice to addicts had changed and was now simply: 'Go and find yourself a private doctor.'

Some of my patients concluded that if they tried to remain 'legal' and attend the clinic, this was likely to make their predicament even worse. They had no faith in Home Office assurances.

'Well, I'm off to rob a chemist. It's the only thing for me to do,' said one. Several made remarks of this kind; several to my knowledge carried out the threat. The first death of a patient of mine from overdose of black-market heroin occurred that week. Others were to follow. At least two others were arrested by the police in the West End. Before this no patient of mine had been arrested in the West End for nearly two years.

Two women patients who felt obliged to return to the black market were, I knew, HIV-positive. They lost their jobs for poor time-keeping and were working as prostitutes when I last heard of them. Yet there was increasing concern about drug users spreading Aids among heterosexual clients.

One of the most depressing things during the first week of the ban on my prescribing was the reaction of some general practitioners. Several shut the door in an addict's face or immediately struck him off their list. This behaviour was directly contrary to the 1984 Guidelines, though I knew it was regarded as acceptable by many. No doctor had ever been disciplined for refusing help to an addict. During the whole of that week I heard of only two GPs out of a possible eighty who were prepared to help my patients in any way, and this was with a small amount of linctus for a few weeks only.

During the same week I received a letter asking me to submit both written and oral evidence to the committee appointed to revise the Guidelines. I found this interesting. The committee had been sitting for several months. Why did they write to me now?

On the day that my ban was enforced I realised that, for the first time ever, I had earned nothing in the practice. I saw only one patient, and he couldn't pay. But the second post contained an unexpected cheque for royalties on my book *Mothers*. It had been published twelve years before and I had thought it was dead, but now I learned that it had sold well in Germany and had been bought by a Swiss book club. I was happy to take this as an indication that I must ease up on clinical work and return to writing.

Later that day, ITV sent a car for me to appear on *Comment*, an excellent three-minute programme that went out after the Channel 4 news, in which someone talked straight to camera for three minutes on a subject of topical interest. It was one of my favourite programmes and I was delighted to be asked. I thought the programme went well and so did the team, though when I saw it I thought I looked rather fierce and serious. 'It's a serious subject; that is as it should be,' said the producer.

Two weeks after the judgment I received a letter from John Wall saying that the MDU had agreed to pay for the opinion of Anthony Lester QC, a leading counsel specialising in European law, with a view to taking the case to the Court of Human Rights. I was pleased about that. Since I had not heard before, I thought the MDU had probably turned it down.

One day Mike Ashton, editor of *Druglink*, telephoned to say that for the first time he had heard complaints about me from my patients. He explained that the ban did not in fact start until the day after the GMC rang to say that I must stop prescribing immediately, so I could legally have continued to prescribe all that day and I could have seen most of the patients. Not knowing that I had been told I could not do this, some patients were saying that I could have done more for them at the end.

This was upsetting: I had done everything I dared to do and everything I had been told to do by the GMC. Mike Ashton seemed to understand and said he would tell any patients with whom he was in contact. I wrote to Phil Webb of DDIG explaining what had happened and asking him to put the record straight as far as possible.

*

Philip and I flew to America for a month. We both needed a rest and a change of scene. I was never so much in need of a holiday, and found it difficult not to remain preoccupied with the case.

After a few days on a warm island in Georgia the fatigue and the strain of the last sixteen months began to emerge. I felt very tired and slept a lot. Barbara Jones of the *Mail on Sunday* telephoned from England, and it seemed strange to be talking to the British press from so far away. But most of the time I just read.

One book that I re-read was Norman Dixon's *On the Psychology of Military Incompetence*. The sections on the authoritarian personality gave me further insights into what has happened in the field of drug dependency. In medicine, as in the military, authoritarians tend to gain control of areas that more able people are not interested in – and in medicine, their lack of humanity ensures that they make a mess of it. Dixon gives as an example the problem of venereal disease in the army. The authoritarians said that the solution was 'chastity'. Montgomery nearly lost his job for suggesting that it lay in practical measures such as condoms.

This was similar to the current approaches to the problems associated with Aids. The drug dependency world had been particularly slow to respond because the authoritarians were in control there. They tended to spend their time arguing about the exact definition of 'maintenance' and whether or not giving clean syringes to addicts spreads addiction.

By the middle of October, a month after the Privy Council's judgment, I had recovered considerably. I felt better and more alert. Some of my children came to stay and brought the mail from England. There was a copy of a letter from John Calderan to John Wall enclosing his descriptions of the GMC's prejudiced behaviour. It made interesting reading but I doubted whether it would lead to anything.

There was also a letter from Dorothy Black saying how satisfactorily everything had gone in the transfer of my patients to the clinics. I could muster only a wry smile. The civil service likes to see what it believes.

Being on the island put things into a different perspective, but I still didn't feel normal. I had been sleeping better but was not enjoying doing anything much, except reading. I still felt angry. I kept dreaming that I was on trial, prosecuted by Preston, his aggressive, sneering manner attacking me across a huge room or hall. I was surrounded by defensive lawyers who were trying to protect me. Just as they nearly succeeded, they could not, for their rules did not encompass the trial.

When we returned to London at the beginning of November, the huge pile of mail contained two important letters. One told me that John Marks had been sacked from his job as Chief of Drug Dependency Services on Merseyside. It had happened as a result of local politics: his outspoken views and radical thinking had upset some powerful people. I had expected this but felt sad.

The other letter was from John Calderan, reporting on the conference with Anthony Lester. Lester's opinion was that going to the European Court was pointless. I was disappointed, and also rather cross that they had held the conference in my absence. But I also felt relieved not to be going through yet another hearing. At last I had reached the end of my dealings with the GMC – or so I thought.

Chapter 16

The Third Hearing

On my return from America I had been trying to wind down my practice with as little suffering to the patients as possible, and trying to find other doctors for them. One day in early November two addicts who didn't know each other telephoned me separately to say they had had visits from the police, who had questioned them about my prescribing. The police had told them that I was in breach of the ban imposed by the GMC. They had been unpleasant to the patients and had made innuendoes about me. 'Oh, she's been supplying you with sleeping pills, has she? And how much does she sting you for those?'

They had also given the impression that these patients would be in trouble with the police for having consulted me. The patients were frightened.

I had prescribed minor tranquillisers, such as Valium and Dalmane, to help some of my patients through the difficult period of leaving my care. Since these were not, in doctor's terms, 'controlled drugs', I did not see what the police could possibly mean. Surely there was some mistake. I rang John Wall and he thought so too. When I told other doctors, the universal response was: 'You must be joking.'

But I wasn't joking, and neither were the police. Unknown to me, the minor tranquillisers had recently been added to two new schedules, 4 and 5, in the Misuse of Drugs Act. This did not concern clinical practice or doctors prescribing but was done to bring Britain into line with international legislation. It affected the import and export of these drugs, not prescribing. But the minor tranquillisers were now, technically, 'controlled drugs' under the Misuse of Drugs Act.

Ironically, it was only the minor and not the major tranquillisers that were included in this new regulation. 'Major tranquilliser' is the term given to the powerful drugs used for calming patients with serious mental illness. It is customary to prescribe milder drugs such as the benzodiazepines, Valium for example, to neurotics and people with anxiety or sleep disorders. I could easily have substituted small doses of major tranquillisers for these had I known.

The GMC had not said anything about this when they imposed the ban. They had not even mentioned the Misuse of Drugs Act. Minor tranquillisers were not classified as controlled in the reference books used by doctors to help with their prescribing. The drugs we all thought of as 'controlled' – such as opiates, amphetamines and barbiturates – were clearly marked *cd*. No other drugs were marked in this manner. A GP friend who telephoned the Home Office to ask about it was told that the regulation concerned only pharmacists, not doctors. And as far as anyone knew, these drugs had never before been included in a similar ban on a doctor, of which there had been many. Was this something that had been specially reserved for me? I couldn't believe that the committee which condemned me had deliberately laid a trap.

If the most common response to what was now happening was, 'You must be joking', the next was 'This is *real* persecution.'

Meanwhile I heard that police from Scotland Yard were interviewing my patients and going round pharmacies collecting prescriptions I had written.

At the same time that this was going on, a campaign was being mounted to have those very drugs classified as controlled drugs! This seemed less like Kafka and more like *Alice in Wonderland*.

When I told Bing Spear, his reaction was similar to when I first told him about the case. 'Words fail me,' he said. 'It's ridiculous.'

'What do you think it's all about?'

'I doubt if there's anything sinister. It's just that the police have nothing better to do.' He suggested that I ask the GMC to clarify the meaning of 'controlled drug'. It seemed extraordinary that, if they had intended a different meaning from the usual one, they had not said so. 'The police mind is black and white,' said Bing. 'I expect someone at Scotland Yard got the idea that he could pursue this and that's how it started.'

I thought it just as likely that someone at the GMC had got the idea that this was a new way to attack me.

'I doubt that the GMC committee intended the ban to extend to those drugs,' Bing said. 'Probably they didn't even know they come under the Act. In earlier procedures where doctors have been banned from prescribing controlled drugs, care has always been taken to see that they can carry on their normal practice. I don't think benzodiazepines have ever been questioned before.'

But he agreed that they might jump at the chance of harassing me further. 'In theory they won the case against you, but they got egg on their faces and that will have made them angry.'

John Calderan was furious. 'This is *persecution* – and I don't mean *prosecution*. I don't care what the police say or what the books say. Dalmane is a mild sleeping drug. It wasn't even mentioned during the case. The intention of the GMC was to stop you prescribing methadone. If you are technically guilty on this, there is lots of mitigation. Clearly this was never intended.

'The police are obviously gathering information at present and it will then be sent to the prosecutor. I don't want you to talk to anyone official unless I'm present.'

Because John was so busy, his colleague John Kelleher dealt with this case. 'It does seem extraordinary,' said one of the lawyers. 'Even if benzodiazepines *are* technically controlled drugs now, why should your prescribing them result in, not a telephone call or a letter but a full-scale police inquiry with a view to bringing criminal charges?'

'Do you think the GMC started it?'

'I don't know. Certainly they have been encouraging the police. The whole thing is a ridiculous, vindictive waste of police time.'

Nearly all the next meeting of AIDA (the Association of Independent Doctors in Addiction) was spent talking about this new problem. Every member had the same idea as I had about the definition of 'controlled drugs'. Michael O'Donnell, when I asked him, gave the same response. He had no idea about the benzodiazepines.

The common view was that it was unlikely that most members of the GMC knew either, but that they might well jump on the bandwagon if it was suggested as a means of damaging me.

When I next spoke to my solicitor he sounded disgusted. 'The police seem determined to complete the investigation and bring a criminal prosecution if they can. It's extraordinary, but they are trying to get you under the Theft Act! They are making out that it is "deception" – that you took fees for prescriptions knowing you were banned from writing them. I don't see how they can do that, but that's what they're after.

'Under normal circumstances we would approach the relevant body and try to clear up the matter with them, but in this case, because of the extraordinary hostility emanating from the GMC in all our dealings with them, I think it would be unwise.'

He had arranged a meeting with the police. We would find out more then.

While all this was going on I was still capable of being amused at events in the field of drug dependency. As I had predicted when 'flexibility' began to be urged on the clinics, some doctors who used to keep quiet about the patients they 'maintained' were coming out into the open to say how they had always prescribed for long-term patients. One consultant was now boasting about his 'flexible' prescribing when I knew that only a few months before he had concealed from his own nurses the fact that, while expressing prohibitionist views in public, he secretly had a number of 'maintenance' patients. When people are proud of what they have once concealed, public opinion has changed.

My solicitors were now convinced that someone was behind it all. 'We don't know who it is,' said John Kelleher, but it means that, absurd as it is, it's likely to be pursued as far as the police can take it, and after that will probably go back to be dealt with by the GMC. If you get a nasty judge, as you well might, it could be very unpleasant indeed. We take a very serious view indeed of the possible consequences.'

Bill Gage advised me not even to see any more addict patients, let alone prescribe anything for them, however free and harmless.

I felt I couldn't do this. I had only a handful of addict patients left, but that was not the point. If I was scared off and dropped them to save my own skin, I would never live easily with myself again.

The solicitors were sympathetic but we seemed to have reached an *impasse*. Bill Gage, master of manipulation, tackled me straight. 'Ann, the GMC clearly intended not only to stop your addict practice but also to get *you*. If you go on seeing addicts, however innocently, they will go on harassing you. The only way to comply is to stop seeing them. It is likely that this new trouble will come before the GMC. The whole thing is ridiculous, but there it is.'

Bill always seemed to win me over to his point of view when I was opposing the solicitors. I had to be convinced that they were right before I could cooperate fully with them.

We agreed that I should see the remaining addicts, but only to say that I couldn't treat them any more. The solicitors were going to Scotland Yard that afternoon to see the policemen in charge of the investigation. They would tell the police that my addict practice was at an end.

We also agreed that the solicitors would set up a meeting with the police to discuss the authenticity of the prescriptions. Then, with Bill

Gage's permission, they would seek clarification from the GMC of the ban imposed on me.

At Scotland Yard, the solicitors discovered that the situation was even worse than we had thought. The police seemed determined to prosecute me for 'deceitfully obtaining fees by illegally prescribing controlled drugs'. Then they wanted to send the case back to the GMC. To get me under the Theft Act, however, the police would have to prove dishonest intent, which none of us thought they could possibly do.

Even more bizarre, the solicitors warned me that I should be prepared for a police raid to see whether I had controlled drugs in my possession. This made life difficult: there were of course benzodiazepines in the house because that was where our practice was based. I had to be sure that none were in *my* possession. So I searched my drawers for any drugs that might be controlled and threw out all that I found.

Like everyone else, David Marjot seemed to take the whole thing as a joke. He was astounded that the minor tranquillisers I had prescribed were now 'controlled'. He offered concrete help. He had taken on several of my patients and thought I had treated them very well in the period after my ban. They would have suffered greatly had I not prescribed for them, and he was prepared to say so in court.

Bill Gage opposed the idea of asking the GMC what they had meant by 'controlled drugs'. He believed that an official inquiry of this sort might precipitate another action against me.

At the moment when the meeting with the police was being arranged my daughter Emma gave birth to Alice Elizabeth. Half an hour later I was at University College Hospital, holding my new granddaughter.

My friend Dr Elizabeth Fletcher came to lunch that day, bringing an article from *General Practitioner* about abuse of the minor tranquillisers. It demanded that they be made into 'controlled drugs'. Yet according to the police they already *were*, and they wanted to prosecute me for prescribing them.

Next day there arrived a letter from Dr John Strang, now consultant in charge of the drug dependency clinic at the Maudsley Hospital. He enclosed a letter he was sending to the *Lancet* and asked me to let him know if I had any comments.

Indirectly, the whole letter seemed a rather unpleasant attack on me. I didn't intend to correspond with him about it. Either I

answered it in the pages of the *Lancet* or not at all. When I happened
to mention it to Debbie Harrison, one of my solicitors, she said she
was most anxious that I should not write for the press while the police
case was going on. I didn't comment on Strang's letter but sent a note
thanking him for sending it.

John Calderan took me out to lunch. I was pleased to see him
again after so long, but I realised how disappointed he had been by
the Law Lords' judgment, and by their refusal to 'rock the boat'. I
also gave him a copy of Strang's letter and said I would like to know
what he thought I should do. I wasn't happy with Debbie's suggestion
that I ignore it, but I had written to Ian Munro, editor of the *Lancet*,
saying that 'On the advice of Senior Counsel, my solicitor is anxious
that I keep out of the public eye while this wearisome police case is
going on. . . . '

December arrived. I had still received no message from John about
the Strang letter when Ian Munro rang. 'I'll have to publish this letter
from Strang. It will be in this week's *Lancet*. I think it's very important
that you reply to it. These things *must* be aired.'

'All right. I'll write something regardless of what my solicitor says.'

I telephoned John, who had read the Strang letter and agreed that
I should reply. 'It is important that you keep a low profile at present,
but Strang has played right into your hands. Here is an opportunity
for you to make a point, not a platform.'

So I wrote my letter to the *Lancet*. In concluding I said: 'There
could be no clearer demonstration that present disagreements about
the treatment of drug addiction are in large part a dispute between
authoritarians and non-authoritarians. History is showing us that the
authoritarians cannot win their "War on Drugs".'

On 7 December Anne Lingham telephoned me in the country
to say that a letter had arrived recorded delivery from the GMC.
I asked her to open it. She read it out.

Written in the GMC's usual formal language, the letter informed
me that they had received information that I had been prescribing
controlled drugs and that this would be put before the Professional
Conduct Committee.

I felt both numb and relieved. They had written as nasty a
letter as they could, presumably hoping to make as much trouble
as possible. But at least, or so it seemed, they did not intend to start
another case immediately. I suspected that they knew it would make
them look ridiculous.

Our meeting with the police had taken place on 16 November at my solicitors' office. We kept the police waiting in the waiting room while we discussed the case and drank tea.

The solicitors reiterated that the sole purpose of the visit, agreed by the police, was for me to authenticate the prescriptions. This would save the police time and save patients from further interrogation.

When the police, a sergeant and a chief inspector, came in it was obvious that they had different intentions. Speaking slowly in heavy police jargon, they made it clear that they were not interested in my authenticating the prescriptions and had no intention of stopping their harassment of patients. They had come with the intention of interrogating me under caution.

'I refuse to allow that,' said one of the solicitors.

Disappointed, the policemen went through the motions of asking me to verify my signature on a number of prescriptions. I could see that they weren't interested. They wouldn't allow Debbie to photocopy the prescriptions, even though she offered to take the sergeant with her while she did it. At the end the inspector, rather exasperated, asked: 'Can't I even ask Dr Dally whether it is her intention to continue along the same path?'

'In what way?' asked the solicitor.

'In issuing prescriptions,' said the policeman.

'No.'

The inspector said that they would probably finish their investigation by the New Year 1988, but the Crown Prosecutor would probably not make up his mind until March. They would inform us as soon as they knew.

It seemed a long time then, but nearly two years later we have still not heard from them.

After they had gone I felt battered. The solicitors tried to comfort me.

One of them said, 'The police case is so weak that they were probably hoping to strengthen it by somehow getting you to incriminate yourself. You may think they were dreadful, but really they were no better or worse than police always are. They're always like that.'

Debbie also told me that John Calderan had been so upset by our appeal that he had asked Debbie to look into the history of such appeals. She found that none had ever succeeded! That shook me and also seemed to shake the lawyers. Later I learned that a few had succeeded early in the century, before the Privy Council was reorganised. That was small comfort.

On 12 December, my letter was published in the *Lancet* along with Strang's. This was much better than having them in different issues.

Two days later Debbie rang to say that Bill Gage had read the letter I had received from the GMC and took a very serious view of it. He wanted to have a legal conference, including John Wall of the MDU. When we met, Bill's first words were: 'This is amazing. Amazing.'

I knew that the whole thing could be made to look very nasty. Anyone who wanted to stick to the letter of the law had the opportunity to make trouble for me. There was talk about whether I should have consulted something more authoritative than *MIMMS*, the pharmaceutical industry's publication which most doctors use because it is known to be reliable and much easier to use than more 'official' publications. But why should *MIMMS* lie? Why should Bing Spear have lied? He had given a clear description of which drugs were controlled and even said that DF118, a mild synthetic opioid, was controlled in its injectable form (which I had never prescribed) but not in tablets. This correlated precisely with the information given in *MIMMS*.

It was decided, since we now knew that the GMC were involved, to prepare a statement for them as soon as possible. Then we would decide whether to show it to the police.

At one point John Wall mentioned the sacking of John Marks. 'Ostensibly it was due to a switch of funds by the Health Authority but everyone who knows anything about it thinks it was really because he had not followed the official line.'

Bill was shaken, but he said something that amused me. 'It's unbelievable! He was *such* a good witness! It suggests,' he went on, 'that there's truth in Marjot's allegations of a conspiracy working in this field.'

I was uncomfortable during the conference and after. Again I had the helpless feeling that people were out to 'get' me. But by Christmas I felt better. Many addicts and other people sent Christmas cards and messages of goodwill.

During the holiday I saw a film on television about Great Ormond Street Hospital, whose dedicated doctors and nurses were such a contrast to the doctors of the drug 'mafia'. Although the situation in the film was exaggerated and dramatised, it emphasised the satisfaction that real doctors get from healing and the commitment they give to it.

I continued to be impressed at the number of people in other fields who seemed to understand what was going on. At a party, a young midwife came up to me and said, 'You didn't have a chance. They stacked everything against you.'

By now Dr Colin Brewer, recently converted to my method of treating long-term addicts, had built up a big practice which included most of my former patients. They no longer had to use the black market, which made me happy. But I also knew it meant the end of DDIG, the self-help group.

Colin had previously applied to join our organisation AIDA. Now that he was becoming involved in the 'unorthodox' treatment of addiction, I felt we must invite him. Former addict patients had been ringing me about him. They were worried that some of his actions would get him into trouble.

At our meeting he talked about his growing practice and his recent change of heart. Until a few months before he had worked in a DDU, treating addicts along standard lines. He had thought of treatment only in terms of abstinence and quick detoxification. Until he started his present practice he had never prescribed injectables. Now he had become converted to my way of treating them, was prescribing injectable drugs and had set up several private clinics in order to treat addicts. He was giving them the same drugs as I had, many in larger doses.

I pointed out some of the things I thought could get him into trouble, and spoke of my sadness that the addicts' attempts to organise themselves had ended. Colin answered benignly, 'They don't need that now they have me to look after them.'

This went against my belief in helping addicts grow up and take responsibility for themselves. I replied: 'Colin, I'm sure you are doing a great deal for them but I think you infantilise them, and this won't help them in the long run.'

I don't think that had occurred to him before. He replied: 'My practice has to be designed not only to help the patients but also to keep myself out of trouble.'

That seemed sensible, in view of what had happened to me, but it made me feel sad.

Rather to my surprise I had been invited to lecture to the Junior Common Room of the Maudsley Hospital. I was looking forward to it. Although the Maudsley has long had a reputation for rigid practice and is often accused of holding back the progress of psychiatry, it is a famous institution and the home of much of the current official thinking in drug dependency. Wendy Savage had talked there and had found her audience stimulating.

Philip came with me. We were met by a pleasant young doctor who took us to lunch in the canteen. Our host was exactly the sort of lively person I expected to find at the Maudsley. During lunch he was openly critical of the hospital. 'Unfortunately the Maudsley is going through a bad phase,' he said.

'Why do you think that is?'

'All the old professors are retiring and the young ones are interested only in building up their own little empires. I don't get much out of it at all. The chief message that comes across from our teachers is, "Look after yourself and keep out of trouble." '

In spite of his warning, I was not prepared for the audience. I had done a good deal of lecturing and had always managed to create spirited, stimulating meetings. But this audience was stolid and unfriendly. At the end, none of the questions challenged me to think further or enlarge my vision, which is usually the greatest pleasure for a speaker. Instead they revealed a crude hostility both to me and to private practice. For example, 'How can you give good treatment if you are being paid a fee for it?' one asked.

I should have answered that providing good treatment in return for fees depends on the character and expertise of the doctor, just as it does if he is being paid a salary. But I was so surprised by the quality and tone of the questions that I was a little irritable. This is never wise.

My invitation to speak at the Maudsley had been accompanied by a request to write an article for the *Maudsley Gazette*, which I did. When the issue appeared, I was angry. My name was misspelt on the cover. The most unflattering press photograph ever taken of me had been blown up and reproduced four times. I truly looked like the monster the establishment made me out to be. The only other photograph was of a girl injecting. I had long tried to raise the self-respect of addicts and improve their public image, yet the editors, by using that picture, fostered the opposite impression.

More than a year later, a pleasant young man spoke to me at a conference about Aids. I did not remember ever seeing him before. He said: 'Dr Dally, I was in the audience when you lectured at the Maudsley. I found your talk fascinating.'

I was surprised. 'Did you, now?' I said with interest. 'That was the worst audience I ever spoke to. The questions afterwards were utterly trivial and unstimulating.'

He did not seem surprised but said, 'Oh, those questions *had* to be asked. It was just after all that publicity.'

I didn't see the connection and said so. In any case, it had been more than a year after the main publicity. He explained, still in his pleasant, accepting manner: 'We were *told* to ask those questions.'

So I learned that the whole thing had been orchestrated. What saddened me most was that the young man, a psychiatrist in training, didn't seem to see anything wrong with it.

Meanwhile the letter to the GMC had been prepared. The first draft arrived for my comments, and I thought it was wimpish and obsequious. When I protested, Debbie said: 'I thought you wouldn't like it.'

The solicitors knew me by now.

'You make it sound as though I accept that I was in the wrong,' I complained. 'What's more, it doesn't even mention the fact that there's a mounting campaign to seek controlled status for the very drugs that I am being persecuted for prescribing on the grounds that they *are* controlled drugs!'

I pointed out that if we accepted what was now being alleged against me, I was not even entitled to carry a Valium tablet or take a codeine cough linctus. 'I'm astonished! We started the case by my sticking up for myself, and now we seem to have come down to licking the boots of the GMC. Even if the lawyers persuade me that it's better to kowtow, they must put more thought into it than that.'

'I'll ask them to think about it further,' said Debbie.

A few days later she read out a less obsequious version. I felt somewhat mollified.

My lawyers had heard nothing from the police and were reluctant to contact them to find out what had happened about their prosecution. 'If we did that the police might take it as an admission of guilt and decide to prosecute.'

I found it interesting that the lawyers generally regarded the police as dishonest, crude and cruel. My experiences in drug dependency had led me to believe that indeed they often are, but something in me still felt shocked. I had been brought up to regard the police as benevolent, honest and protective.

Eventually we heard that the 'information' about me had been put before the president of the GMC. There would be a 'resumed hearing' on my case, beginning on 4 July.

'Three times up before the GMC,' said Bing Spear. 'That's worthy of the *Guinness Book of Records*!'

*

The publication of the Runciman Report, for which I had given evidence, was held up for over two months. I assumed that there was politicking in the background, and later heard that this was so. Among its mild statements was one that Aids posed a greater threat to society than heroin addiction. This was one of those unthinkable ideas, directly contrary to the 'war on drugs'. It seemed to me that the unthinkable represented the pain of an emerging idea.

Eventually the government announced that it had decided to reject the report's proposals and that it would provide no further money for preventing the spread of Aids among drug users. Three months later it was clear that the report had sunk without trace.

Yet a report in the *Guardian* from an Aids conference being held in London, showed that addicts attending St Mary's Hospital DDU had been tested for Aids. I had read previously that those recorded as positive during the summer of 1987 had been 2 per cent. According to the new report, this number had risen to 18 per cent in December 1987 and by the beginning of the following March it had reached 30 per cent. This coincided with the period when most of my injecting addict patients had had to return to the black market.

At our next legal conference John Wall told me how the GMC were likely to respond. If I said I had retired, the GMC would probably restore me to full registration, as they would if I said I had repented and would mend my ways. If I didn't do that, they were likely to try to humiliate me further, perhaps extending the ban or even striking me off the Medical Register. I made it clear that, despite the risk, I did not intend to recant. Bill was sympathetic. Even though I was making his task more difficult, he understood that I felt unable simply to give in. After such a long struggle that would be failure indeed.

Otherwise the conference went well. My views about the letter to the GMC were taken into consideration, and the final version was neither obsequious nor aggressive.

The letter was to be put before the GMC Professional Conduct Committee at the resumed hearing of my case in July.

Meanwhile I was not surprised to hear that one DDU consultant, a fanatic for total abstention, had resigned in protest at the Runciman Report which said that some addicts do better with 'maintenance' prescribing. I also heard that in the specifications for John Marks's job that had been advertised it was stated that 'maintenance' had previously been 'the treatment of choice' and that it was desired to 'move away' from that.

This was a preposterous notion: no one had ever believed in maintenance as the 'treatment of choice'. The term 'maintenance' described the provision of drugs to addicts without reducing the dose. It could never be more than the best available treatment, usually temporary, for an addict who was unable, or convinced that he was unable, to give up drugs or to reduce his dose. Even then it was only given until such time as he could do these things. I don't think it had ever been advocated except for addicts who could not achieve more satisfactory ends. The hostile fantasy that clearly lay behind it accorded with Dr John Strang's recent editorial in the *British Medical Journal* which said that some people advocated 'maintenance for all'. Of course no one ever did this. As before, a number of people wrote to protest at this nonsense. Someone asked for references supporting Strang's extraordinary statement and offered to donate fifty pounds to a medical charity if the author would supply them. He received no reply.

One consolation at this time was that serious newspapers, and some less serious, were questioning the wisdom of the 'war on drugs'. *The Times* published a forthright article by Conor Cruise O'Brien entitled 'The Phoney War on Drugs'. It was largely about America and its foreign policy but was also relevant to Britain. One of his arguments was that the so-called war on drugs corrupted not only the drug dealers but also the anti-drug people. I had seen that myself. The *Economist* and *Daily Mail* devoted major articles to the subject, saying that new ideas were afoot. The *Independent* carried a prominent article based on Bing Spear's ideas. Articles appeared with titles such as 'Thinking the Unthinkable about Drugs'. At last sensible writers were suggesting that it would be better for everyone if long-term addicts were supplied with legal drugs for as long as they needed them.

I was particularly pleased with an article by Ian Turner and Andy Fox in the *SCODA Newsletter*. SCODA (the Standing Conference on Drug Abuse) was funded by the government; its ruling committee was heavy with establishment figures. The article quoted another which pointed out that Aids had 'brought harm reduction into the acceptable centre of drugs policy'. The authors asked why harm reduction, which seemed a constructive and intelligent policy in many areas of human activity, should ever have been consigned to the 'irresponsible fringe' of a drugs policy based on prohibition. 'Why,' they asked, 'do authorities in the UK persist in a policy that has been so discredited?'

The authors attributed the policies to a form of punitive moralism and went on to give my case as an example. 'The criticisms of Dr Dally should be recognised for what they are, moralistic claptrap.' I particularly enjoyed that last phrase. Moralism is usually founded in envy of those who do what the moralists would like to do but dare not.

Douglas Hogg, the relevant government minister, hurried out a press release emphasising the government's commitment to the war on drugs. British politicians were as slow as ever to understand, or at least to lead.

By June my lawyers were concerned that the police investigation was apparently still in progress. We feared what the GMC prosecutors would say about that, and moreover, my defence in the GMC would be the same that we would use if the police finally charged me, and so would be prematurely revealed.

Bill said, 'We ought to find out what they are going to do. You are entitled to know. I can't see what they are up to.' Like so many people when contemplating the actions of the GMC, he seemed puzzled and incredulous.

But next day we knew what they were up to, or at least partially. We received a copy of a statement by John Gerrard, the Home Office inspector who had testified against me at the second hearing. He stated that the drugs which I was now criticised for prescribing were 'controlled drugs' though he didn't say why they had become controlled. The Home Office had taken action under the Misuse of Drugs Act in relation to medical practitioners accused of 'irresponsible prescribing. . . . Having taken such doctors before a tribunal set up under the Act, a Direction has been given prohibiting such doctors from possessing, supplying or prescribing such a drug. . . . '

Gerrard's statement was of the kind now described as 'economical with the truth'. Though technically true it managed to give an entirely false impression. One of my lawyers said it was 'gratuitously nasty'. There had been no question of my having prescribed these drugs irresponsibly or of having to go before a tribunal, yet I was now linked with 'irresponsible doctors', as the GMC had tried to link me in previous trials. Gerrard did not, of course, mention that Home Office spokesmen were informing doctors that these controls did not concern them.

I knew that this statement would not necessarily be used in court, but I had visions of its being passed round the GMC as part of the customary trial by gossip which preceded official trials there. It seemed to me that the GMC was now setting the stage for the final kill. My lawyers seemed to think so too.

Meanwhile the GMC had demanded a list of 'professional colleagues and other persons of standing' from whom they could get evidence about my 'conduct and habits' since January 1987.

I was lucky to have so many loyal friends. Those whom I asked had all known me for periods ranging from twenty to sixty years. I also chose those who were most conspicuously 'persons of standing'; titles and honours seemed to impress the GMC. Some of these friends had already provided references so were well versed in the ways of the GMC.

My lawyers assiduously avoided direct contact with the people I had chosen; they didn't want to be accused of influencing them. Three of them were invited to attend the hearing: Lady Ramsbotham (my old friend Dr Zaida Hall), Dr Elizabeth Fletcher and Austen Kark. When I asked Bill whether Zaida had been invited for her title as well as her professional distinction, he replied with a sly smile: 'It never hurts.'

We talked about the police investigation. It was now twelve days before the hearing and we still awaited the promised information. 'I think we should write to them,' said one of the solicitors. 'They should tell us their intentions.'

'I'm against that,' said another. 'It might stir them up to make trouble.'

'Yes,' agreed John Calderan. 'I certainly don't want the police going to the GMC solicitors and saying: "How do you want us to answer this?".' He thought for a moment and then said: 'I think it would be best to leave it. We can say that the police *were* investigating and said they would let us know if they were taking it further. Since we haven't heard anything, we assume that it's over.'

The solicitors were particularly pleased with a statement from John Wall, soon to be promoted to Secretary (i.e. chief) of the Medical Defence Union. He said categorically that he and many colleagues believed that the 'controlled drugs' which the GMC had banned me from prescribing referred to those in Sections 2 and 3 of the Misuse of Drugs Regulations, 1985. He then explained in some detail how I had consulted him after the ban was imposed, and said that he had not advised me against prescribing the minor tranquillisers.

> Minor tranquillisers including Benzodiazepines . . . were not in
> volved in Dr Dally's case, and were not generally referred to a
> 'controlled drugs' among doctors or in handbooks for prescribers. I
> felt that Dr Dally was seeking to abide by the letter and the spirit
> of the GMC's decision at the time it was made.

He also identified three considerations which he considered important
One of them was that

> lawyers drafting a Notice of Intention to impose a statute-based and
> severe penalty would have identified the statutory source by date and
> number if it had been intended to signal the more punitive of the
> two meanings of a phrase which in the medical context is definitely
> ambiguous.

One of the solicitors said this was crucial because it involved an
important principle in law. Since there was ambiguity, it was the
duty of the GMC to prove what they had meant.

On the Thursday before the third hearing we had our last legal
conference. Christopher Sumner was no longer part of the team: he
had become a judge. I missed him for his immense knowledge of the
papers in the case and because his good humour and dry wit always
made me feel better.

John Calderan came but seemed preoccupied with other things. He
was double-booked and had to leave for another appointment at his
office. This did not help my peace of mind. But there was good news.

'Preston won't be there,' Bill said. 'He's doing a long case in
Winchester. It will be Jeremy Stuart-Smith.'

We knew that the GMC had been trying to retain Timothy Preston
presumably for the final kill. Nothing, I felt, could be nastier than his
prosecuting manner.

Bill started by discussing the question of my giving evidence
The police were still 'pursuing their inquiries' and, if they decided
to bring proceedings, they could use against me anything I had said
at the GMC. They might even have prolonged their inquiries hoping
that this would happen. We were right back in Kafka's world.

'All the same,' Bill said to me, 'I think it will be better if you do
give evidence. After all, you've been open about it from the start and
have nothing to hide.'

I agreed.

We then went through the evidence, with Bill questioning me in much the same way as he would when we got to court. 'I know you don't want me to kowtow,' he said, 'and I won't.' Turning to the other lawyers, he said: 'I think Ann would prefer the worst to happen than that I should be obsequious to the GMC.'

During the weekend before the hearing I tried to keep busy. Having been through all this before I wasn't as tense as in the past, but it was still a strain and I was awake for most of the night.

The papers were full of leaked accounts of the report on the Cleveland child abuse scandal. Lord Hailsham wrote: 'We must not replace trial by doctor for the rigorous standards of law and justice.'

How I agreed! Yet, at least as far as the GMC was concerned, trial by doctor seemed to have increased during the period when Hailsham had been Lord Chancellor.

July 1988: the day of the 'resumed hearing' was exactly five years since the start of the first hearing.

At the GMC building the commissionaire directed me to the scruffy little room allotted to defence. As I opened the door a group of men glared at me. They were lawyers working on another case. Upstairs I discovered that Bill Gage and John Calderan had had the same experience. When we finally got into the defence room, I noticed that it now boasted an electric jug and equipment for making coffee. As a result the room was littered with used coffee cups.

Bill told me that the committee that would judge me was entirely different from before, with the exception of the chairman, Duthie, and the legal assessor. He read me the names of twelve people, two of whom I had known personally. One was Philip Rhodes, the obstetrician who, in the middle of the previous case, had told his audience that I would be struck off the register. When Bill mentioned to Duthie that I knew some members of the committee, Duthie told him that they were aware of this and that it didn't make any difference.

Bill also said that they had found more of my prescriptions. I didn't care – I had nothing to hide – but I thought of all the trouble and expense they had gone to in order to find them. Had they asked me, I would have provided the information.

The council chamber was just as airless as I remembered. There was the usual row of faces, even grimmer than before, on the 'prosecuting' side of the chamber. Apart from the committee itself, I counted eighteen of them.

As I waited for the proceedings to begin, I continued to think about the work my cases had created for the GMC and its lawyers. The cost of my defence was approaching £150,000 and it must be at least as much for the other side, quite apart from the cost of running the hearing and the GMC itself. All those lawyers clocking up their fees, all the committee members receiving their honoraria, their hotel bills, their first-class train fares. And both sides paid by the medical profession. When would ordinary doctors realise what was going on? I had also heard that the GMC was finding its spacious building cramped because of the amount of work it had to do. If my case was anything to go by, this wasn't surprising.

In presenting the prosecution case Jeremy Stuart-Smith didn't hector or bully as Preston had done but spoke to and about me as a normal person. He did try to insinuate a few new implications – for example that I had secretly taken on new addict patients and that the delay in my lawyers' answering the GMC letter might be due to my manipulations – but I felt that these attempts were half-hearted. He did, however, go at some length through what I had *not* been found guilty of, my general method of treating long-term addicts. My lawyers and I thought this irrelevant; I wondered whether it would have been permitted in a real court of law. But at least he did it fairly, mentioning differences of opinion in the medical profession and general agreement that the goal was for the patient to become drug-free.

When the point was raised about my compliance with the ban on prescribing controlled drugs, a huge pile of copies of my prescriptions was produced. I thought, 'What a waste of all that paper.'

The prosecutor was scathing about my having thought that the phrase 'controlled drugs' meant what all doctors (and the books they consulted) took it to mean. Since the committee had statutory powers he said, it was a surprising assertion that it formed its rulings by 'using the vernacular or coffee time chit-chat'. What a meal they made of it References to this regulation and that, number such-and-such, stroke one bracket so-and-so, end bracket. It was all part of the *grativas* emphasising the importance of the occasion and thus of those conducting it.

I had never seen Bill so nervous. Or perhaps I hadn't noticed it during previous hearings. During one pause I said: 'I think you need Christopher to keep you calm. You're really twitchy today.'

But when he stood up to speak his nervousness was gone. He immediately pointed out that the first charge, the bigger one, had not been proved against me, and that much of the evidence for the second charge had come from the much-criticised Guidelines. Since the hearing, he said, the inadequacies of that document had become even more apparent, and the debate made more acute by the spread of Aids. With consummate tact and skill, Bill described how the evidence concerning Khalid had been in dispute. No one had complained about me, not even Khalid. His only criticism of me had been that I discharged him from my care.

'Only you, sir,' Bill said, addressing the chairman, 'only you know on what grounds the committee came to the conclusions they did.' He managed to bring in the skulduggery without being offensive. Several people noticed at this point that Professor Duthie looked uncomfortable and drummed his fingers on the table.

My lawyers had asked the GMC lawyers to circulate John Wall's statement to the committee before the hearing. I thought that once they read that, they might scarcely bother to hold the hearing and I was surprised at all the detail they were listening to. But it turned out that the GMC lawyers had not given it even to the chairman. None of the committee knew anything about it. This amused me after the stories I had heard about 'trials by gossip' before a case was heard. Had that evidence been unfavourable to me, perhaps the lawyers would have seen fit to circulate it.

Bill showed the committee copies of *MIMMS* and the *British National Formulary*, the publications a doctor usually consults when prescribing. Controlled drugs were marked clearly, and the minor tranquillisers were not among them. Since the drugs I had prescribed were not mentioned as being controlled, said Bill, the committee faced two possibilities. Either they never intended these drugs to be included in the ban, in which case there could have been no breach, or the committee had intended the term 'controlled drug' to have 'statutory meaning' but did not say so. Previous bans on other doctors had not used it in this way.

I realised the committee would never admit that the GMC had been wrong in any way. Whatever happened, they would have to save face.

Before we broke for lunch, the chairman started saying things that sounded as though he was talking in my favour. As we left the room, John Calderan told me to take no notice of what the chairman had been saying because it was impossible to know what he was really thinking.

After lunch, Bill finished his submission and then called me to give evidence and led me through the events, which we knew well by now.

Jeremy Stuart-Smith's cross-examination was largely straightforward, though he did make references to an appendix to the Guidelines dealing with the minor tranquillisers. This was irrelevant: it referred to people addicted to those drugs, which my patients were not.

I then had to face some hostile questions from the committee. One of the women said, 'Dr Dally, I find it inconceivable that a woman of your intelligence, having consulted *MIMMS* and the *BNF*, did not look further than you did to discover what were controlled drugs under the Misuse of Drugs Act.'

'I have never known those reference books to be *wrong*,' I replied, 'and those drugs were never mentioned during the whole hearing. Neither was the Misuse of Drugs Act. Had it been, I would have looked at it.'

She then revealed her ignorance of drug addiction by criticising me for prescribing 'something so very addictive' as Valium. I felt embarrassed for her and said: 'A short prescription for Valium to long-term opiate addicts isn't going to cause addiction. They reject it.'

John Wall was the next witness. 'I misled her,' he told the committee, referring to me. 'I talked to her as though she was a run-of-the-mill doctor.'

The implication seemed to be that the GMC had singled me out for special treatment without saying so.

'What advice would you give *now*?' asked the chairman.

'I would ask the committee to say what they mean!'

The woman who had questioned me tried to trip up John Wall, making out that when he had referred to 'a short time' he had meant two or three days and then said something about a month. I could see several other members nodding in agreement. With dignity John Wall pointed out that a month was a short time in this context.

Then came my 'character' witnesses. They all testified as to my good character and were certain I would not deliberately flout the ban. Elizabeth Fletcher said that neither she nor any doctor she talked to had known that these drugs were classified as controlled.

Finally the evidence was over. The order was given for 'strangers to withdraw', and we trooped off to the defence room. As we left I noticed for the first time that high on the wall was the statue of Sir James Paget, the great nineteenth-century clinician who became a member of the GMC and concluded that its work was unsuitable for a doctor to do.

While we were waiting in the defence room, Bill said: 'It won't be for any fault in your evidence if things go against you.'

We didn't have to wait long this time, perhaps a quarter of an hour. The bell rang and we trooped back. I had to stand up. Duthie announced that I was charged with having breached the ban imposed upon me and that the committee found me guilty. But they had decided to do nothing further and not to vary the original sentence. The ban would be lifted on 14 November.

Given that the GMC would never admit that they had been wrong or even unclear in what they had said or intended, it was the minimum they could do. They hadn't dared to carry out the Council's longstanding intention to strike me off the register.

My lawyers were pleased. In the gallery the family was grinning. I was relieved.

Several people said: 'I bet they'll be more careful next time.'

'In future, they'll mention the Misuse of Drugs Act!' said John Calderan.

I thanked all my lawyers. I knew they had given much of themselves to the case.

One of the MDU doctors said: 'I was pleased that a note of common sense finally crept in to the account at the GMC, albeit as grudgingly as ever.'

I hoped that, when John Wall became Secretary of the MDU, he would in time be able to influence the GMC towards common sense and humanity.

Members of the press were waiting for me in the entrance hall.

'How do you feel about it?'

'All right.'

'Do you still believe in "maintenance"?'

'I haven't changed my views. I believe that long-term addicts need long-term treatment.'

'Do you think you have been persecuted?'

'I'm not answering that question.'

'Do you feel bitter about what happened?'

'No, I don't feel bitter. I have learned a lot about human nature.'

This was true. I still felt angry, but bitter, no. I had worked through much of my anger and was ready for the next phase of my life. To hell with the GMC and the drug dependency establishment.

'You've done your stint,' Bing Spear had said. At last I felt I had.

Of course, there was still the police investigation. They had been hoping to convict me in the criminal courts and then get me back before the GMC. They might still do this, though I wondered just how foolish the GMC would allow itself to appear. I thought of Wendy's comment – 'These people *never* give up' – and I felt a twinge of fear. But even after all that had happened, I found it hard to believe that they could persecute me further.

The next morning, something happened that gave me insight into what I had achieved. I was rung up by a young doctor who worked in a drug clinic long known for its rigid establishment views and its hostility to other opinions. In that clinic, patients who did not submit were treated as non-persons.

'Dr Dally,' said the doctor, 'I'm presenting your former patient, Josie M., at our case conference on Friday. She has been addicted for twenty years, since the age of thirteen, and has had many failed treatments. We are thinking of treating her on a long-term basis. Could you tell me something about her?'

I certainly could. Josie had been my patient for years; I knew I had restored her to normal life. As a result she had held a good job as a factory supervisor. One day her landlady had found her injecting and informed the social services. Social workers took away Josie's eleven-year-old son, Damian, on the grounds only that his mother was an addict. That was disgraceful; he was a well-adjusted child and well cared for. They kept him in a children's home for several months, then sent him to foster parents. Damian was miserable. So was Josie. I worked hard with her lawyers and eventually went outside London to give evidence for her in court. The magistrates said they were amazed at what I told them. They had had no idea what was going on in the drug dependency world.

'What you have told us helps us to understand a number of things that puzzled us,' said the chairman. 'You have taught us a lot. Thank you very much.' They then released Damian from care to go home to his mother.

Shortly afterwards Damian sent me a little wooden bookcase he had made at school, together with a note which said:

Dear Dr Dally,
    Thank you for giving me back my Mummy,
            love,
            Damian.

Damian's bookcase is still on my desk. I had wondered what had happened to his mother after I was no longer able to help her. Now I knew at least part of it.

Conclusion

As I write this I have before me three albums of photographs of happy, normal children and their parents. They are ordinary families doing ordinary things such as playing on the grass or the beach, holidaying on a canal barge, opening Christmas presents, laughing. The only unusual thing about these children is that each has at least one parent who is, or was, a heroin addict. Before the events with which this book ends, those addicts were my patients. Some of them managed to quit drugs while under my care. Some, abandoned when I could no longer treat them, are now dead. Some have been unable to find another doctor and are either living on the black market and paying for it by crime or are already in jail, some with their families split and their children in care. Nevertheless, I am as proud of what I did for them and tried to do for them as I am of anything I have ever done in my thirty-six years as a doctor. Yet because of the way I treated them, the ruling body of the medical profession tried to deprive me of my right to practise medicine.

It is now summer 1989, and I have had time to reflect. The ban imposed on my prescribing by the General Medical Council came to an end last autumn but that body continued to act in character. When they sent my annual licence to practise for the year, someone at the GMC had typed on it that it was conditional on my not prescribing controlled drugs. This was not defined, nor was there mention of the Misuse of Drugs Act, nor even a date. Since the 'conditions' were due to be lifted two weeks later and the licence was for a whole year, I regarded this as yet another bit of gratuitous spite of the type I had come to expect from the GMC. I was abroad at the time but my secretary wrote to the Council and pointed out the discrepancy. Back came a letter insisting that there had been no error, but enclosing a 'clean' licence. I hope that is the last communication I ever receive from that peculiarly unpleasant body.

I have had difficulty coming to terms with the fact that I am a member of a profession that allows itself to be governed by a body such as the GMC. I have never heard anyone make a complimentary remark about the Council. Many doctors and others have ideas about what should be done with it but no one, it seems, cares enough to dare stick his neck out in trying to reform it. Friends in other professions assure me that their governing and disciplinary bodies can be almost as rigid, unpleasant and corrupt as the GMC. It appears to be in the nature of professions that they are organised by power-seekers for their own benefit, while those who practise that profession get on with seeing their patients or clients and hope to stay out of trouble. It is sad but true that few good doctors seek power and that many doctors who seek power are unsuited to doctoring. Medicine is in crisis in a changing world. I cannot believe that the GMC as it now exists can cope with the changes that will have to take place. Dr Donald Gould, in his book *The Black and White Medicine Show*, has argued that the GMC should be abolished on the grounds that it does not do its work well and is unnecessary because all its duties could be better carried out by other existing bodies. I should like to agree with this, but I fear that those who would then discipline doctors might be just as blind, self-seeking and bigoted as are the current members of the GMC. Many doctors besides myself have suffered and are suffering from disciplinary injustice, and much of this occurs outside the GMC.

I know that as a result of my struggles with the medical 'mafia' many doctors and other people have had their eyes opened. This fact is frequently drawn to my attention, for example, by journalists and by lawyers. Only yesterday a young barrister whom I had never met before and who had had nothing to do with my case said, 'Your case was much discussed in the Temple. Of course, it's well known that as a legal body the GMC is a joke, but the way they went over the top in your case did highlight it.'

As many people predicted, the situation regarding illegal drugs and problems of addiction has continued to worsen. The steps taken by governments, authorities and the drug dependency establishment to counteract it have been few and cosmetic, and even these are taken only under circumstances of political advantage. One of the biggest of many absurdities is the way in which the US State Department has virtually admitted that there is no such thing as an international 'war on drugs'. The main drug suppliers to the United States (and ultimately to Europe) – Colombia, Panama and the Bahamas – are deliberately left unpenalised by the US, for political reasons. 'Attacks' on them are largely for cosmetic reasons. This was neatly described by Conor Cruise O'Brien, not for the first time, in *The Times*, 10 March 1989.

Seizures of illegal drugs in Britain rose by 60 per cent in 1988 and give every indication of being even more in 1989. Government ministers use these seizures to boast of their success in the war on drugs but privately they know, as many of us know, that increase in seizures is merely an indication of greater smuggling. It is generally thought that seizures are a small proportion, perhaps 10 per cent (many would say much less), of the amount that is successfully smuggled.

It is increasingly clear to thinking people that the war on drugs cannot be won and that the whole approach of Western countries, led by the United States, is in fact making the situation worse. It is a fantasy war, existing in the minds of politicians who feel the need for a visible crusade that supports a common prejudice. This may boost the egos and the popularity of those who pretend that the war is real but it has no effect in curbing the sale of illegal drugs. The present policies cannot work and they compound the problem, not least by the way in which they corrupt those employed to carry them out. But politicians are always out to score points. The increase in the use and smuggling of cocaine has meant that heroin now plays a slightly smaller part in the problem. I have heard David Mellor boasting on television that this means that the policies he imposed when he was a minister at the Home Office have been successful! This is a prime example of what Orwell called Newspeak.

Meanwhile, addiction continues to increase. The 'war on drugs' is indeed a phoney war. It actually supports the illegal drugs industry and has enabled it to become one of the most powerful influences in the world. In the war on drugs it is ordinary people who suffer – because of its cost, because the streets in many towns are no longer safe at night and because they or their children are in danger of becoming hooked. Meanwhile those who run the illegal trade wax fat and encourage the 'war' that makes them rich. At present criminals have little to fear and much to gain. Nothing would damage the drugs trade more than a realistic approach by governments to drugs.

The doctors of the drug dependency 'mafia' continue today on much the same path and with the same policies which are as unacceptable to addicts and as damaging to the community as they have always been, especially in London and certain large cities. They have recently made a few, largely cosmetic, concessions to addicts who have contracted Aids and still fewer to those who might do so. Aids continues to spread through the heterosexual community, largely through drug addicts. As a result of what happened to me, some of my former patients are now spreading it. At scientific meetings about Aids I have been struck by how often doctors attend from every medical specialty except that of drug dependency, though these could probably do the most to prevent the spread of Aids. Although they are deeply involved with Aids patients, or should be, these doctors avoid discussions and meetings. Several times I have heard surprise expressed at their absence and statements that should have come from them being made, *faute de mieux*, by doctors in other specialties.

Although I am now fully registered again, I do not intend to return to treating addicts, despite the enquiries, requests and pleas that I still receive. I believe that were I to resume trying to help addicts, the medical establishment would soon fabricate another case against me. I can be more effective by writing and talking, and with fewer patients I now have more time for this, as well as for my family. All the same, I am disappointed that the addicts' self-help organisation and pressure group, for which I worked hard over many years, failed to develop further. Addicts are among the few disadvantaged people who lack representation and an organisation capable of exerting effective pressure. To help them attain this was one of my aims. I worked for it constantly and I still believe that ultimately it will happen. Perhaps I tried before the time was ripe. Until addicts organise themselves, as they had begun to do, they will not be seen by the general public or by doctors as the normal people that most of them are and they will be at the mercy of hostile doctors, Home Office officials and the medical establishment. The trouble is that few of them have got beyond the stage of thinking that as long as they have drugs for today, tomorrow will take care of itself. As far as I know, no doctor or organisation is now encouraging them to think otherwise, though plenty of charities are, with greater or lesser effect, trying to *do* things to them to help them. Since nearly all addicts lack self-esteem, it is difficult to envisage how they can improve their situation until they themselves are included in decision-making.

People with power often choose certain subjects or groups of people to abuse or attack. It is one of the ways in which they increase or maintain their power and divert attention from other matters. Their focus is often on topics that are surrounded by popular ignorance or prejudice, of which drug dependency is a good example. They attack those who criticise or challenge the party line.

During the middle of the last century most people thought that both birth control and education for women were wrong and dangerous. Doctors of the medical establishment emphasised that this was so, and some went to extremes of insistence. Few sought the truth or accepted it when it was there. The same sort of lies and deception now relate to drug use, again backed by the medical establishment, which often supports extreme political prejudices.

One day it will doubtless be generally realised that heroin addicts are no more sick than smokers or any other addicts, that their particular addiction is less dangerous than many others, and that they are a menace to society only because the way in which they are treated by society, governments and doctors, forces them into criminal activities. It is an astonishing and little-publicised fact that in Britain one person dies every five minutes from the results of tobacco, one every hour from alcohol, and one only every ten days from heroin. The slogan on the government posters, 'Heroin kills', is true only in so far as it reflects the policies of Western governments concerning the drugs they have chosen to make illegal. These are some of the facts that the general public and politicians (including doctor-politicians) are unable or unwilling even to consider. The importance of continuing to tell lies about drugs and to wage the phoney war on drugs is one of the few subjects on which Britain's two main political parties agree.

I am proud to have brought this message to many people who are not too rigid to receive it, and I believe that it will continue to spread long after I have left the field. I am pleased that I was privileged to help so many addicts to lead normal lives and regain their self-respect and that, through them, I have been able to improve their children's chances in life. Persecution by the medical 'mafia' has put an end to my practical work but it cannot take away what was achieved.

Since I finished writing this book President Bush, supported by Mrs Thatcher, has made a new declaration of war against drugs. It remains to be seen whether this will be more successful than those of his predecessors, Presidents Nixon and Regan. It seems to me that politicians in the West do not yet feel able to be honest about drugs or to replace rhetoric with reality. Until this happens, I doubt whether much will be achieved, though perhaps drug use will diminish among certain groups such as the armed services and the middle classes, so that politicians can boast about this while continuing to ignore the true problems.

Glossary and Abbreviations

The following abbreviations and words are used throughout the book. Most of them are explained in the text, but it may be helpful for the reader to have them listed and described.

* = mentioned elsewhere in 'Glossary and Abbreviations'.

abstinence Not taking any drugs at all, the desired goal in the treatment of drug addiction. Some people believe it should be imposed from the outset, or very rapidly, on all addicts, while others believe it should be the ultimate goal, to be worked towards by methods tailored for each patient. Sudden abstinence, whether voluntary or imposed is known as 'cold turkey'*.

ACMD: Advisory Council on the Misuse of Drugs An official committee which advises the government on drug policies.

addiction A word disliked by some medical politicians and workers in the field of drug dependency, largely because it is a medical term. It refers to a type of dependence* on a drug (or anything else) in which withdrawal symptoms* appear when it is not available.

AIDA: Association of Independent Doctors in Addiction Most members are doctors who treat addicts in private or general practice rather than in DDUs*.

Aids: Acquired Immune Deficiency Syndrome A disease carried by a virus which attacks the body's immune system. It spreads rapidly among drug users who have shared needles and is then passed into the rest of the population through sexual activity. In some areas this is the chief way in which Aids is spreading. See also harm reduction*, HIV-positive*.

Alba Association Organisation started by the author in 1983 to help long-term addicts and to encourage them to help themselves.

amphetamine psychosis A mental state resembling schizophrenia* which can be caused by taking amphetamines*.

amphetamines A group of addictive stimulant drugs ('uppers') formerly used widely in psychiatry, now chiefly illegally. Sometimes called the 'poor man's cocaine'*, amphetamines are a common way of becoming 'high'*. They are relatively easily made by someone with a knowledge of chemistry, hence they are usually produced locally rather than smuggled into the country. Heroin addicts often take amphetamines to counteract the sedative effects of heroin. Overdose is common and dangerous. Amphetamines can also cause amphetamine psychosis*, a condition resembling acute schizophrenia*. Long-term use can lead to addiction. Amphetamine addicts tend to be irritable, aggressive and paranoid.

ampoules, 'amps' Glass phials containing pharmaceutical drugs* for injection.

barbiturates A group of addictive sedative drugs* once widely used in medicine and psychiatry but now discouraged, partly because many drug users are attracted to them. They have been largely replaced, both legally and illegally, by the benzodiazepines*, or minor tranquillisers.

benzodiazepines A group of pharmaceutical drugs* which act as sedatives. The best known of the group are Valium and Ativan. They were introduced in the 1950s and gradually replaced the barbiturates* because they seldom cause death if taken in overdose. They are, however, addictive and many thousands of addicts have been created unwittingly by doctors prescribing them.

blood tests Many people think that blood tests should be done to check illegal drug use. This is not valid. Blood tests for drugs are laborious and laboratories prefer to test the urine. A doctor may order blood tests on an addict for other reasons, for example to find out the state of his liver and whether he has anaemia or has been infected with HIV or hepatitis.

BMA: British Medical Association An organisation rather like a trade union for doctors, especially general practitioners. Doctors can join or not, as they please.

BMJ: British Medical Journal Weekly medical publication of the British Medical Association*, sent free to all its members.

BNF: British National Formulary An official publication issued by the BMA* and the Pharmaceutical Society of Great Britain giving information about drugs, prescribing, etc.

'British system' System of treating addicts advocated by the Rolleston report of 1926 which recognises the existence of long-term addicts, addicts who cannot cope with regular reduction in their dosage and addicts who can lead normal lives only if they receive a regular supply of drugs.

'buzz' The sudden pleasurable 'rush' or 'high'* experienced by an addict as he injects intravenously. Said to occur because the passage of the drug from the blood to the brain is quicker than with other methods of administration.

cannabis A plant preparation that is often smoked. It is relatively harmless compared, for instance, with alcohol or tobacco. Most people who smoke cannabis do so only at periods of relaxation such as a Saturday evening, which minimises the likelihood of harm. Although occasionally over-indulged, leading to sleepiness, nausea and occasionally hallucinations, cannabis is seldom addictive. Its danger lies in the fact that it is illegal and so is sold by people who also sell more addictive or dangerous substances. This is its only connection with 'hard' drugs.

'chasing the dragon' Smoking heroin by placing it on silver foil, heating it from below, and inhaling, traditionally through a new, rolled five pound note.

cocaine A stimulant and pain-killing drug prepared from coca leaves. Accepted in many cultures, especially in Latin America and once used freely in the West, it is now a common illegal drug all over the world. In Britain it may be prescribed for the dying and, in theory, to addicts by doctors who hold special licences. Cocaine was widely prescribed to addicts by clinic doctors in Britain in the early days of the DDUs but now is rarely if ever prescribed in this way. See also 'crack'*.

'cold turkey' Sudden withdrawal or abstention from drugs, particularly heroin, so named because of the gooseflesh that accompanies it. Much dreaded by most opiate addicts because of the withdrawal symptoms that go with it.

'crack' A dangerous, highly addictive preparation of cocaine*, now causing considerable problems in the United States and spreading to Britain. Many people believe that its prevalence is an example of how, when the 'war on drugs' attacks relatively benign drugs, such as opium and cocaine, there is a tendency for other, more dangerous drugs to appear on the illegal market.

'cut' Contamination and adulteration of illegal drugs with other substances so that the dealer gets more for his money and the addict gets less. Common substances used include brick dust, Ajax (household cleanser), flour and sugar, all of which are harmful when injected into veins. Some dealers also cut expensive drugs such as heroin and cocaine with cheaper drugs, which will affect the addict and make him less likely to notice that he has been cheated. Thus cocaine* is often cut with amphetamines* and heroin* with barbiturates*.

DDIG: Drug Dependency Improvement Group Organisation set up by long-term opiate addicts to promote their interests and serve their needs.

DDU: Drug Dependency Unit An official drug clinic for people who require help because of their use of illegal drugs. These clinics were set up under the Misuse of Drugs Act, 1967 and are run by consultant psychiatrists specialising in drug dependency*. Most DDUs are sited in hospitals. They attract only a small proportion of addicts (perhaps 5 per cent), and few even of these finish the course of treatment. Of those who do manage to become drug-free under this treatment, many relapse soon after. The DDUs have been widely criticised for rigid thinking and inflexible practices, failure to monitor what they do or to know what is going on in drug dependency, lack of contact with patients and inhumane attitudes towards them.

dependence, dependency: see *drug dependence*

detoxification, 'detox' Withdrawal treatment*: the process of weaning an addict off the drug to which he is addicted, including alcohol. The word is usually used to describe a rapid treatment carried out over a few days in a clinic or hospital.

DF118 A pharmaceutical* preparation of a mild opiate drug, sometimes used during withdrawal* treatment. This drug is despised by heroin addicts and generally regarded as useless during withdrawal.

DHSS: Department of Health and Social Security

Diconal A pharmaceutical* preparation combining dipipanone* with cyclizine, a drug often prescribed for travel sickness. Diconal is highly addictive. It is manufactured to be taken by mouth in cases of severe pain but is often injected by addicts, when it may damage the veins. Many addicts prefer it to heroin or other opiates because the cyclizine, when injected, gives a special kind of 'buzz'*.

dipipanone A synthetic opiate: see *Diconal*

drug A chemical substance, natural or man-made (synthetic*), which, in small quantities (compared with, say, food), has an effect on the body or mind. 'Illegal' and 'addictive' drugs are usually those that alter perception, mood or state of consciousness.

drug abuser, drug misuser Moral condemnatory terms for drug user* that have crept into the jargon of drug dependency as a result of common and official attitudes towards its patients. No other diagnosis in medicine is also a moral judgement, yet it is used without query even in official reports as well as by doctors and other workers in the field.

drug clinic: see *DDU*

drug-crazed A popular term for a drug user who behaves in a violent or mindless way – a state rarely caused by heroin but not uncommon in those who have taken stimulants or alcohol.

drug dependence, drug dependency A modern term for drug addiction*, less medical in connotation and less controversial.

drug misuser: see *drug abuser*

drug user Sensible, neutral term for someone who uses illegal drugs, whether addicted or not.

establishment, medical establishment, drug dependency establishment Those with power and privilege or in secure positions in the medical profession and in drug dependency.

'fix' Injection of drugs

gear Heroin

GMC: General Medical Council A statutory body responsible for the education and discipline of doctors.

GP: General Practitioner Family doctor

'H & C' Popular term for prescriptions for heroin* and cocaine* which were prescribed, often in huge doses, by DDU* doctors in Britain in the early years of the DDUs. Cocaine counteracted the sedative effects of the heroin.

hallucinogen A drug such as LSD* which causes hallucinations, i.e. imaginary perceptions.

harm-reduction An attitude towards drug addicts that accepts that some are unable to give up drugs and that effort should be put into seeing that they cause as little harm as possible to themselves and others. The idea goes against the standard and official drug policies of abstention, rapid reduction and withdrawal. The idea of harm-reduction became common only with the spread of Aids and has so far been used more to prevent the spread of that disease than to help drug users. Thus it is usually associated with sex and drug education, condoms, needle-exchange and maintenance.

heroin Diacetyl morphine, a semi-synthetic opiate and one of the chief commodities of the illegal trade in drugs. Heroin is illegal in the United States, where it cannot even be used to ease the distress of the dying despite evidence that it is often the best drug for this. In Britain any doctor may prescribe heroin to the seriously injured or the dying but only doctors holding special heroin licences* may prescribe it for addicts. Contrary to general belief, heroin, like other opiates*, is a 'gentle', relatively harmless, drug. Its chief bad effect is that it is addictive.

heroin licence Popular term for the licence issued by the DHSS* to certain doctors, almost all of whom are DDU* doctors, to prescribe heroin*, cocaine* and Diconal*.

'high' The state of mind and behaviour of someone who is currently conscious only of the attractive side of life and feels excited or very happy. In such a state the person ignores reality and difficulties and is often unaware of the interests or existence of other people. This state of mind can be induced by many things including drugs, particularly alcohol and stimulants such as cocaine* and amphetamines*.

'hit' Getting the point of the needle into a vein.

HIV-positive Someone who is infected with the virus of Aids* although he may feel well and be without symptoms.

illegal drugs In Britain it is illegal to possess drugs listed in Schedules 1 and 2 of the Misuse of Drugs Act unless they have been prescribed for the person carrying them. These drugs include cocaine*, heroin* and all the major opiates*, amphetamines*, barbiturates* and other drugs which alter mood, perception or states of consciousness.

injecting Ever since the invention of the hypodermic syringe* in the middle of the nineteenth century (the wife of the doctor who invented it became an opium addict), large numbers of addicts for many types of drugs prefer to take the drug by injection, usually intravenously, straight into a vein. The main reason for this is the special sensation or 'buzz'* that results which is not present if the drug is taken by other means. Addicts can become just as addicted to the needle (or rather, to the 'buzz') as to the drug itself and will go to any lengths to inject. Hence the danger of Aids spreading, since the virus lurks in dirty needles.

The commonest site of injection is in the crook of the elbow, but many addicts like to vary the site. Injecting contaminated drugs or using dirty needles encourages infection, the formation of abscesses and the blockage of veins. If veins are difficult to find, addicts often use veins in the groin, ankles, neck, breasts or even eyeballs.

Lancet Weekly medical journal, independent, authoritative and widely respected.

linctus Technically a preparation for coughs, but the term is used in drug dependency to describe liquid oral methadone*, which is made in two strengths, 1 mg/ml and 2 mg/5 ml. This is widely used in treatment, and cannot be injected.

LSD Lysergic Acid, often known as 'acid', an illegal drug. A hallucinogen*, no relation to opiates*.

maintenance A form of help or treatment sometimes given to addicts who are unable to come off drugs at present or who have repeatedly failed in treatment. The method was widely used under the British system* and in the early days of the DDUs* but later became unpopular with those in power, and still is to many despite its recent use as part of harm-reduction*. Maintenance is usually better described as 'stabilisation'* treatment, and the idea is to provide the drugs only until the addict is strong enough and resolved enough to begin reduction. The word is still much maligned by those who believe in total abstinence as the only method of treatment.

management In general medicine, management is an approach to helping a patient in which the whole person and situation is taken into account and of which 'treatment' is only part. In the treatment of drug dependency* the word is used pejoratively to describe the situation in which the doctor considers the circumstances and needs of the individual patient and does not stick closely to the rigid schedules of treatment laid down by the drug dependency 'mafia'.

MDU: Medical Defence Union One of two organisations (the other is the MPS, the Medical Protection Society) which insure doctors against legal costs arising from their practice. Doctors are not permitted to practise unless they belong to one of these organisations.

Medical Register The list of doctors who are permitted to practise in Britain. Since its beginning in 1858, the Medical Register has been kept by the GMC*, whose committees decide who can be on the register and under what conditions, and also have the power to remove ('strike off') doctors' names from the register.

methadone A synthetic opiate* or opioid* drug, more or less interchangeable with heroin* and often substituted for it. It is widely used in the treatment of opiate (usually heroin) addiction, usually in liquid form (linctus*) and sometimes by injection, for which it is manufactured in ampoules*. There are many critics of its use in treatment. Its advantages over heroin are that it does not give the same 'buzz'* and it lasts longer in the body and so needs to be given only once a day. Because of this it is more difficult to overcome addiction to it since the withdrawal symptoms also last longer than those of heroin.

MIMMS A monthly journal published by the pharmaceutical industry containing up-to-date information on pharmaceutical drugs* and prescribing.

morphine A natural opiate* drug that forms approximately 10 per cent of opium*, widely used in medicine.

narcotics In medicine, narcotics are drugs that depress brain function (this includes the opiates*). United States law enforcement officers mistakenly used the term 'narcotics' to cover all the drugs they wished to outlaw. Thus in law enforcement the term refers to drugs such as cocaine* and amphetamines* which are actually stimulants and the very opposite of narcotics, and is not used for prescription drugs, although some of these are true narcotics.

needle exchange A system set up in a few areas of most Western countries whereby addicts can exchange used needles for new ones. This is part of the policy of harm-reduction*, which became more popular when it was realised that addicts were catching and spreading Aids through sharing needles.

NHS: National Health Service The government-run system of medicine which has existed in Britain since 1948.

opiate, opioid A drug derived from opium, or synthesised* with a similar chemical structure. All major opiates have much the same effects and dangers (see heroin*), and all are addictive. They are largely interchangeable. Thus withdrawal symptoms from one opiate can be largely relieved by another opiate.

The word 'opioid' is sometimes used to distinguish synthetic opiates from the rest, but the words are often used interchangeably.

opium The juice of the opium poppy, which grows in most climates, the basic drug from which morphine* is extracted and heroin* manu-factured. It has much the same effect as any other opiate*. It was widely used by the Victorians, who frowned on its excessive use but did not regard it with the horror found today.

overdose (OD) A common cause of death in drug users, especially when they use black-market drugs of uncertain strength and purity. It is not always possible to ascertain whether the cause of death was actually overdose rather than poisoning from the contaminants.

pethidine A synthetic* opiate* widely used in medicine and a common cause of much opiate addiction among doctors and nurses.

pharmaceutical drugs Drugs made and sold by the pharmaceutical industry, as opposed to illegal drugs*.

phenmetrazine: see *Ritalin*

reducing programmes, reduction System of treating drug addicts by gradually reducing their daily dose of drugs. The reduction may last for only a few days or for weeks, months or years.

Ritalin Brand-name for phenmetrazine, a stimulant pharmaceutical* drug, at one time prescribed widely to opiate* addicts to overcome the sedative effects of opiates and to dissuade them from buying black-market amphetamines*, made by amateurs and possibly highly dangerous.

schizophrenia A serious mental illness sometimes simulated or pre-cipitated by taking drugs, especially stimulants* and hallucinogens*. See also amphetamines*.

SCODA: Standing Conference on Drug Abuse An official, government-funded body co-ordinating organisations concerned with illegal drug use.

'script' Prescription

sedatives Drugs which depress the nervous system, 'downers'. Opiates* are sedatives and so is alcohol.

snorting Taking a drug by sniffing.

stabilisation A controversial form of treatment in which an addict is, for a period, provided with the smallest dose of his drug which will enable him to feel normal, work properly and carry on a normal life. It is viewed by some workers with distaste and disapproval and by others as essential for many addicts who are not amenable to any other kind of treatment or who need time in which to organise themselves before embarking on a reducing programme*. See also maintenance*.

stable addict An addict who can lead a normal life both at work and at home as long as he receives a regular supply of the drug to which he is addicted.

synthetic, synthesised drugs Manufactured rather than obtained directly from plants.

syringe An implement for administering injections. Nowadays most syringes are made of plastic and can be fitted with detachable metal needles. The syringes are supposed to be thrown away after one use.

track marks Scars resulting from injection. Recent track marks resemble pinpoints, perhaps surrounded by a small area of inflammation; they can be faked with pins. Long-standing track marks are pigmented and cannot be faked.

tranquilliser Term for sedatives*, commonly used when referring to relatively new drugs. The 'major tranquillisers', such as the phenothiazines, are used mainly in the treatment of serious mental illness. The 'minor tranquillisers' are the benzodiazepines* and other drugs having similar effects.

urine tests These are controversial in the management of drug addiction. Some doctors put great faith in them and insist that they should be done frequently. Others have little faith because they can be easily faked, even when great care is taken to supervise them.

'war on drugs' Term popularised by President and Nancy Reagan describing American policy towards drugs in the twentieth century and copied, more or less, by other Western countries. The emphasis is on the suppliers of drugs, on law enforcement and on considerable publicity about 'success', for example when a quantity of drugs is seized by officers of the law or a treaty concerning drugs is made with a foreign power.

WHO: World Health Organization

withdrawal A type of management of drug dependency in which there is slow or rapid reduction of the addict's dose of drug.

withdrawal symptoms Unpleasant feelings occurring in addicts when deprived of their drug of addiction. Heroin addicts suffer from extreme anxiety and pain, both mental and physical, together with diarrhoea, stomach cramps and an overwhelming desire to obtain the drug. The symptoms may last for days or, as in the case of methadone*, for weeks. See also cold turkey*.

'works' Syringe*, needle

Index

Index

'psychotropic' drugs, 42
'Purple Hearts' *see* Drinamyl

Radio Cleveland, 241
Radio London, 55–6, 184
Rahman, Dr M. L., 184–5
Ramsbotham, Zaida, Lady, *see* Hall, Dr
  Zaida
Regent's Park Nursing Home, 58
'Register', 'registration' of addicts, *see*
  'Addicts' Index' and notification
Release, 195, 248
research, 33–4
Rhodes, Professor Philip, 196, 271
'Ritalin', 291
'Robbie Vincent Show, The', 55–6
Roberts, Margaret, *see* Thatcher, Margaret
Robinson, Jean, *xiii*
Rolleston, Sir Humphry, 88
Rolleston Committee, 88, 96
Rolleston Report, 88–9
Roman Catholics, 2, 31, 37ff
Royal College of Physicians (RCP), 111
Royal College of Psychiatrists
  (RCPsych.), 42, 43, 96, 115,
  138, 144–5; complaints about AD,
  144–5; meeting at Llandudno, 223,
  225–8
Royal Free Hospital, 6
Royal Medico-Psychological Association, 43
Royal Society of Medicine, 118, 138
Runciman Committee, 238, 249, 252
Runciman Report, 266
Rushton, Professor William, 14

St Ebba's Hospital, Epsom, 40
St James's Hospital, Balham, Chapters 2,
  3 and 4
St Thomas's Hospital, *ix*, Chapters 2, 3
  and 4; attitudes to women patients, 33;
  research at, 33–4; and psychiatry, 42
St Thomas's Hospital Medical School, 11, 12
'S', Alan: and GMC, 200; mother talks
  about him, 178; tries to get heroin, 187;
  visits AD, 188–9, 190, 200; contradicts
  mother's evidence, 188, 194;
'S', Mrs, 164, 177ff, 194, 199
Sargant, Dr William, 41, 42–3
Sava, George, 1
Savage, Mrs Wendy, obstetrician, xiiiff, 173,
  218, 237, 239; comparison of her case with
  AD's, 160, 242; helps AD with defence,
  160–1, 173, 184; warns AD, 240; lectures
  at Maudsley Hospital, 263
'savage', to, 209, 210
schizophrenia, 50, 291

SCODA, *see* Standing Conference on Drug
  Abuse
Scott, Dr Jean, 117, 181
Scott Stokes, Susan, *see* Openshaw, Dr
  Susan
'script', 'scrip', 292
second opinion, 137
seizures of illegal drugs, 279
sexism in medical training, 13, 33
Sexton, Alfred, corpse, 15f
Sharpey-Shafer, Professor E. P., 33–4
Sigsworth, Brian, 103–6, 110–20
Simons, Bernie, 224
Slovick, Dr David, 135–6
Smith, Reverend, 171, 181, 183
Smith, Dr Richard, *xiv*
South America, 139, 279
Spear, H. B. (Bing), 72ff, 106, 134; meets
  and encourages AD, 72, 73; opinions, 72;
  tries to avoid trouble, 150; relationship
  with AD, 74, 145, 149, 275; amazement
  at action against AD, 156, 256; comments
  on AD and GMC, 218; criticism of clinics
  and official policies, 71; experience of drug
  situation, 71; identifies DDU group with
  power, 139, 162; illness, 133, 152; tries
  to save AD, 149, 151; warns AD of
  impending trouble, 99, 149; and AIDA,
  85, 100; and *Independent*, 267; and
  'Khalid', 147; and MDU, 109; and
  RCPsych. meeting, 224; letter in the
  Lancet, 231; and 'controlled drugs', 256
Spencer, Robert, 25
Springfield Mental Hospital, 25, 32
stabilisation in treatment of drug
  addiction, 231, 292
Stack, Miss V. E., 7
Standing Conference on Drug Abuse
  (SCODA), 95, 217, 267, 292
SCODA *Newsletter*, 267
Somerville College, 5, 8
Spycatcher case, 234, 249
stable addicts, 91
statistics, manipulation of, 174
Stopes, Dr Marie, 2
Story of San Michele, The, 1
Strang, Dr John, 259–60, 262, 267
Stuart-Smith, Jeremy, 193–4, 270, 272
Summerskill, Dr Shirley, 185
Sumner, Christopher, *x*, 155, 198, 201, 270;
  conference with, 157, 160; on the GMC,
  160, 166; at Privy Council, 234–5
Sunday Times, 115, 232; AD writes article
  for, 115
surgery, 33
syphilis, 18, 40